ECONOMIC ANALYSIS FOR HEALTH SERVICE EFFICIENCY

ECONOMIC ANALYSIS FOR HEALTH SERVICE EFFICIENCY

Econometric Studies of the British National Health Service

MARTIN S. FELDSTEIN

Harvard University

1968

MARKHAM PUBLISHING COMPANY
CHICAGO

MARKHAM Series in Public Policy Analysis
Julius Margolis and Aaron Wildavsky, editors

Library of Congress Catalog Card Number: 67-28015

Sole distributor outside of the U.S.A. and Canada:
North-Holland Publishing Company, Amsterdam

PRINTED IN THE NETHERLANDS

PREFACE

The manuscript of this book was submitted as a doctoral dissertation at Oxford University in 1966. My greatest debt is to my adviser, Professor W. M. Gorman. His frequent help with technical problems and his careful reading of the entire manuscript greatly improved the work and saved me from a number of errors. The influence of his thinking reaches far deeper.

Lady Ursula Hicks and I.M.D. Little encouraged my interest in the economics of public spending for health care and made useful comments as the work developed. John Flemming, John Helliwell, Professor J. Johnston and Maurice Scott read large portions of the manuscript and offered numerous valuable suggestions.

A wife's thanks usually come after all other acknowledgements. I express my debt to Kate at this point to emphasize her contribution to all aspects of the research: the statistical analysis, the interpretation of results, and the style of the final draft.

I have been fortunate to receive advice and information from a number of people in the medical world, particularly Donald Acheson, Odin Anderson, Alexander Barr, Neville Butler, John Cornish, Michael Heasman and Osler Peterson.

The execution of this study would not have been possible without the careful and diligent work of my research assistants, Mrs. Janet Hornby and Mrs. Gillian Leslie. In the early stage of the research, I enjoyed the help of Mrs. Dorothy Edgington, Miss Kathleen Foley, and Mrs. Ann Godfrey.

I wish to thank the Oxford University Computing Laboratory for the use of facilities and its staff members, David Mayers and Christopher Phelps, for assistance and advice. Emil Van Broekhoven of Nuffield College provided valuable help with the analysis for Chapter 9.

Nuffield College has been a stimulating and pleasant environment in which to do this research. I am also grateful for financial support from the Fulbright programme, the United States Public Health Service, the Ministry of Health, and the Health Information Foundation of the University of Chicago.

Finally I am happy to thank Miss Jenny Bond for preparing a typed draft from a difficult manuscript and Mrs. Enid Browne for her special efforts in producing the final typescript with admirable speed and accuracy.

Nuffield College,   MARTIN S. FELDSTEIN
Oxford

CONTENTS

THE HOSPITAL AS A PRODUCING UNIT

NOTATION AND REFERENCES

An appendix to each chapter defines the symbols used in that chapter. No definition is given if a symbol appears on only one page.

A column vector is indicated by a lower case bold symbol. Matrices are always represented by upper case bold symbols but all upper case letters do not represent matrices. Upper and lower case letters do not generally signify different types of variables; in some instances indicated in the text lower case letters do stand for the logarithm of the corresponding upper case variable.

The circumflex over a letter indicates an estimated value of a parameter or variable. A number of general statistical symbols are used without special definition in chapter appendices. Thus r, R and $\bar{R}$ are the correlation coefficient, the multiple correlation coefficient and the adjusted multiple correlation coefficient; σ^2 represents a variance and Ω a covariance matrix. The symbol $\mathscr{E}$ is the expectation operator.

References are cited in the text and footnotes by author and date of publication. Further information is available in the bibliography presented after chapter 10.

CHAPTER 1

INTRODUCTION: ECONOMIC ANALYSIS FOR HEALTH SERVICE EFFICIENCY

The growth of the public sector has been one of the outstanding features of the postwar economy. In response, economists are seeking to develop analytic methods for improving the efficiency of public spending. Attention has focused primarily on evaluating the costs and benefits of individual investments or expenditure programmes. Substantial progress has been achieved in developing a theory of cost-benefit analysis and applications have been made in a wide variety of fields: defence, water resource development, transportation, urban development, education, and health.

The value of costs and benefits is only one type of information that economic analysis can contribute toward improving the operation of public activities. More generally, economics provides a framework for analysing the use of scarce resources. It suggests the information that the responsible decision makers should have in order to operate a public system efficiently. It provides optimizing methods that indicate appropriate policies subject to behavioural and technical constraints. This study is concerned with identifying and estimating relevant decision-making information and with applying optimizing methods to improve the efficiency of the British National Health Service.

Health care is an important area for the application of economic analysis. The health sector absorbs some five per cent of gross national product of all western countries, is generally growing more rapidly than other forms of personal consumption, and lacks the usual market forces to promote efficiency. In recent years, an increasing number of economists have shown concern with the problems of health economics. Several attempts have been made to apply the principles of cost-benefit analysis to measuring the economic value of disease reduction (FEIN, 1958; WEISBROD, 1961; MUSHKIN,

1962; KLARMAN, 1965b).[1] A variety of other economic studies of health care provision have also been done in the United States.[2]

Since its inception in 1948, the National Health Service (N.H.S.) has tried to achieve not only a more just distribution of medical services but also a more efficient use of the nation's health care resources. The prospect of providing health services more efficiently was an important argument used in establishing the National Health Service (ECKSTEIN, 1958). Rapidly rising costs during the early years of the service brought continuing government pressure for greater economy.[3] More recently, the government has sought to increase efficiency by improving longer-term budgeting and planning and by encouraging operational research and management studies.[4]

Any attempt to identify appropriate decision-making information for use in improving the efficiency of the National Health Service must begin by recognising that the structure of N.H.S. administration is highly decentralized. The Treasury, which has always had very little control over detailed health service spending, now restricts its involvement to setting total limits on the N.H.S. budget, to approving major wage and salary changes, and to reminding the Ministry of Health of its responsibility to obtain "value for money". The actual administration by the Ministry of Health retains the three separate divisions inherited from pre-N.H.S. days: the hospital services; the Local Health Authorities which provide home nursing, domiciliary midwifery, domestic helps, mother and baby clinics, ambulance services, etc.; and the local Executive Councils which are responsible for general practitioners, dentists, ophthalmic services, and chemist shops.

---

[1] References cited in the text refer to the bibliography that appears after the final chapter. Further comments on the use of cost-benefit analysis in the health field appear in FELDSTEIN (1963a), KLARMAN (1965a), and PREST and TURVEY (1965).

[2] KLARMAN (1965a) presents a useful survey of almost all work in health economics published before 1965. A collection of papers on different aspects of health economics appears in AXELROD (1964).

[3] FELDSTEIN (1963c) reviews the growth of spending, the ceiling imposed by Chancellor of the Exchequer, Sir Stafford Cripps, and the report of the Guillebaud Committee (Cmd. 9663, 1956). A Select Committee on Estimates reviewed hospital running costs in 1956/57 and made recommendations. For a detailed account of health service developments during this period, see LINDSEY (1962).

[4] The use of longer-term budgets in all public activities was recommended by the Plowden Committee (Cmnd. 1432, 1961). FELDSTEIN (1963c) discusses these recent developments. A list of management and operational research studies in the National Health Service is given in Ministry of Health (1965); for a general survey of this work, see BROTHERSTON (1963a, 1963b).

The hospital service accounts for nearly sixty per cent of total N.H.S. spending; general practitioner services, prescriptions, and local authority care each account for an additional ten per cent.

Each of these divisions is itself highly decentralized. Fifteen semi-autonomous Regional Hospital Boards make their own management and allocation decisions subject to overall budgets negotiated with the Ministry of Health and require specific Ministry approval only for large capital schemes. They in turn delegate much of the authority for making expenditure decisions to the local hospital management groups. Nearly one hundred and fifty Local Health Authorities determine the level and allocation of their own expenditure and obtain central government matching funds that are independent of the pattern of local authority spending. Although the Ministry of Health can prevent any local authority from providing services which are deemed inadequate or excessive, actual levels of expenditure show very great variation. The local Executive Councils have no substantive planning powers. The Ministry of Health influences the national distribution of general practitioners by precluding the establishment of new practices in a few areas and providing small financial incentives for locating in others, but the actual geographical pattern of general practitioner availability largely reflects the preferences of individual doctors.[5]

A most important aspect of National Health Service decentralization is the professional freedom retained by the individual general practitioners and hospital medical staff. The Ministry of Health and the local hospital authorities can made recommendations and can limit the doctor's freedom by the resources that they make available, but the ultimate decisions about the care of each case are made by the individual physician. Because it is the doctor rather than his patient who generally makes the decisions that determine the use of medical services, many improvements in health service efficiency will occur if doctors begin to ask the right types of ques-

---

[5] Further information about the general structure and operation of the National Health Service may be found in Central Office of Information (1964). A summary of current expenditure patterns and a projection of recent trends are presented in PAIGE and JONES (1965). A series of Acton Society Trust booklets (1955, 1956, 1957, 1958, 1959a, 1959b) provides a detailed discussion of health service administration. For a description of local authority services, see GRUNDY (1960). HALL (1952) places the N.H.S. in the wider context of British social services. On the general aspects of the budgetary process, see BEER (1957) and BRITTAIN (1959).

tions and are provided with appropriate decision-making information.[6] The most significant economic characteristic of the National Health Service is the almost complete absence of the market mechanism. As a result, there are no prices to signal relative preferences and opportunity costs to the large number of decentralized decision makers. In addition, the absence of the market means that there are no competitive forces to ensure reasonably uniform efficiency in the production of health services. These conditions determine the problems for economic analysis in the health service and the type of information that the economist can usefully provide to decision makers.[7]

Consider first the problems associated with determining the mix of outputs that the health service should produce. The chapters that follow examine four ways in which the economist can contribute: identifying and estimating the costs relevant for decision making; measuring the benefits of care; monitoring the care being provided by the system; and determining the mix of outputs that maximizes a well-specified preference function subject to behavioural, technical and resource constraints. Brief comments about each of these will make them clear.

In deciding whether a patient should be treated in hospital and, if so, how long he should remain there, neither patient nor doctor faces a charge reflecting the costs that would be incurred by the health services. A knowledge of appropriate marginal cost estimates (including non-financial opportunity costs) may therefore encourage doctors to use facilities more efficiently. The estimation of marginal costs is considered in chapters 3 and 5.

The health service rejects the allocation of health care on the basis of ability (or desire) to pay and seeks to give care to those patients who in some sense will benefit most. The economist may contribute by measuring the "production relations" linking care with better health and, where relevant, by assessing the economic benefits of improved health. If the benefits of a particular set of health care activities can be measured by a single variable, or if a well-defined preference function allows weighting several health

---

[6] This is considered again in chapter 7, section 7.1. For a further discussion, see FELD-STEIN (1963a).

[7] Some economists have argued (LEES, 1960, 1961; JEWKES, 1961, 1963; WISEMAN, 1963; BUCHANAN, 1965) that the problems of obtaining health service efficiency could be solved by returning health care to the marketplace. In this study we take as given the N.H.S. policy of providing health services without charge. For some of the reasons for not relying on the market mechanism, see ROTHENBERG (1951) and ARROW (1963).

"outputs", economic analysis may be able to provide a framework for determining the optimum mix of activities and the best allocation of patients among those activities. This is developed with respect to maternity care in chapter 8.

Because the overall pattern of care reflects the individual decisions of widely distributed doctors, it may diverge substantially from that which the medical profession, acting in unison, would judge to be the best use of available resources. Monitoring the behaviour of the system, – i.e., assessing the factors that affect the allocation of care among different types of conditions and different types of persons, may produce information that will bring about conscious improvements in individual decisions. The estimation of monitoring information is discussed in chapters 7, 8 and 9.

Finally, if health authorities can specify a preference function indicating the relative weights attached to different health service outputs, economic analysis may suggest an appropriate optimizing model in which this may be incorporated. Chapter 6 considers an experimental application of linear programming to determining the mix of cases that maximizes a preference function subject to the technical constraints of hospital production and a set of input constraints. Chapters 7 and 9 discuss the use of a more aggregate model with which health service authorities may select an optimum mix of services.

A different group of problems is associated with the efficient technical production of a given set of health services. What are the effects of hospital size on the costs of providing care? How do changes in the relative quantities of doctors, nurses, beds, and other inputs affect hospital output? What determines the extent to which capacity is utilized? How can the relative costliness and productivity of different hospitals be assessed? Answers to questions such as these can provide both the Ministry of Health and the local hospital authorities with information for improving hospital service efficiency. Chapter 2 discusses the measurement of cost and productivity in acute hospitals. It also introduces the reader to the data and institutional framework that will be used in chapters 3 through 6. Chapter 3 considers the hospital's long-run average cost curve and chapter 4 investigates the problems of estimating a production function for the hospital. Chapter 5 considers several subjects related to the intensity of capacity utilization: the short-run cost curve; marginal costs; and the factors that influence capacity utilization.

The first section of this study (chapters 2–6), dealing with the hospital as a producing unit, is an example of public sector microeconomics. The second section (chapters 7–9) considers the problems of planning the supply and use of health care resources at a generally more aggregate level. In particular, chapter 9 presents a simple aggregate planning model of the health sector that could be used to study the interrelations between population characteristics, the availability of health services (hospital beds, general practitioners, and local authority facilities), and the types of care that the public consumes. Such a model provides a framework within which central authorities may be able to select optimal values of the major health policy instruments.

Estimating the behavioural and technical characteristics of the hospital system raises a number of econometric problems. One subject of general significance deserves comment at this point. It is now well known that the specification of economic relationships for estimation must consider not only the variables and the form in which they enter the model but also the stochastic properties of each relation. A clear distinction is required between endogenous and exogenous variables. If more than one endogenous variable is involved, the equation to be estimated must be considered as if it were part of a larger system of equations. As Nerlove has recently stressed (1965), without a correct stochastic identification the proper interpretation of the parameter estimates of a production relation is unclear.

This raises difficulties for estimating hospital system cost and production functions. Because we begin without a specific theory of hospital production and managerial behaviour, it is not certain which variables should be taken as exogenous. Unlike the private firm, the hospital is not determining all of its inputs and outputs simultaneously in order to maximize profits. Nor can it necessarily be fitted into the model of the regulated private transport or power industry that can be assumed to minimize costs subject to meeting an exogenous demand. It would be unwise to formulate a single model of hospital behaviour and derive all estimates on the basis of these assumptions. If different but equally plausible *a priori* models give rise to estimated structures with different policy implications, this is an important qualification that the economist must bear in mind when profferring advice. This study develops a number of different stochastic formulations of hospital production. Chapters 2, 3 and 5 are primarily concerned with the estimation of cost functions. Chapter 6 combines the estimation of cost functions with a linear programming model. Chapter 4 explores a number of alternative production function specifications and develops a more explicit model of hospital production. Fortunately the major policy implications of each of these approaches are consistent and mutually reinforcing.

PART ONE

THE HOSPITAL AS A PRODUCING UNIT

CHAPTER 2

MEASUREMENT OF COST AND PRODUCTIVITY IN ACUTE HOSPITALS

2.1 Introduction

The measurement and comparison of plant productivity and costs, widely practised in private industry, is of particular importance in public enterprise. Sheltered from the competitive forces that impel cost reduction and lacking the incentive to efficiency provided by the profit motive, the managers of public establishments may fail to achieve a standard of operation comparable to that of private industry. This danger is exacerbated if the public enterprise is wholly or partly financed by government grants or if its products are not sold in competition with privately produced substitutes.

Used judiciously, cost and productivity indices for individual public plants could provide a basis for better budgetary control, could identify particular plants that diverge from national averages, and could stimulate locally responsible managers to seek methods of improving their own efficiency.

The primary difficulty of cost and productivity comparison is that individual plants often produce several products in a way that precludes establishing a separate cost for each. If these products are not sold to private users, there is no natural market-price basis for a "normative" aggregation of output. Although it is often possible to assign shadow prices to these outputs as a basis for aggregation, shadow pricing may sometimes seem impossible, or too arbitrary, to be useful. It is not surprising that economic research in cost and productivity measurement, as well as in the study of economies of scale, has concentrated on industries that seem to produce a single output, such as electricity supply or transport. Even here the single-product assumption is an oversimplification, e.g., electricity generation plants meeting irregular demand with high peaks may incur higher unit costs than those operating at more even output rates.

This chapter develops a method for comparing costs and productivity among public enterprise plants producing multiple products that are not sold to private users and that cannot be satisfactorily aggregated by shadow prices. This method is applied to measuring the performance of 177 acute (general) hospitals.

The acute hospital in the National Health Service embodies all of the problems discussed. Its output, a complex mixture of treated cases and outpatient services, is distributed free while the hospital is financed by Treasury funds. The laborious attempts of individual hospitals to establish internal "standard costs" for different types of cases have never been successful, primarily because accounting conventions cannot provide a useful way of allocating overhead and staff expenditure to individual cases. It is therefore understandable that there have been no attempts to determine case-type "standard costs" for interhospital comparison. Finally, no satisfactory basis exists for valueing or aggregating the output of an acute hospital ward. The acute hospital system is therefore a particularly appropriate field for experimenting with statistical cost and productivity measurement.

Section 2.2 of this chapter presents background information on the development of hospital costing. Section 2.3 discusses the extent of hospital cost variation and its relation to casemix differences. The theoretical framework for cost and productivity measurement is explained in section 2.4. Section 2.5 considers the problems of cost measurement and presents the empirical results. Section 2.6 deals in the same way with the measurement of productivity and input efficiency. The relative importance of productivity and input efficiency as determinants of costliness differences is then considered. The applications of those measures is discussed in section 2.7.

2.2 Hospital costing

Before the National Health Service began, each of the more than 1 000 voluntary and local authority hospitals could employ its own method of accounting and costing. Although most of the voluntary hospitals had adopted a common system of accounts, much diversity remained.

When the National Health Service replaced private and local authority finance with central government funds, it became necessary to have a uniform system of accounts that conformed to Parliamentary appropriations and government audit. A "subjective" costing system, following the pattern of these appropriation accounts, was introduced in April 1950. Each hospital, analysed its expenditure by type of input (for example, nursing salaries, laundry, provisions, etc.) but not by department or programme. Annual reports showed an "average cost per week of maintaining a patient" for each input category (MONTACUTE, 1962; STONE, 1954).

From the very beginning, hospital and Ministry administrators felt that this method of costing was an inadequate guide to hospital performance. In 1952, the Nuffield Provincial Hospitals Trust (1952) and the King Edward's Hospital Fund (1952) proposed the introduction of "departmental" costing – analysing hospital costs by assigning an appropriate proportion of hospital expenditures for nursing salaries, medical salaries, maintenance, heating, etc. to the departments in which they are used: ward, out-patient, X-ray services, etc. This would, they argued, provide the Ministry of Health with comparable data for evaluating hospital efficiency and would give department heads information about costs under their own control. The Ministry appointed a Working Party to study the subject; its report (Ministry of Health, 1955) suggested that departmental costing be started on an experimental basis. The Guillebaud Committee concurred in this suggestion (Guillebaud Committee, 1956), and the 1956/57 Select Committee on Estimates recommended that the "fullest use of departmental costing should be treated as a matter of the highest priority" (Select Committee on Estimates 1957, p. xvii). In 1957/58, 221 hospitals, participated in the Main Costing Scheme and the remaining hospitals in a simpler system of departmental costing. By 1964/65, the number of hospitals in the Main Costing Scheme had increased to 244.

Any assessment of the operation of the costing scheme is extremely difficult. Charles Montacute, in a study of the first three years' experience, concluded that departmental costing had contributed to cost-consciousness and had helped to achieve numerous identifiable savings in hospital housekeeping activities (MONTACUTE, 1962). But as an overall measure of hospital performance, departmental costing has proved inadequate. High cost hospitals have argued that their costs do not indicate inefficiency or an usually extravagant standard of care, but reflect their more difficult casemixes and other factors outside their control. Although Ministry and regional officials have stressed crude cost differences in exhorting hospitals to improve their efficiency, they have wisely refrained from using these crude costs as a basis for altering the allocation of funds. Montacute's opinion summarizes the general attitude of hospital administrators: "for whilst in theory inter-hospital comparison is excellent, the use of crude costs for the purpose is really a comparison of incomparables and even the enthusiast finds he is bogged down by unexpected differences. I am convinced that continuing to compare crude costs is only likely to do a disservice to costing. What is needed, and it is a paramount need in the Service and not merely for costing purposes, is more information about the factors which lead to differences in cost in hospitals and the relative weight of these factors" (p. 209).

In the next section we shall see that hospital administrators are correct to reject crude costs as unsatisfactory and to argue that these are considerably influenced by casemix differences.

2.3 Cost variation and casemix differences

This section shows that there is substantial variation in hospital costs and that this variation remained unchanged during the first five years of the departmental costing scheme. Although the study is restricted to large, acute, non-teaching hospitals, there are substantial differences among the hospitals in the composition of the casemix treated. The section ends with estimates of the extent to which different categories of costs are influenced by casemix.

2.3.1. *Variation in costs*

To assess the extent of cost variation in hospitals of a similar type, attention was focused on large (i.e., with expenditure exceeding £ 50 000 per year), acute, non-teaching hospitals. Information about 177 such institutions was published in the Hospital Costing Returns for the Fiscal Year ended 31st March, 1961 (Ministry of Health, 1961). Table 2.1 presents the mean and coefficient of variation for each of several tyes of ward costs in these 177 hospitals; separate figures are given for costs per patient week and per case. Because of substantial differences in outpatient and laboratory services, this study concentrates on ward costs.

Cost variation is not due to differences in input prices. Staff salaries, which account for the major part of ward costs, are fixed on a single national scale. (Except that some staff salaries in London are slightly higher than elsewhere because of a cost-of-living allowance.) Many other purchases (drugs, dressings, etc.) are at prices established in national purchase agreements between the manufacturers and the Ministry of Health.

TABLE 2.1

Variation in ward cost per case and ward cost per patient week*

	Cost per patient week		Cost per case	
Cost type	Average** (£)	Coefficient of variation	Average** (£)	Coefficient of variation
Total	28.42	12.2	54.62	25.2
Medical	3.02	21.5	5.71	25.0
Nursing	7.02	16.2	13.50	26.3
Domestic (172)***	1.74	53.1	3.49	67.4
Nursing and domestic (172)	8.73	17.7	17.01	31.2
Professional and technical	0.13	84.4	0.26	107.3
Staff	11.75	15.4	22.75	27.5
Clothing, bedding and linen	0.23	35.1	0.45	43.0
Drugs	0.93	25.0	1.77	27.5
Dressings	0.32	32.5	0.60	33.3
Medical and surgical appliances and equipment	0.90	33.6	1.68	32.5
Furniture etc.	0.30	52.3	0.58	59.9
Water, rates and other direct	0.80	32.0	1.52	38.5
Total direct	15.86	13.6	30.44	25.6
Dispensary (175)	0.25	33.1	0.47	38.1
Cleaning, portering and transport (176)	1.38	57.8	2.64	64.6
Medical records service (176)	0.25	47.5	0.49	58.5
Works and maintenance	1.39	36.0	2.71	49.3
Power, light heat, etc.	1.41	23.8	2.72	36.8
Laundry (176)	0.92	23.5	1.77	33.8
Catering	4.79	16.2	9.24	29.1
Total indirect	12.54	16.4	24.14	28.8

* In 177 large, acute, non-teaching hospitals, 1960–61. Numbers in brackets indicate that one or more hospitals reported no costs in category and were omitted from calculation.

** An unweighted mean of the hospitals' average costs.

*** Numbers in brackets indicate that one or more hospitals reported no costs in category and were omitted from calculation.

Most cost types show substantial variation. The coefficient of variation of total ward cost per case is 25.2 per cent. The frequency distribution of hospitals by total ward cost per case is somewhat skewed; fifteen hospitals have costs of less than £ 40 per case and eighteen have costs of more than £ 70. The range extends from less than £ 35 to more than £ 110. The individual cost types in table 2.1 reveal greater variability than the total.

Although costs per patient week are less varied than costs per case, there are still substantial interhospital differences. Total ward cost per patient week has a range from £ 19 to £ 41. Again, the individual cost types are relatively more varied than the total.

TABLE 2.2

*Coefficients of variation in hospital costs**

Cost type	Fiscal year				
	1957–58	1958–59	1959–60	1960–61	1961–62
Ward cost per case	24.84	22.01	22.58	22.58	22.79
Ward cost per week	13.87	11.85	9.96	12.47	10.01
Laundry per week	24.75	23.89	22.79	22.56	24.11
Boiler cost per 1000 lbs steam	37.15	29.82	30.04	26.18	28.41
Catering per person fed per week	11.23	10.58	14.22	9.42	9.61

* 125 large, acute, non-teaching hospitals which participated in the Hospital Costing Scheme during the first five years.

Variation decreased little during the first five years of the costing scheme. The annual coefficients of variation for the 125 large, acute, non-teaching hospitals that were included in the departmental costing scheme from 1957–58 to 1961–62 are presented in table 2.2. In evaluating this information it should be borne in mind that the individual hospitals' figures for the first year were probably subject to substantial error; the reduction in variation between 1957–58 and 1958–59 may largely reflect this. After that year, the coefficient of variation in ward cost per case remained completely stable. Even for such household activities as laundry (per patient week), boiler (per 1 000 lbs. of steam raised), and catering (per person fed per week), relative variation showed little change.

2.3.2. *Differences in casemix*

The extent to which acute hospitals differ in the mix of cases treated is commonly underestimated. The current system of hospital costing and the usual procedure of comparing hospital costs with national averages indicate an assumption that casemix differences are either not substantial or have little influence on costs. We now show that neither assumption is justified.

Hospitals are required to present annual reports of the number of cases treated in each speciality (Form S.H.3). To illustrate the substantial variation among large, acute, non-teaching hospitals in the proportional composition of their casemixes, we have grouped the various specialities into eight mutually exclusive categories: general medicine; paediatrics; general surgery; ear, nose and throat (including tonsils and adenoids); traumatic and orthopaedic surgery; other surgery; gynaecology; and obstetrics. A small number of cases (less than 10 per cent) are considered as a residual.[1] The proportion of cases in each category during the year 1960 was calculated for the 177 hospitals discussed above. Table 2.3 presents the mean and coefficient of variation of each of these proportions. The very high values of the coefficients of variation (for all categories except general medicine and general surgery) must be interpreted cautiously; the actual distributions are bimodal (many hospitals do little or no work in a particular category) and highly skewed (a few hospitals concentrate a much higher than average proportion of their work in these areas). Tables 2.4 and 2.5 indicate more clearly the extent of variation by presenting for each of the case categories the distribution of hospitals by the proportion of their casemixes in that category. Thus, the general medicine column of table 2.4 indicates that in 10.16 per cent of hospitals medical cases constituted less than 10 per cent of total caseload, while in an additional 7.91 per cent of hospitals medical care accounted for between 10 per cent and 12.5 per cent of total caseload;

---

[1] As an alternative, casemix composition could be characterized by the diagnostic category and age distribution of patients. Although this information is collected on a 10 per cent sample basis by the Hospital In-Patient Enquiry, it was not available on an individual hospital basis for use in this study.

TABLE 2.3

Casemix proportions

Speciality	Mean proportion	Coefficient of variation
General medicine	0.174	40.5
Paediatrics	0.034	113.3
General surgery	0.324	35.1
Ear, nose and throat	0.088	98.5
Traumatic and orthopaedic surgery	0.095	86.7
Other surgery	0.066	106.6
Gynaecology	0.082	78.2
Obstetrics	0.077	130.8
Others	0.061	105.5

TABLE 2.4

Variation in hospital casemix: General medicine, general surgery and obstetrics

Proportion of total caseload	Percentage of hospitals with indicated casemix proportion		
	General medicine	General surgery	Obstetrics
<0.025	6.21	1.69	58.19
0.025 —	—	—	1.69
0.050 —	—	—	0.56
0.075 —	3.95	1.13	2.82
0.100 —	7.91	0.56	2.26
0.125 —	12.99	0.56	5.08
0.150 —	20.33	1.69	7.91
0.175 —	15.82	4.52	5.08
0.200 —	12.99	6.78	7.91
0.225 —	10.17	7.34	2.26
0.250 —	4.52	9.04	1.69
0.275 —	2.82	4.52	1.69
0.300 —	0.56	13.56	1.69
0.325 —	—	10.73	—
0.350 —	1.13	15.82	0.56
0.400 —	—	11.30	0.56
0.450 —	0.56	7.34	—
0.500 —	—	1.13	—
0.550 +	—	2.26	—

TABLE 2.5

Variation in hospital casemix: Traumatic and orthopaedic surgery, other surgery, gynaecology, ENT (including tonsils and adenoids) and paediatrics

Proportion of total caseload	Percentage of hospitals with indicated casemix proportion				
	Traumatic and orthopaedic surgery	Other surgery	Gynaecology	ENT (incl. tonsils and adenoids)	Paediatrics
<0.01	22.03	22.60	23.73	23.73	42.94
0.01—	2.82	9.04	3.39	3.95	9.60
0.03—	7.34	13.56	4.52	9.04	18.07
0.05—	7.91	17.51	7.34	9.04	15.82
0.07—	12.43	13.56	10.73	10.17	5.08
0.09—	10.17	10.73	16.38	11.30	2.82
0.11—	7.91	1.69	14.69	4.52	2.26
0.13—	8.47	3.39	9.60	9.04	2.26
0.15—	6.21	0.56	5.08	6.78	
0.17—	2.26	1.69	1.13	4.52	
0.19—	2.26	1.69	1.13	2.26	
0.21—	4.52	0.56	0.56	1.13	
0.23—	1.13	1.13	0.56	1.69	
0.25—	1.69	0.56	1.13	0.56	
0.27—	0.56	1.69		0.56	
0.29—	2.26			1.13	
0.31÷				0.56	

TABLE 2.6

Correlations among case proportions

Department	Paediatrics	General surgery	E.N.T.	T and O surgery	Other surgery	Gynaecology	Obstetrics	"Others"
General medicine	−0.076	0.005	−0.381	−0.142	−0.207	0.013	−0.059	−0.058
Paediatrics		−0.211	−0.131	−0.105	−0.204	0.113	0.154	0.048
General surgery			0.023	−0.100	−0.246	−0.335	−0.398	−0.330
E.N.T.				0.050	0.119	−0.316	−0.352	−0.227
T and O surgery					0.035	−0.330	−0.335	−0.143
Other surgery						−0.201	−0.234	0.053
Gynaecology							0.315	0.093
Obstetrics								−0.033

in contrast, in 2.25 per cent of hospitals, more than 30 per cent of the case-load was general medical cases.

The variation in each of the nine proportions is not attenuated by any substantial tendency for the proportions of different types to vary together. The correlations between the proportions, presented in table 2.6, indicate that although they are not statistically independent of each other (17 of the 36 correlations exceed the 5 per cent significance level of $r = \pm 0.145$), neither is there a high degree of correlation among them. While hospitals with a higher than average proportion of obstetrical cases tend to do relatively more gynaecology ($r = 0.315$), and relatively less general surgery ($r = -0.398$), other categories such as general medicine and general surgery show no correlation ($r = 0.005$).

A general assessment of the extent of interrelationship among all nine proportions was made by a method similar to principal component analysis. Principal component analysis is a technique of transforming a set of correlated variables ($x_{1t}, x_{2t}, \ldots, x_{nt}$; the subscript t referring to the tth observation) to a new set of "principal component" variables ($z_{1t}, z_{2t}, \ldots, z_{kt}$; k is the rank of the X matrix and therefore $k \leq n$). Although it is possible to define principal component variables directly in terms of the original variables, it is often better (and is the practice followed in this study) to transform the original variables to zero mean and unit variance. Then the principal component variables have the properties that: (1) each principal component variable is a linear combination of the standardized original variables ($z_{it} = \sum_j l_{ij} \tilde{x}_{jt}$; $i = 1, \ldots, k$; $j = 1, \ldots, n$; and $\tilde{x}_{jt} = (x_{jt} - \bar{x}_j)/s_j$); (2) the first principal component variable "explains" as much of the variation in the standardized original variables as possible, i.e., there is no other linear combination of the original variables for which the sum of the squared zero-order correlation coefficients with each of the original variables is greater (the l_{1j} are selected to maximize $\sum_j r^2_{z_1 \tilde{x}_j}$ or, equivalently to minimize the sum of the residual sums of squares of the regressions of each $\tilde{x}_j$ on z_1); (3) the second principal component variable is uncorrelated with the first principal component variable and explains as much as possible of the residual variance left by the first principal component; (4) similarly, the $(i+1)$th principal component variable is uncorrelated with each of the previous variables and explains as much as possible of the residual variance left by the ith variable. The weights (l_{ij}'s) are obtained as the elements of the latent vectors of the correlation matrix of the original variables; the vector corresponding to the largest latent root being associated with the first principal component variable. Each latent root of the correlation matrix, when divided by the order of the matrix, indicates the proportion of total standardized variance explained by the corresponding principal component vector (thus, $\lambda_i = \sum_j r^2_{z_i \tilde{x}_j}$ where λ_i is the ith latent root and corresponds to the vector with elements l_{ij}).

If the nine case types are associated in a way that reflects a simple underlying pattern of "casemix types", i.e., if acute hospitals could be characterized by their rating on one or two scales, it would be likely that one or two principal component variables, derived from the latent vectors of the correlation matrix, could explain a high proportion of the total variation in all nine proportions. In contrast, if, after eliminating one of the original nine variables as linearly dependent on the other eight, the remaining variables were completely uncorrelated with each other, each of the principal component variables would represent one-eighth of the total variation. Table 2.7 shows the proportion of total variation explained by each principal component variable.[2] The two largest together account for only 46.1 per cent,

TABLE 2.7

Proportion of total casemix variation
associated with each principal component

Principal component number	Proportion of total variation
1	0.268
2	0.194
3	0.142
4	0.136
5	0.087
6	0.083
7	0.071
8	0.020

[2] For these calculations, an 8×8 matrix was substituted for the full 9×9 matrix by eliminating the row and column referring to "others". Although the values of the individual roots and vectors differ from those that would be obtained for the 9×9 matrix, it seemed appropriate to eliminate this highly heterogeneous residual category in looking for general patterns of hospital casemix. Because the nine proportions are linearly dependent there are only eight non-zero latent roots of the nine by nine correlation matrix.

which must be compared with the 25 per cent that would be obtained if all eight case proportions were independent of each other.

Reviewing tables 2.3 through 2.7 we may conclude that when the case-mixes of large, acute, hospitals are represented by nine broad speciality categories there is a high degree of interhospital variation. The proportion of cases in each of the individual categories varies substantially and in a way that is, in general, not strongly correlated with other categories. In considering the costs and productivity of acute hospitals we can assume neither that they treat similar casemixes nor that it is possible adequately to characterize their casemixes in terms of one or two variables.

2.3.3. *Effect of casemix differences on cost variation*

The multiple correlation coefficient of a regression equation relating a unit cost to the proportion of cases in each category provides an approximate but simple measure of the extent to which cost variation is due to casemix differences. More specifically, $\bar{R}^2$, the square of the multiple correlation coefficient adjusted for degrees of freedom,[3] is an estimate of the proportion of the total variation in the particular cost that would be "explained" by the same casemix proportions if the sample were infinitely large. Although there are nine proportions, the regression is equivalent to finding a constant term and eight additional coefficients. Tables 2.8 and 2.9 therefore present not only $\bar{R}^2$ but also the F value and the corresponding probability associated with the null hypothesis that the true multiple correlation coefficient is zero.

Before turning to these results, we consider some reasons why the calculated values of $\bar{R}^2$ may systematically overstate or understate the extent to which cost variation is due to casemix differences. If some of the cost variation is due to variables other than casemix (e.g., hospital size) and these variables are correlated with any of the case proportions, the explanatory effect of the omitted variables will be attributed to casemix and the $\bar{R}^2$ will overstate the influence of casemix as such on costs. This is surely true to some extent. But against this must be balanced two reasons why the calculated $\bar{R}^2$ values are actually underestimates of the associations between costs and casemix. The relationships assumed in calculating the regression equations were arbitrarily kept linear; a non-linear equation, including, for example, the squares of some of the proportions, would probably increase the

---

[3] $\bar{R}^2 = 1 - (1 - R^2)(176/168)$.

TABLE 2.8

Effects of casemix differences on ward costs per case

Cost type	Average $(\pounds)$	Coefficient of variation	Effect of casemix $(\bar{R}^2)$	F-value	Probability $(<)$
Total	54.62	25.2	0.275	9.33	0.001
Medical	5.71	25.0	0.376	14.27	0.001
Nursing	13.50	26.3	0.223	7.32	0.001
Domestic (172)	3.49	67.4	0.131	4.32	0.001
Nursing and domestic (172)	17.01	31.2	0.237	7.82	0.001
All staff (172)	22.75	27.5	0.264	8.91	0.001
Clothing, bedding and linen	0.45	43.0	0.129	4.25	0.001
Drugs	1.77	27.5	0.303	5.83	0.001
Dressings	0.60	33.3	0.169	5.49	0.001
Medical and surgical appliances and equipment	1.68	32.5	0.076	2.80	0.01
Total direct	30.44	25.6	0.285	9.79	0.001
Catering	9.24	29.1	0.235	7.75	0.001
Laundry (176)	1.77	33.8	0.242	8.03	0.001
Total indirect	24.14	28.8	0.223	7.31	0.001

TABLE 2.9

Effects of casemix differences on ward costs per patient week

Cost type	Average $(\pounds)$	Coefficient of variation	Effect of casemix $(\bar{R}^2)$	F-value	Probability $(<)$
Total	28.42	12.2	0.021	1.47	0.20
Medical	3.02	21.5	0.247	8.20	0.001
Nursing	7.02	16.2	0.045	2.04	0.05
Domestic (172)	1.74	53.1	0.046	2.05	0.05
Nursing and domestic (172)	8.73	17.7	0.049	2.13	0.05
All staff (172)	11.75	15.4	0.049	2.14	0.05
Clothing, bedding and linen	0.23	35.1	0.005	1.10	*
Drugs	0.93	25.0	0.002	1.05	*
Dressings	0.32	32.5	0.140	4.57	0.001
Medical and surgical appliances and equipment	0.90	33.6	0.053	2.22	0.05
Total direct	15.86	13.6	0.061	2.43	0.05
Catering	4.79	16.2	0.007	1.15	*
Laundry (176)	0.92	23.5	0.117	3.92	0.001
Total indirect	12.54	16.4	0.036	1.83	0.10

* $P > 0.20$.

ability to explain cost variation by the nine case proportions. We might also be able to increase the equation's explanatory power by selecting a different set of nine categories or by dividing cases into a larger number of types. Our selection of nine case types, although perhaps not the best for explaining cost variations, does however provide a medically meaningful way of dividing a hospital's casemix. Experiments with larger numbers of case proportions do not show very much greater explanatory power. While the relationship between ward cost per case and the nine case proportions shows an $\bar{R}^2$ of 0.275, a relationship with twenty-eight case proportions shows only $\bar{R}^2 =$ $= 0.320$. Although this increase is "statistically significant" ($P < 0.10$), the difference is not very substantial when weighed against the computational difficulties of using the larger number of case types. The use of different specifications of casemix are considered in more detail below in section 2.5.2. Now we need only be satisfied that the $\bar{R}^2$ associated with this linear regression provides a useful indication of the extent to which casemix differences are responsible for hospital cost variation.

Table 2.8 presents the results for various categories of cost per case. Casemix differences have explained 27.5 per cent of the variation in overall ward costs per case. Even more sensitive to casemix differences is medical cost per case; here 37.6 per cent of interhospital variation is explained. At the other extreme only 7.6 per cent of variation in expenditure for medical and surgical appliances is accounted for. In such costs as medical salaries and drug expenditures, casemix differences have a direct effect through patients in different specialities requiring different kinds and amounts of these services. In contrast, variations in cost per case of such categories as domestic services and patients clothing are more likely to reflect casemix differences indirectly through their effect on patients' average durations of stay.

This is confirmed by table 2.9 which presents the results for various costs on a per patient week basis. Here only 2.1 per cent of the variation in overall ward costs is accounted for by casemix differences. Certain cost categories – those in which the effect of casemix was indicated as more direct – are more substantially influenced: 24.7 per cent of the variation in medical costs and 14.0per cent of the variation in expenditure for dressings are explained by casemix differences.

The general conclusions to be drawn from these results is quite clear. Ward costs per case and, to a lesser extent, per patient week, are substantially influenced by the casemix composition of the hospital's workload. Any attempts to compare hospitals' costs for administrative or research purposes or to establish relationships between costs and other characteristics (e.g., number of beds) should, therefore, generally take casemix into account. But although there are important associations between costs and casemix, the proportion of total variation that remains unexplained is quite large. Thus, interhospital cost variations are not merely a reflection of casemix but indicate differences in hospital efficiency, management efficiency, and standards of service. In the next section we develop a theoretical framework which incorporates casemix differences into the comparison of hospital costs and efficiency.

2.4 Theoretical framework for cost and productivity measurement

2.4.1. The unit of output

Before considering the framework for dealing with the multiproduct character of hospital output, we must choose between two basic units of output measurement: the case and the patient week.

Although the case seems the natural output unit, health service officials at present use both cost per case and cost per patient week indiscriminately on the assumption that they are alternative measures of the same thing. Unfortunately the assumption is unwarranted; the correlation between cost per case and cost per patient week in the 177 acute hospitals is only 0.232.

Some hospital administrators have argued that cost per week is the more appropriate index of hospital performance. Since case cost is very much dependent on length of stay, which in turn is partly a reflection of casemix, their argument is persuasive as long as costs are not adjusted for casemix. But it need not influence our choice of output for measuring casemix-adjusted costs.

The possibility of a trade-off between length of stay and cost per week is the most important reason for measuring output in terms of the number of cases treated. If increasing nursing or medical costs per week, for example, could decrease average stay sufficiently to reduce cost per case, hospital costs should not be measured in a way that penalizes this substitution.[4] Hospitals should be free to select a combination of length of stay and cost per week and should be evaluated on the resulting cost per case.

If length of stay is itself an aspect of the quality of patient care, this must be borne in mind in assessing a hospital's casemix-adjusted costs. But

---

[4] If a capital cost per patient day were imputed, total cost per case would fall even if the absolute elasticity of length of stay to operating cost per week were less than one.

as long as adjusted costs are not used as a direct measure of efficiency, these differences in quality are not an objection to using the case as the unit of output. Moreover, it is easy to exaggerate the extent to which length of stay differences do imply differences in the medical quality of care. It may be better to assume that the doctor's decision to discharge a patient indicates that the patient's medical care is adequately completed; although longer stay may not be wholly without medical benefit, such benefit would be imperceptibly small. Longer stays may generally be a service of convenience to patients and their families or a reflection of hospital inefficiency.

A more serious difficulty in using the case as an output measure is that the number of cases treated by a hospital is measured by the number of hospital spells, i.e., the number of deaths and discharges. An individual patient who spends a period of time at home between two inpatient spells would be counted as two "cases". Hospitals that follow a policy of discharge and readmission, or that accept a number of cases transferring from other hospitals, or that can transfer patients for convalescence in another hospital, will thereby enjoy shorter stays and lower costs per case. Fortunately for this study these practices are neither very substantial nor very varied among hospitals. Nevertheless it might be useful to include information on transfer patients in assessing hospital costs. Unfortunately, data on this subject, although collected in the Hospital In-Patient Enquiry, was not available for the study.

Measuring the quality of medical care remains an unsolved problem. If useful quality indices are ever developed, a new dimension could be added to the assessment of hospital costs. But the existence of differences in the quality of care is not an excuse for abandoning the attempt to measure and compare hospital costs. If a hospital can convincingly argue that its higher adjusted costs reflect higher quality care, regional and Ministry authorities must decide whether they want these differences in hospital standards or will adjust budgets to achieve greater uniformity. Again, it is easy to exaggerate the extent to which expenditure differences affect the medical quality of care. It may be more correct to assume that among large acute hospitals expenditure affects the standard of the hospital's "hotel" activities but has little effect on patient health.

2.4.2. Costliness index

We shall refer to casemix-adjusted ward cost per case as "costliness" and define it as a Paasche index number:

$$C_i^* = \frac{\sum_j n_{ij} c_{ij}}{\sum_j n_{ij} c_{.j}}$$

where

C_i^* costliness of hospital i

n_{ij} number of cases of type j treated per year in hospital i

c_{ij} average ward cost per case of type j in hospital i

$c_{.j}$ national average cost per case of type j.

Costliness is thus an index number comparing the hospital's costs for specific case types with the corresponding national average costs, weighting by the composition of the hospital's casemix.

C_i^* can also be interpreted in terms of an underlying linear model of hospital costs; this interpretation provides the basis for the estimation procedure described below. Using a single value to represent the cost of each case type implies that each average cost is constant, i.e., that the total cost function is a linear combination of the individual cost types (total cost in hospital $i = \sum_j n_{ij} c_{ij}$). This is not unreasonable since most capital costs are excluded.[5]

Alternatively, we can consider the average costs as useful approximations to a non-linear function. Two types of non-linearity are possible: (1) general economies (or diseconomies) of scale characterized by the overall average cost per case changing with hospital scale, and (2) individual economies of scale in particular case types or economies of specialization. Chapters 3 and 4 show that general economies of scale are of little or no importance. Non-linear cost behaviour of the individual case types is discussed in chapter 5.

Although it is not possible to estimate the corresponding Laspeyres cost index,

$$C_i^{**} = \frac{\sum_j n_{.j} c_{ij}}{\sum_j n_{.j} c_{.j}}$$

where $n_{.j}$ is the national average number of cases of type j treated by a hospital in a year, it is likely that $C_i^* \leq C_i^{**}$. If the unit cost of producing cases of each particular type decreases as a higher proportion of the hospital's caseload is concentrated on that type, or if hospitals tend to produce rela-

---

[5] The assumption is explicitly examined in chapter 6 and is shown to be satisfactory.

tively more of those types of cases in which they enjoy a comparative advantage, then weighting individual case costs (c_{ij}) by the number of such cases in that hospital (n_{ij}) will give greater weight than in the Laspeyres index to the hospital's relatively lower-cost cases. The costliness value therefore probably measures the hospital's performance in a more favourable light than would a Laspeyres index.

It must be emphasized that costliness is not a measure of management efficiency.[6] A number of factors outside management control may influence costliness: hospital size and age, physical characteristics of the hospital building, regional price and wage differences, the existence and size of nurses' training facilities. Although hospital size and nurses' training can be shown to be irrelevant to our results, other factors affecting costliness cannot be dismissed.

Although the n_{ij} can be estimated on a basis of the annual Hospital Return (S.H.3 form) that each hospital files with the Ministry, we cannot directly measure c_{ij} and $c_{.j}$. Fortunately there is no need to estimate c_{ij} since the numerator of the costliness index, $\sum_j n_{ij} c_{ij}$ is equal to the total ward cost of hospital i and is directly available from the Hospital Costing Return.[7] The $c_{.j}$ are estimated by a least squares regression of average ward cost per case on the proportion of cases of each case-type:

$$c_{i.} = \sum_{j=1}^{k} c_{.j} p_{ij} + u_i \qquad (2.1)$$

where $c_{i.}$ is the average ward cost per case in hospital i, p_{ij} is the proportion of all cases in hospital i that are of type j $(p_{ij} = n_{ij}(\sum_j n_{ij})^{-1})$ and u_i is a random error with $\mathscr{E}(u_i) = 0$.[8]

Using a statistical model in terms of *average* case cost has two advantages over a total expenditure model of the form:

$$E_i = \sum_{j=1}^{k} c_{.j} n_{ij} + v_i \qquad (2.2)$$

---

[6] For a discussion of the parallel difference between social efficiency and managerial efficiency, see HALL and WINSTEN (1959).

[7] A minor difficulty arises because the Hospital Return (S.H.3) indicates the number of cases treated in the calendar year while the Costing Return covers the fiscal year ending March 31st. The n_{ij} were estimated on the assumption that the cases treated in each hospital during the fiscal year 1960–61 had the same proportional distribution as the cases of the calendar year ending 31st December 1960.

[8] The problem of choosing a particular aggregation into the case types is considered below.

where E_i is the total expenditure on ward care in hospital i. First, although there is substantial multicollinearity among the n_{ij} there is little correlation among the p_{ij}; see above, table 2.6. The coefficients of (2.1) can therefore be estimated more accurately than those of (2.2). Second, the heteroscedasticity of the total cost function is likely to be greater than that of the average cost function.[9] This too will make the estimates of (2.1) more accurate than the estimates of (2.2).

This method of estimating the $c_{.j}$ suggests an alternative interpretation of the costliness index. If we replace the n_{ij} in the costliness index by the p_{ij} (i.e., divide numerator and denominator by the total number of cases in hospital i) the value of C_i^* is unchanged but the numerator is now the observed average cost per case $(c_{i.})$ and the denominator is the cost per case expected on a basis of equation (2.1), $(\hat{c}_{i.})$. Costliness is therefore the ratio of the observed case cost to the cost per case that would be expected with that hospital's casemix if cost per case in each speciality were equal to the corresponding national average.

Regarding costliness as the ratio of observed to expected average cost and using the stochastic model of equation (2.1) simplifies the logic of estimating the sampling variance of the costliness statistic for each hospital. Since costliness is a *non-linear* function of two random variables, its variance is obtained as an approximation which is strictly valid only at C_i^*. The approximate variance of the ratio $C_i^* = c_{i.}/\hat{c}_{i.}$ is given by

$$\operatorname{var}(C_i^*) = \frac{\operatorname{var}(c_{i.})}{(\hat{c}_{i.})^2} + \frac{c_{i.}^2 \operatorname{var}(\hat{c}_{i.})}{(\hat{c}_{i.})^4} - \frac{2c_{i.}\operatorname{cov}(c_{i.}, \hat{c}_{i.})}{(\hat{c}_{i.})^3}. \tag{2.3}$$

We obtain estimates of $\operatorname{var}(c_{i.})$, $\operatorname{var}(\hat{c}_{i.})$ and $\operatorname{covar}(c_{i.}, \hat{c}_{i.})$ from the least squares regression procedure used to estimate the $c_{.j}$ by treating the p_{ij} as non-random. The observed cost per case, although known "exactly" from accounting data, is nevertheless a random variable with non-zero sampling variance. In effect, if fiscal year 1960–61 occurred again, we would expect to observe a different $c_{i.}$. Equation (2.1) indicates that this variance of observed cost per case is σ_u^2, the variance in cost per case not due to differences in casemix. More precisely, if $\hat{u}_i = c_{i.} - \sum_{j=1}^k \hat{c}_{.j} p_{ij}$, the estimate of $\operatorname{var}(c_{i.}) = \hat{\sigma}_u^2 = (\hat{u}'\hat{u})(T-k)^{-1}$ where T is the number of observations. The estimated variance of the expected cost per case, $\operatorname{var}(\hat{c}_{i.})$, depends on the residual variance (σ_u^2) as well as the sampling variances and covariances

---

[9] See appendix 2A of this chapter.

of $\hat{c}_{.j}$.[10] More precisely, estimated $\text{var}(\hat{c}_{i.}) = p_i'\hat{\Omega}p_i$ where p_i is the vector whose jth element is the proportion of cases in hospital i that are of case type j and where Ω is the covariance matrix of the regression coefficients. Finally, we estimate covariance $(c_{i.}, \hat{c}_{i.})$ by the corresponding sample covariance. Note that covariance $(c_{i.}, \hat{c}_{i.}) = [\text{var}(c_{i.})]^{\frac{1}{2}}[\text{var}(\hat{c}_{i.})]^{\frac{1}{2}} R$ where R is the multiple correlation coefficient of equation (2.1).

There is no difficulty in extending the costliness measure to individual inputs such as medical cost or nursing cost. Nursing costliness is the ratio of observed nursing cost per case to expected nursing cost per case. Such specific costliness values could be useful as measures of the hospital casemix-adjusted use of particular inputs. But they may be more limited than the general costliness value as a measure of efficiency if hospitals are able to substitute one type of input for another; we return to this in chapters 4 and 5 where we consider the possibility and extent of input substitution.

2.4.3. *Productivity index*

A productivity index provides an additional way of assessing a hospital's performance. Instead of examining the costs incurred by the hospital to produce a particular output, we now consider the output which the hospital produces with a given set of inputs. The inputs are measured either in money terms or in physical units (doctor sessions, nursing hours, bed-days, etc.) without regard to their prices.

To simplify the discussion, we postpone the crucial problem of aggregating the hospital's heterogeneous mix of cases and assume that there is a single-valued measure of output, $W_i = \sum_{j=1}^{k} \lambda_j n_{ij}$. The λ_j's indicate the marginal social values of the individual cases; society's marginal rate of substitution of cases of type j for cases of type k is the ratio of λ_k to λ_j (i.e., $MRS_{jk} = \lambda_k/\lambda_j$).

The hospital's production function may be expressed as:

$$W_i = \phi(X_{i1}, X_{i2}, \ldots, X_{is}, \varepsilon_i) \tag{2.4}$$

where the X_{ir} are the physical quantities of the inputs used by hospital i per annum, W_i is the "output" per annum, and ε_i is a random term indicating that the output that each hospital would obtain from given inputs will not be the same. More specifically, at this point we shall assume a

---

[10] $\hat{c}_{.j}$ is the vector whose elements are the $\hat{c}_{.j}$'s. An approximation is introduced since $\hat{c}_{.j}$ has been derived from the sample for which the predictions are being made.

Cobb-Douglas production function

$$W_i = A(\prod_r X_{ir}^{\alpha_r})\varepsilon_i \qquad (2.5)$$

with no restriction on the sum of the α_r's. The parameters of equation (2.5) can be estimated by ordinary least squares if W_i and the X_{ir} are first transformed into logs.[11]

We measure a hospital's productivity as the ratio of its actual output, W_i, to the output expected from a hospital of "average" productivity using that set of inputs, $\hat{W}_i$. Because we assume that the production functions of all hospitals have the same values for the α_r's, the measured productivity is equal to $\hat{\varepsilon}_i$. Thus,

$$P_i^* = \frac{W_i}{\hat{W}_i} = \hat{\varepsilon}_i. \qquad (2.6)$$

Instead of this assumption of "neutral" productivity differences, we could generalize the production function of equation (2.5) by replacing each α_r by an α_{ir}. Our productivity index could therefore be interpreted as an index number for comparing not only ε_i with 1 but also the α_{ir}'s with average α_r's:

$$P_i^* = \frac{\exp(\sum_r x_{ir}\alpha_{ir}+\log \varepsilon_i)}{\exp(\sum_r x_{ir}\alpha_{.r})} = \varepsilon_i+\exp[\sum_r x_{ir}(\alpha_{ir}-\alpha_{.r})] \qquad (2.7)$$

where $x_{ir} = \log X_{ir}$.

We now return to the problem of aggregating the individual cases to obtain a suitable measure of output. In effect, we ask: what are the relative shadow prices (λ_j's) with which society should value the various types of cases produced by a hospital? Although we may not be able to establish a set of shadow prices reflecting the relative desirability of an additional treated case of each type, an alternative approach is possible. The hospital system already produces a large number of cases of each type. If hospital i produces an additional case of type j, one less case of that type can be produced elsewhere without changing the total amount of hospital care in the sytem as a whole.[12] The relative values to society of the different cases produced at hospital i may be measured approximately by the relative marginal costs of those cases elsewhere in the hospital system. To estimate λ_k/λ_j we re-

---

[11] The specification of the production function and its stochastic properties is discussed in chapter 4. Alternative estimation methods are also used.
[12] This simplifies by assuming that the value of a case does not depend on its location.

place the *normative* MRS_{jk} with the *technical* marginal rate of transformation, MRT_{jk}. Unfortunately we do not have information about the relative marginal costs of different case types. We must go one step further and replace relative marginal costs with relative average costs; thus, $\lambda_k/\lambda_j = c_{.k}/c_{.j}$. This cannot be justified by arguing that equilibrium conditions assure that relative average costs are the same as relative social values. Rather we assert as a plausible and useful assumption that society might value the cases of different types produced in a particular hospital in proportion to the average costs of producing those cases elsewhere in the hospital system.[13]

The form of the production function implies that only the constant term (A) is affected by a change in the scale on which output is measured. Since this term cancels out in calculating P_i^*, we may take $\lambda_j = c_{.j}$ and therefore define output as: $W_i = \sum_{j=1}^{k} \lambda_j n_{ij} = \sum_{j=1}^{k} c_{.j} n_{ij}$, the expected total ward cost of producing the casemix of hospital i.

This solution to the problem of output measurement is far from wholly satisfactory but seems the best available. The results shown in section 2.6 below, and in chapter 4 are sufficiently plausible to support the conclusion that this method is not without value.

2.4.4. *The relation of costliness and productivity*

We now consider the relation of costliness to productivity and, in so doing, derive a third measure of hospital performance, the relative efficiency of input combination, I^*.[14] No attempt is made to provide a rigorous analysis. Rather we seek to suggest a plausible basis for analyzing differences in costliness into (1) differences in productivity, and (2) differences in input efficiency.[15] This can be shown diagrammatically if we simplify by assuming that hospitals use only two inputs (X_1, X_2) and produce a single output, W.

---

[13] This assumes that average money costs are proportional to average social costs. Since money costs exclude capital costs, the opportunity costs of the beds used by different case types is ignored. Fortunately lengths of stay are roughly proportional to average money costs.

[14] This analysis is related to the work of FARRELL (1957). Farrell used a linear activity analysis model. NERLOVE's study (1965), using a Cobb-Douglas production function, appeared after the preparation of this chapter. For a basic difference between their approach and that of this chapter, see footnote 16, p. 32.

[15] The distinction was first made by MARSCHAK and ANDREWS (1944) who called the corresponding entities "technical" and "economic" disturbances. The analysis uses the fact that all hospitals can be assumed to face the same input prices.

The solid line isoquant in figure 2.1 corresponds to the production function of the "average" hospital[16] ($W_0 = AX_1^{\alpha_1}X_2^{\alpha_2}$) and indicates the alternative input combinations of X_1 and X_2 that yield the specified output, W_0. The broken-line isoquant refers to the same quantity of output but corresponds to the production function of an individual hospital that is below average in productivity ($W_i = AX_{i1}^{\alpha_1}X_{i2}^{\alpha_2}\varepsilon_i$, $\varepsilon_i < 1$).[17] The common slope of the isocost lines, B_1 to B_5, indicates the relative proces of the two inputs.

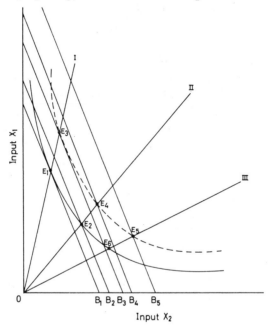

Fig. 2.1. Costliness, productivity and input efficiency.

The hospital of average productivity ($\varepsilon = 1$) can produce W_0 at least cost by using the input combination indicated by point E_1, incurring cost B_1. But the average hospital is *not* perfectly efficient in its choice of inputs

---

[16] The analysis thus differs from that of Farrell and Nerlove who use an estimated "best-practice" isoquant. Although their procedure conforms more closely to the standard microeconomic analysis, their estimation methods are far more complicated than ours. Farrell's method also has the disadvantage of using only a small fraction of the total number of observations.

[17] We assume that productivity differences are neutral (i.e., the values of α_1 and α_2 are the same in all hospitals) and therefore draw the isoquants so that along any ray from the origin the tangents to the isoquants have the same slope.

and therefore produces at a point on a different input-ratio ray, say point E_2 on ray II where total cost is B_2. If the lower productivity hospital used this input ratio it would produce at point E_4 with cost B_4. Alternatively, the hospital might select a more or less appropriate input ratio; on input ratio ray I its cost would be least (B_3) while input ratio III would be less appropriate than average and increase its costs to B_5.

We can now express costliness, productivity and appropriateness of input ratio for a hospital producing quantity W_0 of a homogeneous output at E_5. Costliness is the ratio of actual cost (B_5) to average cost for the same output (B_2); $C_i^* = B_5/B_2$. Productivity is the ratio of actual output to the output expected, on average, for a given set of inputs. With constant returns to scale,[18] a proportional increase in the distance from the origin along a ray corresponds to an equiproportional increase in the hospital's output. If the "average" hospital used the inputs corresponding to point E_5, its output would be higher: $(E_50/E_60)W_0$. Productivity is the ratio of W_0 to $(E_50/E_60)W_0$, i.e., $P_i^* = E_60/E_50$. By a similar argument it is clear that $P_i^* = E_40/E_20$. The ratio of B_4 to B_2 therefore measures the individual hospital's proportional increase in costs over the average due to lower productivity. We may now denote the ratio of B_4 to B_5 as the measure of the hospital's appropriateness of input proportions, I_i^*. To obtain a numerical value for I_i^* we note that $C_i^* = B_5/B_2 = B_4/B_2 \cdot B_5/B_4 = = (B_4/B_2)(I_i^*)^{-1}$ and then replace (B_2/B_4) by our productivity measure, (P_i^*). We therefore define $I_i^* = [C_i^* P_i^*]^{-1}$.

Section 2.5 discusses the measurement of costliness and presents the results which we obtained. Estimates of P_i^* and I_i^* are then considered in section 2.6.

2.5 Measuring hospital costliness

Specifying the casemix is the principal problem in costliness measurement. Section 2.5.1 presents the results obtained when cases ware aggregated into 28 different types. For several reasons, such a detailed casemix specification may be less suitable than a cruder one. Alternative aggregations with fewer case types and the use of principal component variables are considered in section 2.5.2. The best of these, a specification of casemix by nine case types, is developed in section 2.5.3. The costliness measure is extended to individual cost types in section 2.5.4.

---

[18] Chapter 4 shows that this assumption is reasonable. Of course, we require this assumption only for this diagrammatic representation of productivity and not for the algebraic measures discussed above.

TABLE 2.10

Costliness regression: 28 case types

No.	Case type	Mean proportion ***	Regr. coeff.	Standard error	Average cost per case (£)
(1)	(2)	(3)	(4)	(5)	(6)
1	(General medicine)*	0.1738	—	—	102.17
2	Paediatrics	0.0335	−77.40	28.65	24.77
3	Infectious diseases	0.0031	−22.92	31.88	79.25
4	Diseases of chest	0.0044	26.66	82.43	128.83
5	Dermatology	0.0048	−89.29	104.99	12.88
6	Neurology	0.0033	133.74	74.82	235.91
7	Cardiology	0.0003	−142.13	345.11	−39.96
8	Physical medicine	0.0004	−367.76	413.64	−265.59
9	Venereal disease	0.0005	563.28	252.33	665.45
10	Geriatrics and chronic sick**	0.0035	−2.48	115.23	99.69
11	General surgery	0.3238	−61.83	16.25	40.34
12	E.N.T. (Excl. T. and A)	0.0504	−76.98	23.70	25.19
13	Tonsils and adenoids	0.0379	−89.44	32.78	12.73
14	Traumatic and orthopaedic surgery	0.0952	−57.27	17.85	44.90
15	Ophthamology	0.0263	−26.03	35.80	76.14
16	Radiotherapy	0.0058	−99.60	53.96	2.57
17	Urology	0.0108	−11.88	33.77	90.29
18	Plastic surgery	0.0067	45.97	45.11	148.14
19	Thoracic surgery	0.0049	2.46	49.46	104.63
20	Dentistry	0.0083	−81.09	75.07	21.08
21	Neurosurgery	0.0029	−6.87	76.32	95.30
22	Gynaecology	0.0820	−52.91	21.08	49.26
23	Obstetrics	0.0766	−57.04	18.52	45.13
24	Special care babies	0.0079	−107.10	67.73	−4.93
25	Mental illness	0.0008	25.23	266.94	127.40
26	G. P. and pre-convalescent	0.0057	−80.67	27.60	21.50
27	Staff and private beds**	0.0250	−27.02	34.24	75.15
28	Other specialities	0.0021	68.58	81.17	170.75
	Constant term	—	102.17	11.93	—

  * General medicine was the omitted variable; see text.

  ** Contains more than one of the original thirty-three categories.

*** An unweighted mean of the 177 proportions.

2.5.1. *Costliness with 28 case types*

The annual hospital reports (form S.H.3) state the number of cases treated in each of 33 distinct and non-zero categories.[19] Although we originally intended to derive costliness by a regression of cost per case on 33 case proportions, limitations of the computer made it necessary to reduce this to a maximum of 28 explanatory variables.[20]

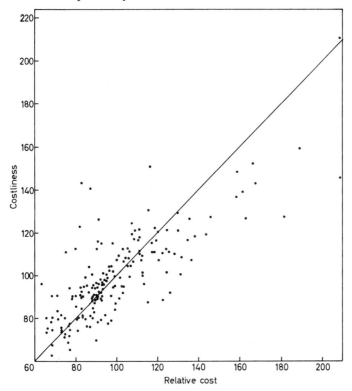

Fig. 2.2. Costliness and relative cost (28 case types).

---

[19] A few additional categories are indicated on the form. Some hospitals understandably do not distinguish, for example, antenatal obstetrics from postnatal obstetrics. There were no cases in the 177 acute hospitals in the categories: child guidance, subnormality, and convalescent.

[20] Regressions were computed in two stages. In the first, a data matrix (177×34) of the cost per case and *numbers* of cases of each type in each hospital was used to derive the moment matrix (29×29) of the case proportions, and the vector whose 29 elements are the cross products of cost and case proportions. By limiting the moment matrix to order 29, the calculations could be carried out efficiently in the working store of the Mercury

Table 2.10 shows the 28 case types and the mean proportion of cases in each category. A least squares regression of cost per case[21] on the 28 explanatory variables accounted for 42.4 per cent of the variation in cost per case ($R^2 = 0.424$) or, after adjustment for the number of degrees of freedom used, for 32.0 per cent of the variation ($\bar{R}^2 = 0.320$). The actual regression produced a constant term and 27 regression coefficients; these coefficients and their standard errors appear in columns (4) and (5). If we add the constant term (102.17) to a regression coefficient we obtain an estimate of the average cost per case in that category ($c_{.j}$); these estimates are presented in column 6.

Before considering the individual regression coefficients, we examine the costliness values derived from them.[22] The scatter diagram of figure 2.2 shows the costliness and relative cost (observed cost as a percentage of the national average) of each hospital.[23] The diagonal line indicates the points at which costliness and relative costs are equal. The wide scatter of points away from this line indicates a substantial divergence between costliness and the crude relative cost values; the correlation between the two is only 0.729. The regression of costliness (C_i^*) on relative costs ($c_{i.}/c_{..}$)

$$C_i^* = 1.973 + \frac{0.9791}{(0.0696)} \left(\frac{c_{i.}}{c_{..}}\right) \tag{2.8}$$

indicates that *on average* relative cost is an unbiased (although "inefficient") measure of costliness. This unbiasedness property does not hold when we consider separately the hospitals with low and high relative costs. Among high relative cost hospitals ($c_{i.}/c_{..} > 100$), relative cost generally exceeded costliness; among low relative cost hospitals ($c_{i.}/c_{..} < 100$) the converse is therefore also true.

Figure 2.3 shows the extent of this asymmetry. Among hospitals with relative costs below 100, costliness exceeds relative cost by more than ten points in 32 hospitals while relative cost exceeds costliness in only seven.

---

computer. The regression coefficients were calculated from these with a programme provided by Mr. P. Vandome.

[21] Unless otherwise specified, cost per case refers to ward cost per case.

[22] Recall that a hospital's costliness, although defined in terms of an index number, may be measured as the ratio of observed cost per case to the cost per case predicted by the regression equation for a hospital with that casemix. For convenience these values have been multiplied by 100.

[23] A tabulation of costliness and relative cost for all hospitals will be found in FELDSTEIN (1965a).

For hospitals with relative costs above 100, the corresponding numbers are eight and twenty-two.

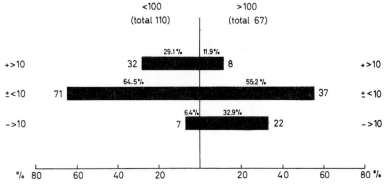

Fig. 2.3. Percentages of hospitals with relative costs below and above average, in which costliness differs from relative cost by more than 10 points (based on 28 case types).

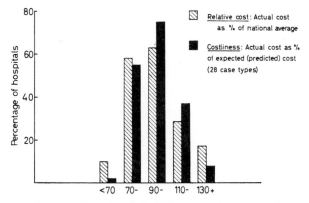

Fig. 2.4. Distribution of hospitals by relative cost and costliness (28 case types).

Crude relative costs are therefore not only inappropriate measures of the cost performance of individual hospitals but also overstate the variation in hospital cost performance. Figure 2.2 shows the greater dispersion among relative costs than among costliness values. This is shown more clearly in figure 2.4. Although there are then hospitals with relative costs below 70, only two have costliness below that level; similarly there are 17 hospitals with relative costs at or above 130 but only eight with costliness in that range.

Table 2.11 shows the relative cost and costliness values for the ten hospitals with highest relative cost and the ten with lowest relative cost. In every hospital except number 135 the costliness is nearer than relative cost to 100.

TABLE 2.11

A comparison of the relative cost and costliness of ten high and low relative cost hospitals

Hospital number	Relative cost	Costliness (28 types)	Costliness (9 types)
45	145.89	123.08	127.33
12	158.18	102.83	136.73
59	158.95	152.58	148.55
63	161.30	117.69	139.63
81	162.93	95.87	126.69
74	166.14	153.52	152.24
107	181.47	114.03	127.78
55	188.88	167.12	159.30
60	208.55	192.93	210.49
101	209.08	110.17	146.20
25	63.98	85.30	96.11
158	66.00	77.91	80.23
130	66.09	77.15	73.36
14	66.66	77.34	75.63
162	68.35	85.50	90.41
176	68.60	74.11	78.56
135	68.63	65.04	62.79
102	68.98	83.79	80.27
100	68.99	79.70	74.78
32	69.61	83.01	67.93

But the extent to which replacing relative cost by costliness alters a hospital's apparent cost performance varies substantially. For example. the casemix of hospital 101 explains most of its high relative cost [$c_i/c_{..}$ = 209.08, C_i^* = 110.17] but the high cost of hospital 60 does not reflect its casemix [$c_i/c_{..}$ = 208.55, C_i^* = 192.93].

Although the specification of casemix by 28 case types seems to provide a satisfactory basis for costliness measurement, there are a number of reasons for considering alternative aggregations. The set of estimated "average costs" of the individual case types (derived from the regression coefficients and presented in column 6 of table 2.10) contains several impossible and implausible values: three "average costs" are negative, six more are less than £ 25, and three are above £ 150. In part, these values reflect coefficients estimated on the basis of very small numbers of cases; of the twelve case types with clearly implausible coefficients, only one mean proportion exceeds 0.01 and four are less than 0.001. This and the multicollinearity among case proportions is reflected in the large standard errors of a number of coefficients. These problems would be reduced if casemix were specified by a smaller number of case types. Moreover this would reduce the susceptibility of the results to ambiguities in the original assignment of cases to the 33 categories.[24] A less disaggregated casemix specification would reduce calculations, an advantage if standard errors of the costliness values are to be obtained. Finally, a set of alternative costliness values will indicate how sensitive this measure is to the particular method of specifying casemix.

2.5.2. *Alternative casemix specifications*

The 28 case types might be aggregated into fewer categories by grouping cases with similar regression coefficients in the 28 case type equation (i.e., similar estimated average costs). We have chosen, however, to follow more closely the medical character of the cases; because this parallels the pattern of hospital organization, the costliness values will be less susceptible to ambiguities in the assignment of cases to the original 33 categories.

As a preliminary aggregation, cases were grouped into nine categories: general medicine (case type 1); paediatrics (2); general surgery (11); ear, nose and throat (12, 13); traumatic and orthopaedic surgery (14); other surgery (15–21); gynaecology (22); obstetrics (23); and miscellaneous others [25] (3–10, 24–28). The mean proportions of cases in each category are presented in table 2.12, column 3. The regression on nine case proportions accounted for 27.5 per cent of the interhospital variation in average cost per case ($\bar{R}^2 = 0.275$). The explanatory power of the 28 variable equation is somewhat greater ($\bar{R}^2 = 0.320$); an F-test shows that this difference is "significant" at the 10 per cent level.[26] Nevertheless, the 9 variable equation may be more suitable for calculation of costliness values. The estimated average cost values (table 2.12, column 6) are more reasonable than those obtained for the large number of case types, standard errors are smaller,

---

[24] This will occur most commonly when cases in medical (surgical) specialities are assigned to general medicine (surgery).

[25] As indicated by the case type numbers, these are primarily but not exclusively medical cases.

[26] Although some variables that appear in the 9 variable equation do not appear in the 28 variable equation, the F-test is still appropriate; since the 9 variables are linear combinations of the 28, the 28 could be specified in terms of the 9 variables and 19 others. This equivalence assures us that the two chi-square distributions are independent.

TABLE 2.12

Costliness regression: 9 case types

No.	Case type	Mean proportion	Regression coefficient	Standard error	Average cost per case ($£$)	Squared zero order correlation**
(1)	(2)	(3)	(4)	(5)	(6)	(7)
1	General medicine	0.1738	44.97	18.89	114.48	0.1423
2	Paediatrics	0.0335	−44.54	28.51	24.97	0.0074
3	General surgery	0.3238	−36.81	14.88	32.70	0.0343
4	E.N.T.	0.0882	−54.26	16.52	15.25	0.0947
5	Traumatic and orthopaedic surgery	0.0952	−29.82	17.18	39.69	0.0062
6	Other surgery	0.0656	28.51	20.27	98.02	0.0478
7	Gynaecology	0.0819	−10.79	21.47	58.72	0.0099
8	Obstetrics	0.0766	−34.63	16.34	34.88	0.0011
9	Others*	—	0	—	69.51	—
	Constant term	—	69.51	—	—	—

* Omitted variable.
** The square of the correlation of the average cost per case and the proportion of cases in the specified category.

TABLE 2.13

Explanatory power of alternative casemix specifications

Equation	Explanatory variables*	Residual sum of squares**	$\bar{R}^2$
(1)	(2)	(3)	(4)
1	M, P, S, E, T, OS, G, Ob, Oth.	23 311	0.2746
2	M, S, (P+E+T+OS+G+Ob+Oth).	27 696	0.1679
3	(M+P), (S+E+T+OS), G, Ob, Oth.	28 996	0.1188
4	(M+S), P, E, T, OS, G, Ob, Oth.	27 013	0.1645
5	M, P, (S+OS), E, T, G, Ob, Oth.	26 294	0.1867
6	(M+Oth), P, S, E, T, OS, G, Ob.	24 098	0.2546

* M = Medical; P = Paediatrics; S = General surgery; E = ENT; T = Traumatic and orthopaedic surgery; OS = Other surgery; G = Gynaecology; Ob = Obstetrics; Oth = misc. others.
** Total sum of squares equals 33 668.

and the dangers of ambiguous classification of cases is reduced. In section 2.5.3 these costliness values are examined and compared with those for 28 case types.

Five alternative aggregations were derived by further grouping of these 9 categories. The explanatory power of these alternative specifications are shown in table 2.13. In the best of these (number 6), "miscellaneous other" cases were grouped with medical cases and one fewer variable used; but when an F-test is used to compare the sum of the squared residuals from this equation with the corresponding sum for the nine variable equation (number 1), the nine variable equation is significantly better at the 5 per cent level.

No single case category had substantial explanatory ability. The squared zero-order correlations of average cost per case and the individual case type proportion, shown in column 7 of table 2.12, indicate that the best single explanatory variable, the proportion of medical cases, accounted for only 14.2 per cent of the variation in cost per case.

As an alternative and completely different approach to defining casemix aggregates, we derived principal component variables from the eight basic case types. The definition and calculation of principal component variables were described in section 2.3.2 above. The first two principal component variables accounted for 46.1 per cent of the variation in the standardized casemix proportions. A regression of cost per case on these two principal components explained only 11.2 per cent of the cost per case variation. Similarly unimpressive results were obtained with three principal components which accounted for 60.3 per cent of the casemix variation, but explained only 16.5 per cent of the cost per case variation.

2.5.3. *Costliness with 9 case types*

We now consider the costliness values obtained with 9 case categories and the corresponding regression coefficients presented in table 2.12. The error properties of these costliness values are then examined.

Figure 2.5 shows the close agreement between the two measures of costliness.[27] The correlation between 9-case type costliness (C_9^*) and 28-case type costliness (C_{28}^*) is 0.906. Of course, this reflects the correlation of expected cost per case estimated by the two methods (0.911).

---

[27] For a full tabulation of costliness by 9-case type categories see FELDSTEIN (1965a). This also contains costliness values by individual input categories.

The relationship of relative cost and costliness, shown in figure 2.6, therefore closely resembles the analogous scatter diagram for 28 case types (figure 2.2). The one noticeable difference is that now costliness values for the hospitals with high relative cost are frequently not as low as the costliness values derived on a basis of 28 case types. When high observed costs are due to a number of cases in particular medical and surgical specialities, the more

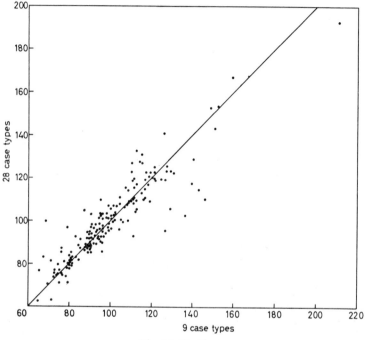

Fig. 2.5. Costliness.

aggregated nine-case type costliness values will fail to reflect this adequately. But the 28-case type costliness values may, in fact, be biased in the opposite way. If a particular hospital treated only cases of one type and no other hospital treated that type of case, the regression coefficient for that case type would be such that implied "average cost" was equal to that hospital's average cost per case and the hospital would have a costliness of 100. Although this extreme situation does not exist, the use of 28 case types increases the extent to which a hospital's estimated expected cost is likely to be based on regression coefficients which reflect that hospital's observed costs. This seems another reason for preferring the more aggregate casemix specification.

Figure 2.7 shows the same asymmetry as figure 2.3. The number of hospitals in which costliness differs from relative cost by more than ten points has decreased from 69 to 66. Comparing figures 2.8 and 2.4 shows that nine

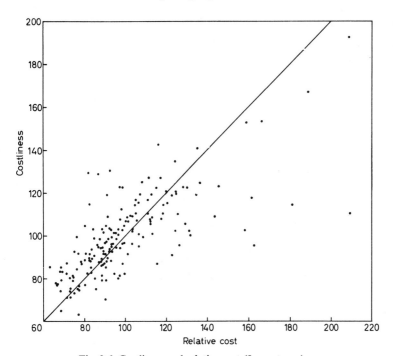

Fig. 2.6. Costliness and relative cost (9 case types).

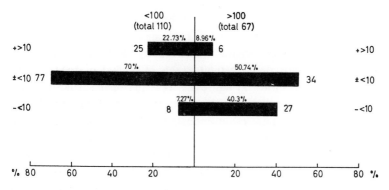

Fig. 2.7. Percentages of hospitals with relative costs below and above average, in which costliness differs from relative cost by more than 10 points (based on 9 case types).

case type costliness is less dispersed than relative costs but more dispersed than the 28-case type costliness values.

Although the individual regression coefficients and corresponding estimated "average costs" (table 2.12, columns 4 and 6) appear reasonable, it might be objected "intuitively" that in comparison to an overall average cost per case of £ 54.62 the implied cost of medical cases (£ 114.48) is too high while the cost of surgical cases (£ 32.70) is too low. As a compromise with this *a priori* intuition, a new set of costliness values were calculated as follows: the cost of medical cases was lowered by deducting an amount

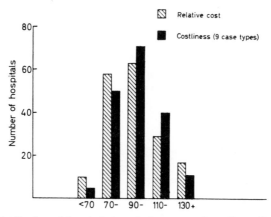

Fig. 2.8. Distribution of hospitals by relative cost and costliness (9 case types).

equal to one standard error of the estimated regression coefficient (£ 114.48– £ 18.89 = £ 95.59) and an amount was added to the cost of surgical cases (£ 32.70 + £ 10.15 = £ 42.85) so that a hospital with average casemix would still have an average cost of £ 54.62.[28] These modified costliness values were highly correlated with the original 9-case type costliness values ($r = 0.978$), reflecting a correlation between the two sets of estimated expected cost per case of 0.984; this is shown in figure 2.9. It is reassuring to know that the costliness values are not very sensitive to a variation of one standard error in the regression coefficient of an important case type.

---

[28] Prior beliefs about the "correct" average cost values could alternatively be incorporated by specifying constraints within which estimates must fall. For an example of quadratic programming used in this way, see MAYER and GLAUBER (1964). Other non-Bayesian methods of incorporating prior information are discussed by THEIL and GOLDBERGER (1960) and THEIL (1963).

To assess the extent to which the differences between costliness and relative cost are due to chance, the differences between observed and expected costs were compared with the standard error of the expected cost (standard error of $\hat{c}_{i.} = (p_i' \Omega p_i)^{\frac{1}{2}}$ where Ω is the covariance matrix of the nine regression coefficients and p_i is the vector of casemix proportions in hospital i). This provided a simpler approach than calculation of the standard errors of the costliness values by the method discussed in section 2.4.2. On the null hypothesis that observed cost per case equals expected cost per case, $[(c_{i.} - \hat{c}_{i.})/(p_i' \hat{\Omega} p_i)^{\frac{1}{2}}]$ is normally distributed with mean zero and variance one. The actual distribution of this statistic, presented in figure 2.10, shows that 115 hospitals (65 per cent) lie outside the range -2 to $+2$ and 78 hospitals (44 percent) are outside the range -4 to $+4$.

Finally, the costliness values were recalculated for the fiscal year 1963–64.[29] The regression coefficients implied average costs for each case type that were very similar to those for 1960–61. Costliness values for the two years were also highly correlated: $r = 0.849$.

2.6 Measuring productivity and input efficiency

This section describes the productivity and input efficiency values that have been obtained and examines their relation to costliness.

The productivity index (P_i^*) for an individual hospital is the ratio of its observed output[30] (W) to the output expected on the basis of the inputs of nurses (N), doctors (M), beds (B) and "other variable inputs (S)".[31] The production function used to calculate productivity values was:

$$W = (4.677) \, N^{0.047} \, M^{0.387} \, B^{0.465} \, S^{0.069}. \tag{2.9}$$

The parameters were estimated by ordinary least squares regression in the logarithms of the variables. In chapter 4 we consider in detail the appropriate form of the production function, the specification and measurement of inputs, the use of alternative methods of statistical estimation, and the implications of the input elasticities; we disregard these problems at this point and

---

[29] I am grateful to the Ministry of Health for preparing these calculations.

[30] Output is defined as a weighted sum of the numbers of cases treated in each diagnostic category. See above, p. 31.

[31] See above, p. 30. Except for the number of beds (B), these inputs are measured in value terms.

accept equation (2.9) as a useful working assumption. Productivity values calculated from alternative production functions and discussed in the appendix to chapter 4 agree well with the ones considered here.

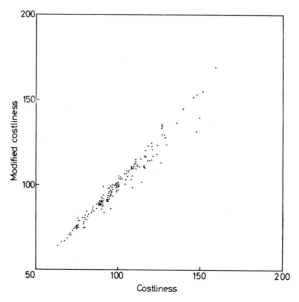

Fig. 2.9. Costliness and modified costliness.

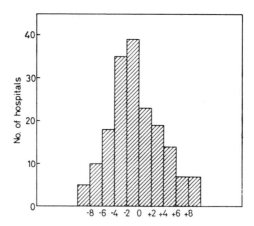

Fig. 2.10. Distribution of hospitals by standardized difference between actual and expected cost per case.

The distribution of hospitals by productivity is shown in figure 2.11. Seventy-one hospitals (40 per cent) had costliness values between 90 and 110; there were 82 hospitals (46 per cent) with productivity in that range. Seventeen hospitals had low productivity ($P^* \leqq 80$) and 21 had high productivity ($P^* \geqq 120$).

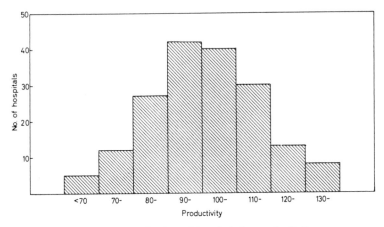

Fig. 2.11. Distribution of hospitals by productivity.

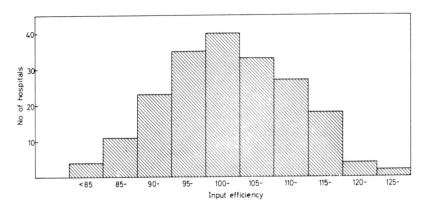

Fig. 2.12. Distribution of hospitals by input efficiency.

The input efficiency index (I^*) is not estimated directly but is calculated from casemix and productivity values by the identity $C_i^* = (P_i^*)^{-1}(I_i^*)$. Figure 2.12, the frequency distribution of hospitals by input efficiency, shows that input efficiency is less varied than costliness or productivity. No hospital had a value less than 80 or more than 130. The range between 90 and 110 contained 131 hospitals (74 per cent).

Rather surprisingly, the relation between productvity and input efficiency is quite weak. This is shown in figure 2.13, the correlation between $P*$ and $I*$ is only 0.048. Because both indices are measures of a hospital's performance in using its budget to produce treated cases, we might have expected a higher

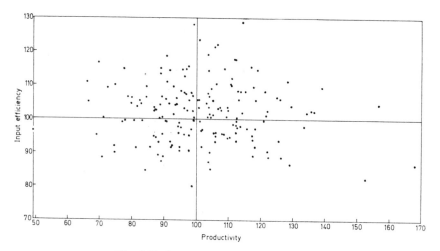

Fig. 2.13. Input efficiency and productivity.

correlation. A high correlation would indicate that "good hospital management" obtains an efficient input combination and achieves high productivity while "bad hospital management" combines inputs inefficiently and uses them with low productivity. One reason for the observed low correlation may be that budget allocation decisions (input combinations) are not made by the same persons, nor in the same way, as the decisions which affect the productivity of these inputs. Input combinations reflect administrative decisions, not only at the hospital level but also at group and regional levels, as well as the inherited pattern of past allocation. The productivity with which resources are used is more likely to be determined by medical and nursing staff within the individual hospital. The low correlations may also be due to imperfections in our indices as measures of *managerial* performance; productivity and input efficiency may reflect not only management but hospital age, local supply of medical and nursing staff, etc.

Costliness variation is primarily a reflection of productivity differences.

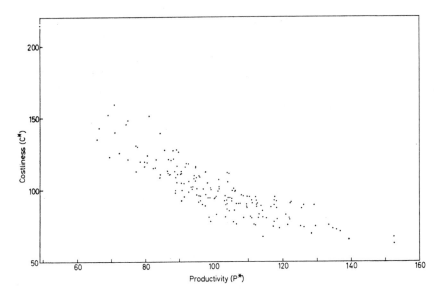

Fig. 2.14. Costliness and productivity.

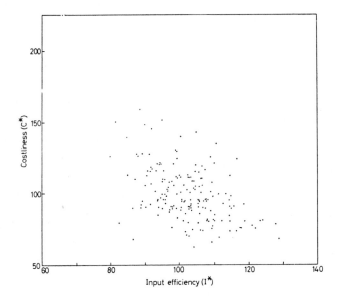

Fig. 2.15. Costliness and input efficiency.

This is seen by comparing figures 2.14 and 2.15. Seventy-one per cent of the variation in costliness can be explained by a linear regression on productivity while only 18 per cent can be explained by a similar regression on input efficiency. If high costliness values are to be lowered, attention must be focused primarily on increasing productivity. But the small effect which differences in input efficiency have on costliness must not be interpreted as indicating that input proportions are generally appropriate; in chapter 4 we show that the average absolute efficiency of input combination may be substantially below the optimum feasible level.

2.7 Applications in national health service management

Costliness, productivity, and input efficiency are proffered as indices of hospital performance in the selection and use of resources. For this purpose they are a considerable improvement over the crude cost per case or cost per week values currently used.

These indices should not, however, be interpreted uncritically as measures of the efficiency of each hospital's management.[32] Factors outside the control of hospital management may influence costs: hospital size, age and conditions of building, local availability of medical and nursing staff, etc. The output measure used in the three performance indices does not allow for differences in patient age distribution, quality of care, or extent of transfers. But the practical significance of these limitations should not be exaggerated. As shown in the next chapter, it is safe to disregard hospital size. Transfer and readmission rates are low in large acute hospitals and do not vary substantially among these hospitals; it might nevertheless be useful to develop a costliness index containing this information. A variable to indicate the proportion of patients over sixty-five years old could be included. Although to use these performance indices as measures of management *efficiency* it would be desirable to adjust them for differences in the quality of care, for an index of management *costliness* we do want a measure that shows that a management's costs are high whether this is due to low efficiency or high quality. The words "productivity" and "input efficiency" should, of course, also be purged of some of their usual connotation and interpreted in the same way as costliness. Unfortunately, until clinicians have developed a

---

[32] The word "management" is used here to include not only administrators but also medical and nursing staff.

useful measure of the quality of patient care we cannot distinguish between the effects of efficiency and quality. It may be best to assume that the medical care in large acute hospitals is generally of the same standard and that quality differences are limited to the hospitals' hotel activities.

In practice, the costliness index could provide administrators with a summary measure of hospital performance. As such it could direct the attention of regional and Ministry authorities to those hospitals that differ substantially from average. While it cannot be advocated as the sole basis for budgetary reallocations, it is no doubt a better guide than the crude cost values currently available.

The indices of productivity and input efficiency may be of value in identifying the cause of a hospital's high or low costliness value. If a hospital has high costliness but average or above average productivity, its staffing ratios and general expenditure pattern should be re-examined.

On a more general level, by studying the hospitals in which productivity and input efficiency values are very high or very low, hospital authorities may better understand the factors that influence hospital costs. Although our investigation of productivity and input efficiency indicates that costliness differences are due primarily to differences in productivity, we shall see in chapter 4 that there is evidence to indicate that the average absolute level of input efficiency is unnecessarily low.

Finally, the demonstration that approximately one third of the observed interhospital variation in cost per case is due to casemix differences has implications for further research. First it indicates that there is substantial cost variation that is not due to casemix differences. Hospital service efficiency can be improved if the reasons for this variation can be determined. Second, in studying the factors that influence hospital costs, biased and possibly misleading results may be obtained if casemix differences are not taken into account.

Heteroscedasticity and generalized least squares estimates

The optimum properties of ordinary least squares estimates depend on the assumption that the error variances of all observations are equal; i.e., for the equation $y = X\beta + u$ it is assumed that $\mathscr{E}(uu') = \sigma_u^2 I$. When the assumption of homoscedasticity is not satisfied, ordinary least squares estimates are unbiased but inefficient and the estimated standard errors of the coefficients are biased. Efficient parameter estimates are obtained if each observation is transformed by weighting it inversely proportional to the square root of its error variance; i.e., weighting by $\sigma_{u_i}^{-1}$. The transformation is equivalent to the generalized least squares procedure of replacing the ordinary least squares estimators $[\hat{\beta} = (X'X)^{-1}X'y]$ by $\hat{\beta} = (X'\hat{\Omega}^{-1}X)^{-1}X'\hat{\Omega}^{-1}y$ where $\Omega = \mathscr{E}(uu')$, a diagonal matrix (JOHNSTON, 1963, pp. 179–187, 207–210).

Because the σ_{u_i} are unknown, it is common to assume that they are equal (and therefore to use ordinary least squares) or that they are proportional to one of the explanatory variables or to its square root (JOHNSTON, 1963, p. 210). An alternative approach is developed in this appendix.

The observations are arranged in order of anticipated increasing error variance. When no single explanatory variable would provide a satisfactory ordering, the ordinary least squares predicted values of the dependent variable are used. The observations are then divided into quartiles and a likelihood ratio test of homoscedasticity is applied to the residuals of the ordinary least squares estimation. If heteroscedasticity is indicated, the estimated intra-quartile error variances are used to determine weights for transforming the original observations. Ordinary least squares is then applied to the transformed variables. The likelihood ratio test and weighting procedure is then repeated until the errors are homoscedastic. In practice, this occurred after the first generalized least squares estimates were obtained.

Equation (2A-1) relates the average ward cost per case in hospital i $(c_{i.})$ to the proportion of cases in each category (p_{ij}) and an error term (u_i). The national average costs in each category $(c_{.j})$ are unknown and are estimated from the regression of $c_{i.}$ on the p_{ij}'s.

$$c_{i.} = \sum_{j=1}^{k} c_{.j} p_{ij} + u_i \qquad (2A-1)$$

There is no reason to assume that $\sigma_{u_i}^2$ is correlated with any of the p_{ij}'s. A more plausible assumption is that the error variance increases with the average case cost. The ordinary least squares parameter estimates, $\hat{c}_{.j}$, were therefore used to calculate $\hat{c}_{i.}$ and hospitals were arranged in increasing order of $\hat{c}_{i.}$. This ordering was then divided into quartiles. The maximum likelihood estimate of the error variance in a particular quartile $(\hat{\sigma}_{u_q}^2)$ is equal to the sum of squared residuals $(\sum_{i \in q} \hat{u}_i^2)$ divided by the number of observations in the quartile (T_q); i.e., $\hat{\sigma}_{u_q}^2 = \sum \hat{u}_i^2 / T_q$. The values obtained were: 71.47; 114.82; 102.81; 239.34. There is a clear pattern. The error variance rises with increasing predicted cost per case. The difference between the second and third quartile variances is small in comparison to the other differences.

The test of homoscedasticity that will now be stated is an application of the general likelihood ratio test of the equality of several variances (MOOD, 1950, p. 269). As such, it ignores the order of the four quartiles and considers only whether the variances are equal. More specifically, the likelihood ratio compares the probability of the observed residuals given homoscedastic errors to the probability of the observed residuals given that the error variances are not necessarily the same in the four quartiles. The equation of the likelihood ratio (λ) is given in (2A-2):

$$\lambda = \frac{\prod_{q=1}^{4} (\hat{\sigma}_{u_q})^{T_q}}{(\hat{\sigma}_u)^T} \qquad (2A-2)$$

where $\hat{\sigma}_u^2$ is the maximum likelihood estimate of the error variance if there is homoscedasticity. As usual, $-2 \log \lambda$ is distributed as χ^2 with 3 degrees of freedom.

The error variances imply a likelihood ratio of $\lambda = 1.081 \cdot 10^{-4}$, indicating substantial heteroscedasticity. The value of $-2 \log \lambda$ is 18.265; the probability of observing a value greater than 11.341 in a chi-square distribution with 3 degrees of freedom is 0.01.

Generalized least squares estimates were therefore calculated by weighting each observation in proportion to $\hat{\sigma}_{u_q}^{-1}$. The weights, normalized to make their average equal one, were: 1.2599; 0.9940; 1.0504; 0.6885. The new error variances were much more equal: 106.34; 110.71; 114.99; and 117.06. The implied likelihood ratio is $\lambda = 0.941$. The associated χ^2 value (0.121) is not different from zero at the fifty per cent level.

TABLE 2A-1

Ordinary least squares and generalized least squares estimates of average costs by case type

Case type	Average cost per case $(\hat{c}_j)$	
	Ordinary least squares	Generalized least squares
General medicine	114.48	111.81
Paediatrics	24.97	28.35
General surgery	32.70	35.07
E.N.T.	15.25	15.58
Traumatic and orthopaedic surgery	39.69	36.04
Other surgery	98.02	101.38
Gynaecology	58.72	58.48
Obstetrics	34.88	34.50
Others	69.51	66.26

The generalized least squares parameter estimates, presented in table 2A-1 are very similar to those obtained by ordinary least squares. The analysis of this chapter therefore remains generally unaffected by the heteroscedasticity of the untransformed variables. Only the discussion of the standard error of the differences between observed and predicted cost merits revision. Because generalized least squares are more efficient than ordinary least squares, the standard errors of those differences would be decreased. This further reduces the probability that the observed differences are due to chance.

SYMBOLS IN CHAPTER 2

c_{ij} average ward cost per case of type j in hospital i

$c_{i.}$ average ward cost per case in hospital i

$c_{.j}$ average ward cost per case of type j in all hospitals

$\hat{c}_{i.}$ average ward cost per case predicted for hospital i

C_i^* costliness of hospital i

C_i^{**} a Laspeyres cost index

E_i total ward expenditure in hospital i

I_i^* input efficiency of hospital i

n_{ij} number of cases of type j in hospital i

p_{ij} proportion of cases of type j in hospital i

P_i^* productivity of hospital i

W_i output of hospital i

CHAPTER 3

EFFECTS OF SCALE ON HOSPITAL COSTS

3.1 Introduction

The existence of substantial economies or diseconomies of scale in the provision of hospital in-patient care would be an important determinant of the optimum pattern of hospital size and location. In this chapter we investigate the extent to which the size of acute hospitals influences their costs per case.

The measurable effect of hospital size on the cost of in-patient care is one of three factors that should determine the pattern of hospital size and location. Size may also influence the "quality" of care provided and the cost of "distributing" hospital services. Advocates of increasing hospital size argue that large hospitals bring together a range of facilities and medical specialists that cannot be provided in smaller units. Against this must be balanced the evidence that the quality of "personal" care (the "standards of human relations in hospital") deteriorates with hospital size (REVANS, 1954; CARTWRIGHT, 1964). Hospital "distribution costs" per case, including social as well as money costs, increase with the size of the catchment area served. These costs include the operation of the ambulance service, the use of patients' time in transit to hospital, the risk due to distance to be travelled in emergencies, the provision of in-patient care for persons who would have been seen as out-patients if they lived closer to hospital, and the reduction in use of hospital services by persons living at a distance. Our investigation of the economies of scale in the production of hospital in-patient services therefore provides only part of the evidence on which hospital size should be determined.

Some of the reasons why we might expect hospital size to influence costs are suggested in section 3.2. The work of a number of previous writers is considered briefly. Section 3.3 discusses the advantages and disadvantages of the data available for this study. Section 3.4 shows that on balance size has little effect on cost. The analysis considers the specification bias that results if a description of the casemix is not included in the cost function. In a more detailed analysis, hospitals are divided into size classes and some or all of the parameters of the cost function are allowed to vary among size classes.

Section 3.5 shows that the apparently horizontal average cost curve represents a balance of the effects of scale on length of stay and on cost per day. Larger hospitals treat somewhat fewer cases per bed. If it were not for this lower intensity with which the hospital plant is used, these larger hospitals would have lower costs per case. This is demonstrated by incorporating a capacity utilization variable (cases per bed) in the cost function. If this variable is endogenous to the system of hospital production, ordinary least squares will give biased estimates; an alternative set of estimates, using an instrumental variable approach, is presented.

In the sixth section we consider the possibility of estimating separate cost curves for the individual components of cost, e.g., nurses' salaries. Because input substitution cannot be clearly distinguished from true economies of scale, these results are proffered with caution.

An appendix deals with the problems of heteroscedasticity.

As a background for these studies, it should be noted that acute hospitals today have an average of some 200 beds, but range in size from less than 100 to more than 1 000 beds. The *Hospital Plan for England and Wales*, (Cmnd. 1604, 1962) presented to Parliament in 1962, indicates that in the future hospital system the great majority of cases will be treated in district general hospitals of 600 to 800 beds. A substantial reduction in the number of small hospitals is planned by 1975. While 46.8 per cent of all non-mental hospitals in 1961 had less than 250 beds, by 1975 only 28.1 per cent of non-mental hospitals will be in this size class; in contrast, the percentage of non-mental hospitals with more than 650 beds will rise from 16.4 in 1961 to 40.1 in 1975 (COWAN, 1963).

3.2 The nature of scale effects

Traditional economic analysis posits a U-shaped cost curve for the manufacturing plant. Technical economies, the division of labour, and the spreading of overheads cause unit costs to decline as scale increases (ROBINSON, 1935; CLARK, 1923). Eventually, the costs and difficulty of managing a large scale enterprise cause unit costs to increase (ROBINSON, 1935, ch. 3). A number of writers have criticized the theoretical basis of the U-shaped curve, arguing instead that the cost curve is flat or L-shaped (ANDREWS, 1948; WILES, 1956). Andrews argues that "technical costs" per unit fall continuously with increasing scale while "managerial costs"[1] fall for part and then rise. Wiles denies the potential importance of managerial diseconomies and concludes that costs stop falling or rise only because labour efficiency may decrease with scale: "whenever the human factor is important there may be a U-shaped cost curve, or at least a very flat L". (WILES, 1961, p. 221).

Empirical cost curve estimates give overwhelming support to the view that costs do not increase with size. This has been shown in individual studies relating to gas supply (VERHULST, 1948; LOMAX, 1951; GRIBBEN, 1953), electricity supply (JOHNSTON, 1952; NERLOVE, 1963), road transport (JOHNSTON, 1956; CHISOLM, 1959; MEYER and KRAFT, 1961), rail transport (BORTS, 1952; BORTS, 1960), retail distribution (DEAN and JAMES, 1942; HALL and WINSTEN, 1961), and local authority licence issuing (OLIVFR, 1962). Surveys of other cost curve estimates may be found in MASON (1943), SMITH (1955), WILES (1956), JOHNSTON (1960), and WALTERS (1963). The conclusion based on cost studies are confirmed by production function estimates of economies of scale in rail transport (KLEIN, 1953) and electricity supply (DHRYMES and KURZ, 1964).

A number of writers have suggested that the cost curve estimates may be biased towards linearity.[2] But in the absence of evidence or stronger theoretical arguments in favour of the U-shaped cost curve, it must be concluded that within the broad range of current observation costs generally do not rise with scale.[3]

What can be expected of the cost curve of an acute hospital? If the mix of cases and the quality of care remain constant, larger scale could lower

---

[1] These "managerial costs" include not only the costs of management but also the "excess" costs of non-managerial factors of production that are attributable to a lower level of managerial efficiency.

[2] Some of these arguments will be considered below in relation to the estimation of the hospital cost curve. For a general critical summary, see JOHNSTON (1958 and 1960).

[3] It is unfortunate that empirical studies have concentrated on power, transportation and distribution. Evidence about manufacturing industry is still very scarce.

cost per case by permitting higher percentage occupancy of available beds and providing opportunities for economies of scale in the operation of centralized housekeeping activities (laundry, kitchen, boiler room, etc.). Beyond a certain size, managerial diseconomies and decreasing labour efficiency might cause case costs to rise.

In fact, among hospitals of the size studied in this chapter (approximately 100 to 1 000 beds), scale has little effect on percentage occupancy. But routine central housekeeping activities do constitute a large portion of total costs and larger scale allows the mechanization and specialization of function that could produce economies of scale.

The primary managerial problem of a large hospital is maintaining staff efficiency. Despite the formal structure of staff relations, the "production process" is itself quite informal in comparison with industrial production. The pace of operation is therefore critically dependent upon the attitudes and behaviour of staff members. There is evidence that staff morale may be lower in larger institutions (Acton Society, 1953; REVANS, 1964). Revans argues further that hospital efficiency reflects the ease of communication among different types of staff and that communication is likely to be worse in larger hospitals (REVANS, 1962 and 1964). Decreasing staff efficiency, and poor communications in particular, are likely to raise case cost by increasing patients' average duration of stay.

The overall effect to be anticipated is unclear. The shape of the cost curve will depend on the relative importance of technical economies and managerial or staff diseconomies. Stated differently, technical economies may lower cost per day but managerial or staff diseconomies may increase costs through longer durations of stay.

There is unfortunately little previous evidence about the effects of scale on hospital costs. A few studies have been made in the United States and France, none in Britain. The hospitals in each study were heterogeneous in the types of cases treated, the quality of service provided, the extent of teaching activities, and the prices paid for inputs and staff. These factors were not specifically allowed for in the cost curve estimation. Moreover, estimates were related to cost per patient day rather than cost per case, thus ignoring the possible influence of hospital size on duration of stay. In view of these shortcomings, it is not surprising that the available evidence is inconclusive. JONES (1938) and HAYES (1959) found U-shaped cost curves in studies of New York hospitals. In a later study, decreasing average costs were inferred from the positive intercept of a linear total cost function fitted to 60 hospitals varying in size from 48 to 453 beds (P. J. FELDSTEIN, 1961). For a summary of these findings, see KLARMAN (1965, pp. 104–108). SKINNER (1962) studied more than 200 Michigan short term general hospitals; 41 per cent had less than 50 beds and only three per cent had more than 500 beds. He found a strong positive association between cost per patient day and hospital size, but stated that most of this could probably be attributed to differences in the types of cases treated and the range of services provided.

3.3 Hospital cost data: Advantages and disadvantages[4]

The data used in this study refers to the costs and cases treated in 177 large acute non-teaching hospitals in England and Wales. Cost data for the fiscal year ending 31st March 1961 was obtained from the *Annual Costing Return* (Ministry of Health, 1961). Detailed data on the types of cases treated during 1960 were obtained from annual Hospital Return (S.H.3) forms provided by the Ministry of Health. This material has already been described in chapter 2.

We are fortunate in having a comparatively large number of observations over a wide range of hospital sizes. The smallest hospital has only 72 beds while the largest has 1 064; associated with the mean of 302.9 is a coefficient of variation of 61.4. The distribution of hospital sizes reflects factors of history and location rather than conscious choice of economically efficient sizes. The criticism (FRIEDMAN, 1955; MALMGREN, 1958; WALTERS, 1961) that estimated cost curves show constant average costs because competition forces all firms to build plants only within the minimum average cost size range will therefore not be relevant to our study.

Because we have separate measures of hospital capacity (the number of available beds) and hospital output (the number of cases treated), we are able to avoid two problems that arise when output is used as a measure of scale in the estimation of cost functions. The first of these problems, raised by FRIEDMAN (1955), is generally referred to as the "regression fallacy". Friedman has argued that the usual finding that long-run average cost curves are L-shaped or flat (i.e., that marginal costs do not rise with scale) is due to the incorrect measurement of scale and costs. If scale is

---

[4] For discussions of the usual disadvantages of accounting data for cost studies, see JOHNSTON (195?), MALMGREN (1958), and JOHNSTON (1960).

measured by output rather than by capacity, a transitory component in output will cause the output-capacity ratio to be positively correlated with scale.[5] Since conventional accounting does not increase plant depreciation when output rises, the unit cost of production will, *ceteris paribus*, be negatively correlated with the output-capacity ratio. As a result of these two things, the regression of unit cost on scale (i.e., output) is biased downward toward constant marginal costs.[6] The second problem that we avoid by using capacity as the measure of scale is the possibility of simultaneous equations bias. If a hospital's output and cost per case are determined simultaneously (i.e., if cost per case is a determinant of how many cases a hospital treats), the output variable will not be independent of the error term in the cost function; the ordinary least squares regression of cost per case on output would give biased coefficients.[7]

No attempt has been made to adjust costs for local price differences. Although a correction for the London area would have been desirable, the implicit assumption of uniform prices in the rest of the country is quite tenable. Wages and salaries, which account for substantially more than half of hospital costs, are paid on a uniform national scale with a London "cost of living" allowance. Other equipment and supplies are often obtained at uniform prices through national purchase agreements between the manufacturer and the Ministry of Health. The failure to adjust London costs for higher prices would bias the estimated cost curve only if the size distribution of London hospitals were different from the distribution of hospitals in the country as a whole. Table 3.1 shows that the two distributions are remarkably similar.

Capital costs are not included in the data. Costs refer to operating costs including maintenance and the normal replacement of equipment but exclude depreciation, building costs and the purchase of major long-lived equipment. Charges for rent, rates and water average less than three per cent of total cost. (In drawing policy conclusions from the empirical results, it is also important to note that higher levels of capacity utilization, i.e., higher case-bed ratios, reduce the capital cost per case.)

---

[5] Friedman assumes that there would be no correlation if scale were measured by capacity.
[6] For additional discussion of the regression fallacy, see BORTS (1960), NERLOVE (1963), and WALTERS (1963).
[7] Not all research workers agree that scale should be measured by a capacity variable. HALL and WINSTEN (1961) argue that measuring size by output has logical priority over measuring size by input.

TABLE 3.1

Frequency distributions of hospitals by number of available beds

No. of available beds	No. of hospitals in England and Wales	No. of hospitals in London	% of hospitals in England and Wales	% of hospitals in London
1 —	6	2	3.4	3.6
101 —	57	18	32.3	32.5
201 —	45	11	25.6	20.0
301 —	23	9	13.2	16.3
401 —	22	6	12.5	10.8
501 —	10	4	5.6	7.2
601 —	6	2	3.4	3.6
701 —	3	1	1.7	1.8
801 —	1	0	0.6	0
901 —	1	1	0.6	1.8
1001 +	2	1	1.1	1.8
Total	177	55	100	100
Mean	303	299	—	—

Although environmental factors such as hospital age and location may influence cost, this will bias the estimated cost curve only if these factors are associated with size. There are no *a priori* reasons to suspect a source of bias but the subject has not been investigated.

The problems of measuring hospital output have already been discussed in chapter 2. Our basic unit of output is the case. Since this is measured by the number of discharges and deaths, cost will be affected by the extent of interhospital transfers. No evidence was available on whether transfers are associated with size; in the absence of such association, transfers would not affect the parameters of the cost curve. The incorporation of casemix differences is considered in detail in the next section.

3.4 Estimation of the average cost functions

By estimating the relation between size and cost as an *average* cost function instead of a total cost function we obtain several advantages.[8]

---

[8] A total cost curve is presented in chapter 5. Its properties support the conclusions of the current chapter.

First, we reduce the problem of heteroscedasticity. With homoscedastic errors, the regression coefficients are efficient and their estimated standard errors are free of bias. The appendix of this chapter indicates that there would be substantial heteroscedasticity in a total cost function but that this is not so for the average cost functions that have been estimated.

Second, we are able to measure output as the number of cases and scale as the number of beds. As explained above, the case is a more appropriate measure of output than the patient-day or bed-day. Measuring scale by number of available beds avoids the regression fallacy difficulties and the simultaneous equations problem encountered if output is used as a measure of scale.

Third, our cost function implies that if no cases were treated the total cost would be zero. Consider the basic average cost function, $c_i = \alpha + \beta B_i$, where B_i = number of available beds. Multiplying both sides by the number of cases gives: $E_i = n_i c_i = \alpha n_i + \beta B_i n_i$, from which it is clear that total cost would be zero if no cases were treated. This is desirable since our cost data excludes capital cost and is most appropriately considered as long-run variable cost.

Finally, the *proportional* composition of cases provides a suitable casemix specification for an average cost curve. If the equation $c_i = \beta B_i + \sum_{j=1}^{k} \gamma_j p_{ij}$ (where p_{ij} is the proportion of cases of type j) is multiplied by the number of cases, the casemix in the resulting total cost curve is specified as the actual number of cases in each of the k categories. The proportional casemix specification effectively removes the problem of multicollinearity in the workload specification that would be present in severe form if the actual numbers of cases were used.

3.4.1. Preliminary estimates without casemix

Basic estimates of linear and quadratic average cost functions are presented in equations (3.1) and (3.2). It should be recalled that the average cost per case is £ 54.62.

$$c_i = 49.71 + 1.62\ (10^{-2})B_i$$
$$\qquad\quad (0.55) \qquad\qquad\qquad R^2 = 0.048 \qquad (3.1)$$

$$c_i = 49.16 + 1.96\ (10^{-2})B_i - 0.38\ (10^{-5})B_i^2$$
$$\qquad\quad (1.77) \qquad\qquad (1.89) \qquad R^2 = 0.048 \qquad (3.2)$$

These equations make no allowance for the association between hospital size and casemix composition. We shall therefore give them little attention. For what it is worth, however, we may note that differences in hospital size explain very little of the variation in cost per case. Although the large number of observations make even the low R^2 values ($R^2 = 0.048$) "significant" at the 5 per cent level, this must be interpreted with caution. As shown below, large hospitals are associated with more costly casemixes; some of the correlation between casemix and cost per case is therefore attributed to hospital size. Disregarding the bias that may be due to casemix differences, and using the regression coefficients as point estimates, we see that, throughout the currently observed range of hospital sizes, cost per case increases with hospital size; the quadratic cost curve does not reach its maximum until 2 580 beds. The expected cost per case for small (100 beds), average (300 beds), and large (1 000 beds) hospitals is shown in table 3.2. It must be emphasized that these values are shown only so that they may be compared with the unbiased estimates presented later.

TABLE 3.2

Expected case cost at three hospital sizes

Cost function and equation	Expected cost per case ($£$)		
	100 Beds	300 Beds	1 000 Beds
Linear	51.33	54.57	65.91
Quadratic	51.09	54.70	64.97

3.4.2. *Casemix omission and specification bias*

Because equations (3.1) and (3.2) do not include any measure of the casemix, the estimates of the coefficients of B and B^2 may be biased.[9] More specifically, let the correct specification be

$$c_. = [BB^2]\beta + P\gamma + u \tag{3.3}$$

[9] For a more general discussion of specification bias see GRILICHES (1957) and THEIL (1961).

where $c_.$ is the vector of average costs, $[BB^2]$ is the matrix of hospital size variables, and P is the matrix of case proportions. If instead we estimate

$$c_. = \alpha + [BB^2]\beta^* + v, \qquad (3.4)$$

β^* will be a biased estimator of β unless there is no association between scale and casemix or no net association between casemix and cost per case $(\gamma = O)$.

If the casemix variables in (3.3) are redefined so that the first column of P is the unit vector and the remaining columns denoted $\tilde{P}$, the asymptotic bias may be expressed as

$$\text{plim} \begin{bmatrix} \hat{\beta}^* - \beta \\ \hat{\alpha} - \gamma_1 \end{bmatrix} = \text{plim}(X'X)^{-1} X'\tilde{P}\tilde{\gamma} \qquad (3.5)$$

where $X = [BB^2 i]$. We are not interested in deriving this bias directly, since we shall be estimating equation (3.3) itself. It will therefore be sufficient to indicate that size and casemix are not uncorrelated. For this purpose, we specify P in terms of the same 9 case-types used in chapter 2; thus P is $177 \times 9.$[10] Instead of estimating $(X'X)^{-1}X'\tilde{P}$ we shall take the easier course of showing that $(P'P)^{-1}P'X \neq O$. This is shown by the multiple correlation coefficients associated with the regression of B on P ($R^2 = 0.29$) and B^2 on P ($R^2 = 0.20$). More important, the evidence suggests that the larger hospitals have more costly workloads. Equations (3.6) and (3.7) show that the expected cost per case, calculated on the basis of proportional casemix in 9 categories, increases with hospital size.

$$\hat{c}_{i.} = 50.34 + 1.41 \cdot 10^{-2} B_i$$
$$(0.29) \qquad\qquad\qquad R^2 = 0.12 \qquad (3.6)$$

$$\hat{c}_{i.} = 48.42 + 2.61 \cdot 10^{-2} B_i - 1.34 \cdot 10^{-5} B_i^2$$
$$(0.94) \qquad\quad (1.01) \qquad R^2 = 0.13 \qquad (3.7)$$

where $\hat{c}_{i.} = P(P'P)^{-1}P'c_{i.}$.

Again, this must be interpreted with some caution since the values derived in the regression of average cost on casemix are themselves influenced by the relation between scale and cost. Nevertheless, equations (3.1) and (3.2) are likely to be biased.

---

[10] For a discussion of this specification see chapter 2, p. 39.

3.4.3. *The average cost function with casemix specified*

When a vector of nine case proportions is included in the average cost function, we obtain the following estimated equations:[11]

$$c_{i.} = 0.295 \cdot 10^{-2}B_i + p_i' \hat{\gamma}$$
$$(0.567) \qquad\qquad\qquad\qquad R^2 = 0.308 \qquad (3.8)$$

$$c_{i.} = -0.581 \cdot 10^{-2}B_i + 0.934 \cdot 10^{-5}B_i^2 + p_i' \hat{\gamma}$$
$$(1.728) \qquad\quad (1.741) \qquad\qquad R^2 = 0.310 \qquad (3.9)$$

Both equations indicate that when allowance is made for differences in casemix the average cost per case is unaffected by hospital size.

Comparing equations (3.1) and (3.8), we note that introducing casemix reduces the size of the coefficient of B and increases its standard error. The R^2 values are due almost entirely to the effect of casemix; for the regression of cost per case on casemix, we calculated $R^2 = 0.303$.

With casemix omitted, the quadratic cost function equation (3.2) indicated increasing costs throughout the relevant range; the linear term was positive and exceeded its standard error while the negative quadratic term was only 20 per cent of its standard error. In contrast, equation (3.9), a quadratic cost function with casemix included, implies that cost is unaffected by size. If we disregard the standard errors, (3.9) indicates a shallow U-shaped curve with minimum average cost per case at approximately 310 beds. The current average size appears to be that of minimum average cost. Smaller hospitals show little increase in average cost (with 100 beds, average cost would be £ 55), larger hospitals show a somewhat more substantial increase in cost (with 1 000 beds, average cost would be £ 59).

Table 3.3 summarizes the casemix-adjusted estimates of average costs in hospitals of three sizes.

Comparing tables 3.2 and 3.3 shows that omitting casemix may substantially bias the cost-curve estimates.

Although the standard errors of the coefficients in equations (3.8) and (3.9) are quite large, we must not disregard as "insignificant" the possibility that cost per case does increase substantially as hospitals exceed the current average size. The "cost" of incorrectly assuming that size is irrelevant justifies further investigation. If an increase from 300 to 1 000

---

[11] For economy of space we omit $\hat{\gamma}$, the estimated coefficients of the casemix variables, simply adding the term $p_i' \hat{\gamma}$.

beds raises average cost by almost ten per cent, as indicated by the point estimates for the quadratic cost function shown in table 3.3, this might have important implications for hospital planning and location. It would also compel us to revise our costliness measure to include an explicit size variable.

TABLE 3.3

Expected case cost at three hospital sizes with average casemix*

Cost function equation	Expected cost per case (£)		
	100 beds	300 beds	1 000 beds
Linear	54.00	54.61	56.68
Quadratic	54.72	54.30	58.73

* The "average casemix" is the mean proportion of cases of each case type.

We will therefore examine the cost curve in more detail. Two approaches are followed. First, we focus attention on the large hospitals (with more than 500 beds) and examine their actual costs, costliness values, and regression residuals. Second, we divide hospitals by size classes and examine the shape of the cost curve within each class. Both of these approaches support the conclusion that any tendency to increased costs in larger hospitals is of no importance. There are neither substantial economies nor diseconomies of scale. The costliness index need not be adjusted for hospital size.

3.4.4. *Examination of actual costs and residuals of large hospitals*

Table 3.4 presents, for the 23 hospitals with 500 or more beds, the observed cost per case (col. 3), the costliness per case (col. 4), the residual of the regression of cost per case on the nine case proportions (col. 5), and the residual from the quadratic cost equation (col. 6).

We examine the actual cost per case (col. 3) to see whether larger hospitals do have higher cost when no account is taken of casemix. Only 12 of the 23 hospitals have a cost above the overall average. The average of these 23 hospitals" costs is £ 61.92 (standard error = 2.69). Although this indicates that costs are higher in larger hospitals, as already shown in equations (3.1) and (3.2), caution must be used in considering observed costs without adjustment for casemix.

TABLE 3.4

Hospital costs and residuals

Ident. no.	Beds avail.	Cost per case (£)	Costliness	Res. from (P)	Res. from (B, B², P)
(1)	(2)	(3)	(4)	(5)	(6)
128	518	72.06	108.29	5.5	5.60
1	532	67.14	88.61	−8.6	−8.60
100	532	37.69	74.78	−12.7	−12.87
101	533	114.21	146.20	36.1	36.33
47	533	50.45	89.75	−5.8	−5.75
12	537	86.40	136.73	23.2	22.96
89	546	55.35	89.66	−6.4	−6.44
69	571	65.75	107.14	4.5	4.35
106	573	50.57	89.36	−6.0	−6.15
88	589	59.22	106.17	3.4	3.13
166	615	53.87	85.36	−9.2	−9.65
28	627	61.37	101.46	−0.9	0.54
46	631	73.54	116.73	10.5	10.15
27	645	49.00	94.50	−2.9	−3.64
151	647	52.97	102.68	13.8	0.77
57	689	49.70	88.88	−6.3	−7.20
26	729	54.51	94.13	−3.4	−4.57
87	744	64.41	111.23	6.5	5.23
127	799	40.01	74.29	−13.9	−15.57
165	850	64.31	115.30	8.5	6.22
54	954	53.41	111.27	7.0	3.59
45	1043	79.69	127.33	17.1	12.73
164	1064	53.19	81.40	−12.2	−16.88
Mean	—	61.92	101.79	2.08	2.09
S.E.	—	2.69	3.88	2.17	2.52

Column 4 shows the "costliness" of these hospitals: 100 times the ratio of actual cost to the cost expected on the basis of casemix.[12] Similarly, column 5 shows the residual of actual cost from cost expected on a basis of casemix. To see whether, after taking casemix into account, large hospitals are more costly than smaller ones we note whether the costliness values are generally greater than 100 or, equivalently, the residuals of

---

[12] For a full discussion of the costliness measure, see chapter 2.

column 5 are greater than zero. Although this avoids the bias that results from examining the crude case costs of column 3, it underestimates the extent to which higher costs are associated with hospital size. This occurs because, to the extent that size is correlated with individual casemix proportions and that size is correlated with cost per case, the casemix regression coefficients will reflect the indirect association with higher costs; when these coefficients are used to "predict" case cost they predict that larger hospitals have higher costs than they should predict. The nature of this specification bias is analogous to that discussed in section 3.4.2. It must be borne in mind in examining columns 4 and 5. In the absence of this bias, if cost were actually higher in large hospitals, we would expect a high proportion of the estimated residuals in equation (2.13) to be positive. In fact, only 11 of the 23 residuals (48 per cent) are positive. The average of the residuals is 2.08 with a standard error of 2.17. A one-tailed t-test does not indicate this to be different from zero at the 15 per cent level. Even allowing for the possibility of bias, there is little reason to believe that ignoring hospital size causes any systematic tendency to underestimate cost. The evidence may be interpreted as indicating that diseconomies of scale, if any, are quite small.

Finally, we consider the residuals from the casemix adjusted quadratic function (equation 3.9). The equation predicts that cost rises with hospital size above 300 beds. If costs do not rise with size in the way predicted, we expect that the residuals for large hospitals would tend to be negative. Column 6 shows that only 11 of the 23 residuals are negative. The average of the residuals is 2.09; with a standard error of 2.52, this is not significantly different from zero. It would not, however, be correct to infer that, since cost in larger hospitals is not overestimated by the quadratic function, cost actually rises with size. If costs in medium size hospitals are underestimated, the shape of the function would be wrong but would produce unbiased prediction for large hospitals. To explore this further we consider the cost function in individual size categories and estimate functions other than the quadratic.

3.4.5. *Cost functions for hospitals in different size groups*

It is a substantial simplification to assume that the cost-size relationship can be represented by a single quadratic function over the entire size range, i.e., that the regression coefficients have the same expected values in each size group. By dividing hospitals into size groups and estimating a separate cost function for each group, we may obtain better estimates of the size-cost relationship in each group. This would be achieved not only because the relationship is allowed to differ between size groups but also because the estimates for each size group are not influenced by hospitals outside the group. Such improved cost functions would be important for several reasons. First, they would provide more accurate evidence of whether there are any general diseconomies of scale. Second, they might be of practical importance when the policy problem is to choose between hospitals of 200 to 300 beds and hospitals of 300 to 500 beds; for this question, the cost function in the 500 to 1 000 bed region would be irrelevant. Third, if hospital size is to be incorporated into the costliness measure, the size effect should be one appropriate to the hospital's size group. Finally, it would be interesting to compare the shape of the single quadratic cost function estimated for the entire 75 to 1 000 bed range with the shape of the cost curve for the same range that might have been estimated on the basis of observations on hospitals with less varied numbers of beds.

For this purpose we have divided hospitals into two subgroups (above and below the mean). A further analysis was done by dividing hospitals into four subgroups (adding the mean ±one standard deviation as division points). A summary of the hospital population and the subgroups is given in table 3.5.

TABLE 3.5

Characteristics of hospital population and hospital subgroups

	Population	Two subgroups		Four subgroups			
Min	72	72	303	72	118	303	489
Max	1064	302	1064	117	302	488	1064
Mean	302.9	189.8	493.0	99.0	204.0	389.1	652.9
S.D.	185.8	60.6	169.5	13.9	52.2	53.7	162.3
Number	177	111	66	15	96	40	26

We have estimated a separate equation of type (3.9) for each size group on the assumption that all eleven parameters of the cost function vary between size groups; this assumption will be referred to as hypothesis one. A more restricted assumption (hypothesis two) is that the workload coefficients (γ) are the same in all subgroups with only an additive constant term and the size coefficients differing between size groups.[13] These cost functions are estimated by a single equation, using a set of dummy variables. Equation (3.10) for, example, was used to estimate the coefficients when hospitals were divided into two subgroups.

$$c_{i.} = \beta_{11}(B_i d_{1i}) + \beta_{12}(B_i^2 d_{1i}) + \beta_{21}(P_i d_{2i}) + \beta_{22}(B_i^2 d_{2i}) + \delta(d_{2i}) + p_i' \gamma \quad (3.10)$$

where

$$d_{1i} = 1 \text{ if } B_i \leq 302; \; d_{1i} = 0 \text{ otherwise}$$

$$d_{2i} = 1 \text{ if } B_i \geq 303; \; d_{2i} = 0 \text{ otherwise}$$

Hypothesis two is therefore more economical of degrees of freedom than hypothesis one. When hospitals are divided into two groups, we estimate 14 parameters instead of 22; for four groups, we estimate 20 instead of 44.

The more disaggregated models do not provide a better model of the relation between size and average cost per case than the original single equation (3.9). Allowing a constant term and the coefficients of the size variables (B and B^2) to vary (hypothesis two) does not substantially improve the explanation of the variation in average costs. Introducing divisions into two and four groups reduces the residual sums of squares by only 1.6 per cent (two groups) and 4.8 per cent (four groups). Examination of F-ratios[4] shows that the null hypotheses of equality between the residuals for one and two groups, one and four groups, and two and four groups, cannot be rejected at the twenty per cent probability level.

This conclusion is confirmed if we examine the estimated coefficients for the individual cost curves, their standard errors, and the implied turning point of the cost function; these are presented in table 3.6. The regression coefficients of the size variables are not significant in the single equation model, nor, in general, in the equations of the four disaggregated models. But all four of these models indicate a cost curve of the same general shape as that implied by the single equation: a slightly U-shaped curve with a minimum in the range of 250 to 350 beds. When hospitals are divided into two groups, both hypotheses indicate a minimum cost at 250 beds; among hospitals with more than 300 beds, the cost curve is described as rising

---

[13] This is similar to Nerlove's estimation of "neutral" economies of scale (1965, pp. 119–125).

[14] The ratios of the sums of squared residuals, adjusted for degrees of freedom, are distributed as F. The required independence of the numerator and denominator is clear when it is recognized that the variables of the more disaggregated equation could be rewritten in terms of the more aggregated variables plus additional variables.

TABLE 3.6

Average cost functions in hospital size groups

Division	Min	Max	No. of hospitals	Tot. S.S. (10^{4})	Hypothesis one (separate equations)				Hypothesis two (single equations)			
					B (10^{-2})	B^2 (10^{-5})	Min.* (Max)	Res. S.S. (10^{4})	B (10^{-2})	B^2 (10^{-5})	Min.* (Max)	Res. S.S. (10^{4})
One group	72	1064	177	3.367	−0.58 (1.73)	0.93 (1.74)	311	2.323				
Two groups	72	302	111	1.446	−7.97 (10.79)	16.09 (27.75)	248	0.982	−11.3 (12.5)	22.9 (32.0)	247	2.286
	303	1064	66	1.763	2.79 (6.13)	−2.39 (4.82)	(585)	1.069	2.6 (4.9)	−1.70 (3.82)	(818)	
Four groups	72	117	15	0.153	−18.30 (394.08)	−135.60 (1939.81)	No T.P. decr.	0.031	17.3 (350.4)	−195.0 (1836.0)	(44)	2.212
	118	302	96	1.282	−34.61 (17.99)	75.43 (42.82)	229	0.848	−38.8 (20.8)	85.0 (49.3)	288	
	303	488	40	0.935	−16.82 (93.39)	24.54 (122.56)	342	0.607	−4.50 (64.43)	8.6 (83.9)	263	
	489	1064	26	0.735	1.51 (19.09)	−1.39 (12.58)	(540)	0.228	−15.6 (141.1)	9.8 (92.2)	787	

* Minimum (or maximum) cost per case occurs at indicated number of beds. No. T. P. indicates no turning point in the relevant range.

to a maximum in the 600–800 bed range. Of course, because of the relatively large standard errors these turning points must be regarded with caution. The four separate equations also indicate a decline until 230 to 340 beds, followed by a rise to a (false) maximum at 540 beds. It may be noted that the coefficients for the equation related to the group of hospitals with 117 to 303 beds are nearly twice their standard errors and support the conclusion that there is a turning point in the range indicated. The single-equation four-group model (hypothesis two) shows a similar pattern, except for the apparent minimum point in the middle of the group of largest hospitals. Thus, although the assumption that the cost-size relationship can be represented by a single quadratic function over the entire range is, *a priori*, a substantial simplification, the results obtained when the coefficients are allowed to vary among size groups are substantially the same.

The investigation of models with varying coefficients was undertaken to examine whether the diseconomies of scale suggested by the single quadratic cost curve was more than a statistical artifact. The coefficients for the two and four group models do not provide firm evidence for or against the theory that costs rise among the largest hospitals. The division into two groups provides contradictory evidence. Hypothesis one suggests a rising average cost from 300 to 600 beds followed by a decline among the largest hospitals; hypothesis two indicates that costs do rise until 820 beds, after which there may be some decline. Similarly for the division into four groups. Hypothesis one indicates that costs rise from 340 to 540 beds and then decline; hypothesis two shows costs declining in the largest group until 790 beds and then possibly rising. We can neither accept nor reject the theory that there are overall diseconomies of scale among the largest hospitals. What does appear most likely is that a true minimum does exist in the 250 to 300 bed range; this is generally agreed by all models and gives rise to a quadratic equation in the corresponding size group with coefficients nearly twice their standard errors. Beyond 300 beds it would seem that costs do rise until about 600 beds and then probably flatten out at this higher level. In short, costs rise slightly with scale beyond the current average size but cease rising at twice that size.

3.5 Effects of capacity utilization differences

The estimates of section 3.4 indicate that there are no economies of scale. We now look "behind" the casemix-adjusted quadratic cost curve and show that the apparent absence of any influence of size is the resultant of a *pure scale effect* that decreases cost per case in larger hospitals and a *case-flow effect* that increases these costs.

This section shows that if the number of cases treated per bed per year (the "case flow", F) were the same for hospitals of all sizes, the cost per case would decrease with scale. Larger hospitals have lower flow rates and this case-flow effect increases cost per case in a way that balances the pure scale effect which, *ceteris paribus*, would cause larger hospitals to have lower costs per case. However, even if flow rates were the same, the economies of scale would be small; the evidence indicates that cost per case would be only ten per cent lower in 1 000 bed hospitals than in hospitals of 300 beds.

3.5.1. *Variation in flow rates with hospital size*

The average case flow is 23.18 cases treated per bed year, reflecting a range from 9.41 to 40.48 and a standard deviation of 5.33.

The flow rate is negatively correlated with hospital size; the correlation of F and B is -0.432. A more general relationship, taking into account casemix differences, is given in equation (3.11):

$$F_i = -1.616 \cdot 10^{-2} \, B_i + 8.317 \cdot 10^{-6} \, B_i^2 + p_i' \hat{y} \qquad (3.11)$$
$$(0.613) \qquad\quad (6.173)$$

Despite the correlation between B and B^2, each of the coefficients exceeds its standard error with the coefficient of B being more than $2\frac{1}{2}$ times its standard error. Although the positive quadratic term exceeds its standard error, the coefficients indicate that F decreases throughout the relevant range; there are only two observations with more beds than the 970 at which F reaches its fitted minimum in equation (3.11).

Of course, the association of scale and flow rate shown in equation (3.11) does not *prove* that larger size "causes" F to decrease or creates an environment that decreases F. But the estimate does lend strong support to the arguments of section 3.2 above that the pace of hospital activity may decrease with size. The inference is consistent with the more general economic argument that the specific diseconomy of large units is managerial or labour inefficiency and the increasing complexity of communications.

3.5.2. *The average cost function adjusted for flow rates*

The effect of this correlation on the relationship between size and cost is shown in the flow-adjusted quadratic cost curve equation (3.12).[15]

$$c_{i.} = -3.54 \cdot 10^{-2} B_i + 1.96 \cdot 10^{-5} B_i^2 - 7.14 F_i + 0.109 F_i^2 + p_i' \hat{\gamma} \qquad (3.12)$$
$$(1.01) \qquad\qquad (1.07) \qquad\qquad (0.64) \quad (0.013) \qquad R^2 = 0.744$$

In contrast to equation (3.9), each of the coefficients of B and B^2 is greater than its standard error. Instead of an approximately linear relationship with the slight suggestion of a minimum at 310 and costs then rising to *increase* some ten per cent by $B = 1\,000$, equation (3.12) indicates that costs *decrease* to a minimum of £ 49.30 at $B = 903$, a decrease of 12 per cent from the mean cost per case. This theoretical turning point is an artifact of the quadratic form of the function. While there are too few hospitals larger than this (only three exceed 900 beds) for direct tests, the quadratic curve is not better than some monotonic functions at explaining the variation in cost per case. Of these, the semilogarithmic and logarithmic equations are presented:

$$c_{i.} = -6.01 \log B_i - 7.03 F_i + 0.106 F_i^2 + p_i' \hat{\gamma} \qquad (3.13)$$
$$(1.21) \qquad (0.63) \quad (0.013) \qquad R^2 = 0.744$$

$$\log c_{i.} = -0.099 \log B_i - 0.093 F_i + 0.126 \cdot 10^{-2} F_i^2 + p_i' \hat{\gamma} \qquad (3.14)$$
$$(0.020) \qquad (0.110) \quad (0.022) \qquad R^2 = 0.734$$

Both equations indicate a negative elasticity of cost per case with respect to scale of approximately -0.1. Although error variance tests are not directly applicable to the comparison of equations (3.12) and (3.13)[16], the two residual sums of squares are practically equal and the R^2 values of (3.12), (3.13), and (3.14) provide no basis for choice among the three specifications.

It therefore seems appropriate to conclude that if flow rates were uniform, larger hospitals would enjoy lower costs per case.

---

[15] F, unlike B, is not an exogenous variable. The coefficients of equation (3.12) are therefore not necessarily unbiased. Consistent instrumental variable estimates presented in 3.5.6 support the ordinary least squares results presented here.

[16] The F-test or equivalent likelihood ratio test requires that the errors in the two equations be independent; this they clearly are not.

3.5.3. *Flow-rate adjusted cost functions in different size groups*

To obtain a more accurate picture of the flow-rate adjusted relation between size and cost, hospitals were divided into two and four subgroups in the same way as was done for the general quadratic cost curve in section 3.4.5 above. In that section two hypotheses were considered: hypothesis one specified a completely separate cost function for each size group; hypothesis two specified that the coefficients of the casemix were the same in all size groups while the other coefficients might differ. In this section we also consider a third hypothesis; we restrict the equation further by assuming that the coefficients of F and F^2 are the same in all size groups.

When only the constant term and coefficients of the size variables (B and B^2) are allowed to vary (hypothesis three), the estimation of separate cost functions does not significantly improve the explanatory ability of the model. The sum of squared residuals is reduced by only 1.4 per cent with

Average cost functions in hospita

No. of Groups	Min.	Max.	No. of hosp.	Total S.S. (10^4)	β_1 (10^{-2})	β_2 (10^{-5})	Min* (Max.)	Res
					Hypothesis one			
One	72	1064	177	3.367	−3.54 (1.08)	1.96 (1.07)	903	
Two	72	302	111	1.446	−4.78 (7.42)	5.65 (18.94)	423	
	303	1064	66	1.763	7.09 (37.14)	1.13 (2.92)	(318)	
Four	72	117	15	0.153	4.87 (2.46)	−2.58 (1.21)	(96)	
	118	302	96	1.282	−0.07 (12.02)	−5.63 (28.62)	No T.P. decr.	
	303	488	40	0.935	−4.49 (54.38)	6.41 (71.33)	No T.P. decr.	
	489	1064	26	0.735	−1.49 (1.24)	7.51 (8.10)	1985	

* Minimum (or maximum) cost per case occurs at indicated number of beds. "No T

two size groups and 3.7 per cent with four size groups. Examination of the corresponding F-ratios indicates that the reductions are not significant at the twenty per cent level.

Similar results are obtained when the coefficients of the case-flow variables (F, F^2) are also allowed to vary (hypothesis two). The sum of squared residuals is now reduced by 2.7 per cent (two groups) and 8.6 per cent (four groups). Again, these reductions are not significant at the twenty per cent level.

Examining the coefficients of the cost curves, presented in table 3.7 confirms that the same general size-cost relation is indicated by each of the models. We have seen that when no division into groups is made, cost per case decreases with hospital size to a (false) minimum at 905 beds; more appropriately costs decrease, but at a decreasing rate, as a function of size. Each of the models in which hospitals are divided into two groups follows the same pattern. Among smaller hospitals, costs fall toward a minimum at

s: Adjusted for case-flow rates

	Hypothesis two				Hypothesis three			
f ps	β_1 (10^{-2})	β_2 (10^{-5})	Min* (Max.)	Res. S.S. (10^4)	β_1 (10^{-2})	β_2 (10^{-5})	Min* (Max.)	Res. S.S. (10^4)
	—	—	—	—	—	—	—	—
	−6.27 (7.84)	9.53 (19.94)	329	0.837	−4.64 (7.76)	5.89 (19.76)	394	0.848
	0.61 (3.00)	−1.05 (2.35)	(289)	—	0.28 (2.99)	−0.81 (2.34)	(170)	—
	180.3 (271.1)	−1025.6 (1394.9)	(88)	0.786	192.3 (221.6)	−1082.7 (1158.3)	(89)	0.828
	0.933 (13.115)	−6.483 (31.041)	(72)	—	−0.283 (13.06)	−4.066 (30.93)	No T.P. decr.	—
	19.458 (40.689)	−26.643 (53.040)	(365)	—	28.78 (40.25)	−39.09 (52.43)	(368)	—
	−9.167 (8.834)	5.158 (5.770)	889	—	−8.64 (8.75)	4.69 (5.71)	921	—

tes no turning point in the relevant range.

a hospital size that exceeds the upper bound of the size group. Among larger hospitals, costs fall from a maximum at a hospital size that is at the beginning of the size group or below its lower bound. In short, costs continually decrease although, in contrast to the fixed-coefficients model, costs first fall at a decreasing rate and then at an increasing rate. This should be interpreted with caution since the coefficients of the two group model are, under all these hypotheses, less than their standard errors. The same general pattern appears in each of the models in which hospitals are divided into four groups: decreasing costs, followed by a range of constant costs, followed by further decrease in costs. Again, the large standard errors require us to be cautious about attaching too much weight to these slight changes. But the overall pattern is clear: a general decline in costs over the entire range of observed hospital sizes. Further, the simplification of expressing the cost-size relation by a fixed coefficient model appears to be warranted.

3.5.4. *Components of case flow*

The flow rate is proportional to the percentage occupancy of available beds divided by the average duration of stay per case.[17] We may therefore enquire whether the case flow effect is due primarily to percentage occupancy or length of stay.

Although there is some variation in percentage occupancy – a standard deviation of 4.94 is associated with the mean occupancy of 81.7 per cent – this variation is small in comparison to the overall variation in flow (a standard deviation of 5.32 and a mean of 23.2).

More important, introducing the occupancy rate (R) into the standard quadratic cost curve[18] shows that percentage occupancy does not itself affect cost and causes little change in the coefficients of B and B^2. In equation (3.9) the coefficient of B was -0.581 (10^{-2}) and of B^2 was 0.934 (10^{-5}), implying a minimum cost at 310 beds. The coefficients in equation

---

[17] $F = \dfrac{\text{cases per year}}{\text{available beds}} = \dfrac{\text{cases per year}}{\text{occupied beds}} \cdot \dfrac{\text{occupied beds}}{\text{available beds}} =$

$\dfrac{365}{\text{average stay per case}} \cdot \dfrac{\text{proportional occupancy}}{\text{of available beds.}}$

[18] R, like F, is not an exogenous variable. The results of this section are maintained when ordinary least squares estimates are replaced by instrumental variable estimates. See section 3.5.6.

(3.15) imply a minimum cost at 318 beds. This reflects an absence

$$c_{i.} = -0.626 \cdot 10^{-2} \; B_i + 0.989 \cdot 10^{-5} \; B_i^2 - 0.462 \; R_i + 0.002 \; R_i^2 + p_i'\hat{\gamma}$$
$$\quad\;\; (1.747) \qquad\qquad (1.756) \qquad\qquad (4.154) \quad\; (0.026) \qquad\qquad (3.15)$$

of correlation between percentage utilization and number of beds: $r = -0.009$.

In contrast, a quadratic cost curve with a duration of stay variable (S) shows results more similar to the flow-adjusted cost curve than to the general curve of equation (3.9).[19] The coefficients of equation (3.16)

$$c_{i.} = -3.63 \cdot 10^{-2} \; B_i + 1.85 \cdot 10^{-5} \; B_i^2 + 1.94 \; S_i + 5.52 \cdot 10^{-2} \; S_i^2 + p_i'\hat{\gamma}$$
$$\quad\;\; (0.86) \qquad\qquad (0.86) \qquad\quad (0.77) \quad\; (2.25) \qquad\qquad (3.16)$$

may be compared with those of equation (3.12) (the coefficient of B was $-3.54 \cdot 10^{-2}$ and of B^2 was $1.96 \cdot 10^{-5}$); the implied minimum cost size, 981 beds, is similar to the flow-adjusted minimum cost size of 903 beds. We may therefore conclude that the most important flow effect is due to differences in length of stay.

3.5.5. *A note on the regression fallacy*

The discussion of the effects of case flow rate on the shape of the estimated cost curve is reminiscent of Friedman's analysis of the "regression fallacy" that can be introduced by differences in capacity utilization.[20]

In some ways the hospital cost results are illustrative of Friedman's position. Although we have measured scale by capacity (number of beds) we may consider the effect of measuring it by output (number of cases, n_i). If scale is measured by output, capacity utilization (F_i) no longer decreases with scale (compare equations (3.17) and (3.11)). There is, as Friedman would predict, a positive correlation of output and the output-capacity ratio; F reaches a maximum at n greater than 30 000 in contrast to reaching a minimum at $B = 970$. As a result of this, the quadratic cost curve

$$F_i = 1.693 \cdot 10^{-4} \; n_i - 2.575 \cdot 10^{-9} \; n_i^2 + p_i'\hat{\gamma} \qquad\qquad (3.17)$$

$$F_i = -1.616 \cdot 10^{-2} \; B_i + 8.317 \cdot 10^{-6} \; B_i^2 + p_i'\hat{\gamma}$$
$$\quad\;\; (0.613) \qquad\qquad (0.617) \qquad\qquad\qquad\qquad (3.11)$$

---

[19] See section 3.5.6. for similar instrumental variable estimates.
[20] For a discussion of Friedman's hypothesis, see above, p. 60-61.

relating cost per case to output shows decreasing costs (compare equations (3.18) and (3.4)). Thus, measuring scale by output biases downward the cost of "large" hospitals. In (3.18), $\hat{c}_{i.}$ decreases throughout the observed range of scale while in (3.9) it increases for B greater than its average value (310).

$$c_{i.} = 2.563 \cdot 10^{-3} \, n_i + 8.23 \cdot 10^{-8} \, n'_i + p'_i \hat{\gamma}$$
$$\quad (0.902) \qquad\qquad (4.66) \qquad\qquad\qquad (3.18)$$

$$c_{i.} = -5.809 \cdot 10^{-3} \, B_i + 9.34 \cdot 10^{-6} \, B_i^2 + p'_i \hat{\gamma}$$
$$\quad (17.278) \qquad\qquad (17.41) \qquad\qquad\qquad (3.9)$$

Although these results support Friedman, the reason is somewhat different. In Friedman's analysis, higher utilization rates decrease unit costs because depreciation costs are not fully measured. In the study of hospital costs, higher utilization decreases unit costs not because of the definition of costs but because of the definition of output units. A higher output-capacity ratio means shorter hospital stay per case and therefore lower costs.

Since we have been able to measure scale by capacity, the general problem of the regression fallacy need not concern us. We should, however, recognize the implication of omitting capital depreciation from our cost data. To the extent that true depreciation costs increase with more intensive utilization of capacity, the omission of capital depreciation will cause our cost curves to underestimate the actual economies of scale. But intensive utilization is unlikely to have a very important effect on hospital depreciation. The more significant result of omitting capital depreciation is an underestimate of the extent to which total cost per case, including capital costs, rises with scale. Since larger hospitals have lower case-bed ratios they would have higher capital costs per case unless there are very substantial economies in large scale building.

3.5.6. *Instrumental variable estimates*

Unlike the number of beds, the case-flow rate is not an exogenous variable. It might therefore not be independent of the error in the average cost equation, thus making ordinary least squares estimates biased. Although it would in principle be better to analyze the adjusted cost curve in the context of a complete model, we limit ourselves to a single equation estimate. As a compromise, however, we consider an instrumental variable estimate.

We divide hospitals into four and six groups on F and use group numbers as instruments.[21] The estimated coefficients will be consistent if the group number is uncorrelated with the corresponding error in the equation. This assumption may be quite plausible. Although staff and other expenditures may influence the actual F value that a hospital achieves, the group in which a hospital falls may reflect primarily exogenous factors such as the scarcity of beds in the area, local social conditions (which influence length of stay), etc. As shown in chapters 4 and 5, the only input expenditures which do have a substantial direct effect on F are drugs, dressings and doctors' salaries. Since these are a small component of cost, and since doctors' salaries may themselves be largely exogenously determined, it may be relatively innocuous to employ ordinary least squares or such an instrumental variable approach.

Table 3.8 compares the ordinary least squares and instrumental variable estimates of the coefficients of B and B^2 in long-run average cost equations adjusted for F, S and R. The instrumental variable estimates support the basic conclusions derived from the ordinary least squares equations. Adjustment for case-flow rate or average duration of stay shifts the minimum cost scale from the current average size (about 300 beds) to the largest sizes in the observed range.[22] The elasticity of cost per case with respect to scale, calculated at 300 beds, remains negative but very low. Adjustment for percentage occupancy still has little effect on the scale parameters.

3.6 Cost functions for individual cost categories

All of the cost functions in this chapter have referred to total ward cost per case. A similar analysis could be done for individual cost categories, e.g., medical salaries per case. In this way we might hope to see whether, for example, medical cost per case decreased with hospital size or nursing cost per case increased with size.

Such an analysis is unbiased only if there is no tendency to substitute one type of input for another as hospital size increases. Although there seems

---

[21] If the quartile number had been used for both F and F^2, the normal matrix would have been singular.

[22] Although the new case-flow adjusted equation indicates a smaller minimum cost size than the ordinary least squares value (738 beds instead of 903), there are too few hospitals above this size (only nine) to give much weight to this as evidence of a turning point.

TABLE 3.8

Comparison of ordinary least squares and instrumental variable estimates of long-run average cost function parameters*

Adjustment for capacity utilization	Estimation method**	Coefficient of		Minimum cost size	Cost elasticity***
		B (10^{-2})	B^2 (10^{-5})		
F, F^2	O.L.S.	−3.54 (1.08)	1.96 (1.07)	903	−0.1298
F, F^2	I.V.	−2.76 (1.40)	1.87 (1.40)	738	−0.0900
S, S^2	O.L.S.	−3.63 (0.86)	1.85 (0.86)	981	−0.1384
S, S^2	I.V.	−3.04 (1.14)	1.37 (1.14)	1109	−0.1218
R, R^2	O.L.S.	−0.63 (1.75)	0.99 (1.76)	318	−0.0020
R, R^2	I.V.	−0.53 (1.75)	0.91 (1.76)	291	−0.0090

 * All equations include a vector of nine case proportions.
 ** O.L.S. = Ordinary least squares; I.V. = Instrumental variables.
 *** Elasticity of cost per case with respect to number of beds evaluated at $B = 300$.

no reason to expect such substitution, we cannot test the hypothesis that size does not influence input substitution. Any evidence on changes in the composition of cost per patient day could not be used as evidence about input substitution; rather, a change in the proportional distribution of cost per patient day would be the resultant of both input substitution and the relative economies of scale of specific inputs. We must therefore accept as a working hypothesis the assumption that any tendency to substitute one type of input for another is unaffected by size. An alternative examination of whether there are specific economies of scale for individual inputs will be considered in the next chapter as part of our investigation of hospital production functions.

It should be emphasized that the existence of possible or actual substitution as such does not preclude valid estimation of individual cost curves.[23] Only the association of scale and input substitution would bias the results. The existence of substitution as such would only increase the variance of the estimated cost curve coefficients[24].

Table 3.9 presents the relevant coefficients from three cost functions for each input category. All cost functions include a casemix vector representing nine case-type proportions. Column 3 refers to a linear cost curve, columns 4–6 to a quadratic curve, and columns 7–9 to a quadratic function which also contains case-flow variables (F, F^2). Because substitution among different staff types, especially between nurses and domestics, might be more common than other forms of substitution, two joint input categories are also presented. Subtotals for direct and indirect costs are also indicated. For reference, the values for total ward cost are also given.

The simple linear functions suggest that several categories of direct costs increase with size – domestic staff, drugs, dressings, clothing – while in no category do costs decrease significantly.

The quadratic cost function confirms the result that domestic staff cost per case increases continuously with size. Nursing costs are at a minimum in hospitals that are somewhat larger than average (409 beds) and then increase. Medical costs decrease until 548 beds and then begin to rise. Unlike the coefficients of the cost curve for total costs, the coefficients of these individual curves substantially exceed their standard errors. Adjusting each of these functions has the effect of increasing the hospital size at which costs begin to rise. Domestic costs now rise above 366 beds. These cost patterns agree well with our general theory that the potential economies of scale in the hospital are at some point outbalanced by the lower intensity with which capacity is utilized and, even when this case-flow effect is taken into account, by the lower efficiency with which staff work in a larger hospital is carried out.

The remaining cost categories show that it is only in respect to ward staff – the pure labour component of hospital cost – that, after adjusting for case-flow rates, there are still diseconomies of scale. In the other cost

---

[23] DHRYMES and KURZ (1964) obtain an individual cost curve only when they have shown (by estimating a general constant elasticity of substitution production function) that substitution is not possible. Their procedure is obviously safer than ours since their exclusion of all substitution obviates the assumption that size does not influence substitution.

[24] We consider the extent of input substitution and substitution possibilities in the next chapter.

TABLE 3.9

Average cost functions for individual cost types

Cost category	Mean	Linear function B (10^{-2})	Quadratic function			Quadratic function with caseflow variables		
			$B(10^{-2})$	B^2 (10^{-5})	Min* (Max)	B (10^{-2})	B^2 (10^{-5})	Min* (Max)
(1)	(2)	(3)	(4)	(5)	(6)	(7)	(8)	(9)
Medical	5.71	−0.030 (0.054)	−0.206 (0.165)	0.188 (0.166)	548	−0.393 (0.144)	0.252 (0.143)	780
Nursing	13.50	0.955 (1.473)	−0.656 (0.445)	0.802 (0.448)	409	−1.415 (0.308)	1.094 (0.307)	646
Domestic	3.40	0.298 (0.105)	0.095 (0.321)	0.216 (0.324)	No T.P. increasing	−0.234 (0.285)	0.320 (0.284)	366
Nursing and domestic	16.93	0.394 (0.217)	−0.561 (0.659)	1.018 (0.663)	276	−1.649 (0.453)	1.415 (0.451)	587
Staff	22.75	0.364	−0.767	1.206	318	−2.041	1.666	612

		(0.021)	(0.064)	(0.065)		(0.061)	(0.061)	
Dressings	0.60	0.008 (0.009)	0.028 (0.027)	−0.021 (0.028)	(667)	0.012 (0.026)	−0.016 (0.026)	(375)
Appliances and equipment	1.68	0.005 (0.025)	0.020 (0.077)	−0.016 (0.078)	(612)	−0.014 (0.077)	−0.006 (0.077)	No T.P. decreasing
Clothing, etc.	0.45	0.011 (0.008)	0.015 (0.026)	−0.005 (0.026)	No T.P. increasing	−0.010 (0.025)	0.006 (0.025)	833
Total direct costs	30.44	0.484 (0.309)	−0.568 (0.937)	1.122 (0.944)	253	−2.097 (0.645)	1.665 (0.641)	630
Catering	9.24	−0.042 (0.119)	−0.009 (0.346)	0.054 (0.349)	83	0.022 (0.071)	−0.035 (0.070)	(315)
Laundry	1.76	0.053 (0.027)	0.110 (0.082)	−0.062 (0.083)	(887)	−0.533 (0.258)	0.240 (0.256)	No T.P. decreasing
Total indirect costs	24.14	−0.160 (0.296)	0.062 (0.903)	−0.237 (0.910)	(131)	−1.349 (0.622)	0.229 (0.618)	No T.P. decreasing
Total ward costs	54.62	0.295 (0.567)	−0.581 (1.728)	0.934 (1.741)	311	−3.541 (1.080)	1.957 (1.074)	905

* Minimum (or maximum) cost per case occurs at indicated number of beds. "No T.P." indicates no turning point in relevant range.

categories, the advantages of large scale outweigh the tendency of individuals to be less efficient. For drugs and dressings, after adjustment for case-flow rates, costs decrease (slightly and not significantly) in hospitals above the 375 to 470 bed range. In the two other categories of indirect cost, adjusted costs per case decrease throughout the relevant range. Similarly catering costs decrease beyond 315 beds and laundry costs decrease throughout the entire range.

3.7 Conclusions

The general empirical results presented in this chapter can be summarized briefly. The average cost function, when adjusted for casemix, is a shallow U-shaped curve with a minimum at the current average size (310 beds). Costs rise beyond this size but level off after 600 beds at about 10 per cent above the minimum cost. The failure to achieve economies of scale is primarily due to the lower case-bed ratio in larger hospitals, even after adjusting for casemix differences. This probably reflects a lower level of "managerial" or labour efficiency and, in particular, a slower hospital pace. When costs are adjusted for case-flow rates, cost per case decreases throughout the observed range of hospital size to a value of £ 49.30 at 905 beds, some 12 per cent below average cost. Cost curves for individual input categories show that the pure labour component – ward staff costs – have the greatest diseconomies of scale while direct costs and other indirect costs generally enjoy increasing returns to scale when adjustment is made for case-flow rates.

These results indicate that the medium size hospital of 300 to 500 beds is at least as efficient at providing general ward care as are larger hospitals. But although the medium size hospital must not be rejected as uneconomically small, it cannot be defended as substantially less costly than the larger hospital. If the case-flow rate of larger hospitals could be improved so that it was not lower than the rate in other hospitals – primarily by decreasing average lengths of stay – operating cost per case in larger hospitals could be reduced to better than 12 per cent below current average cost. Additional savings in capital costs would also be achieved. Further economies could be obtained by larger hospitals if they lowered their expenditure on ward staff into line with the rest of the hospitals.

Finally, the results of this chapter indicate that the costliness index would gain little if hospital size were explicitly included.

Generalized least squares estimates

The appendix of the previous chapter presented a likelihood ratio test of homoscedasticity and described the use of estimated error variances in generalized least squares estimation. Application of this method to the quadratic average cost function adjusted for capacity utilization (equation 3.12A) shows

$$c_{i.} = \beta_1 B_i + \beta_2 B_i^2 + \beta_3 F_i + \beta_4 F_i^2 + p_i' \gamma + u_i \qquad (3.12A)$$

that although there is heteroscedasticity in the original equation, generalized least squares estimates are almost identical to those obtained by ordinary least squares. This is described below. An alternative method is then discussed.

Hospitals were ordered by the value of $\hat{c}_i$ calculated from the ordinary least squares estimates of equation (3.12A). Maximum likelihood estimates of the error variances in each quartile $(\hat{\sigma}_{u_q}^2)$ are: 26.01; 41.39; 33.76 and 92.47. The implied likelihood ratio, $\lambda = 1.706 \cdot 10^{-5}$, indicates the presence of heteroscedasticity. This is confirmed by the value of $-2 \log \lambda = 21.964$ which greatly exceeds the critical value of the χ^2 distribution for the 0.01 probability level (11.341).

The estimated error variances were used to calculate weights for generalized least squares regression. The weights do not change gradually with $\hat{c}_i$; the most substantial difference is between the first three weights (1.251, 0.992, 1.098) and the final weight (0.663). The new error variances are essentially homoscedastic. The likelihood ratio is 0.905; the associated χ^2 variable, 0.199 is not different from zero at the fifty per cent level.

The generalized least squares coefficients are almost identical with those obtained by ordinary least squares. Table 3A-1 compares the values for the coefficients of B and B^2. (The values for F and F^2 are also very similar; these are discussed in section 5.3.2.2 of chapter 5.)

TABLE 3A-1

Ordinary least squares and generalized least squares estimates of parameters of average cost function

Variable	OLS estimate	GLS estimate
B	$-3.54 \cdot 10^{-2}$	$-3.50 \cdot 10^{-2}$
B^2	$1.96 \cdot 10^{-5}$	$2.09 \cdot 10^{-5}$

An alternative method of deriving weights was also investigated. Instead of assuming that σ_u was a monotonic function of $\hat{c}_i$, we related the absolute values of the residuals of the ordinary least squares equation ($|\hat{u}_i|$) to the variables of equation (3.12A) by an equation of the form:

$$|\hat{u}_i| = a + bB_i + b_2 B_i^2 + b_3 F_i + b_4 F_i^2 + p'\gamma + \varepsilon_i. \qquad (3A-1)$$

Such a regression explained 23 per cent of the variance of $|u_i|$. The estimated equation was then used to calculate values of $|u_i|$ and the inverses of this calculated variable were the weights used in a generalized least squares regression. The importance of this method is that it allows the estimated value of $|u_i|$ to vary freely among hospitals and permits each of the explanatory variables to influence the estimation of $|u_i|$.

The parameter estimates obtained in this way are again very similar to the ordinary least squares values: the coefficient of B is $-3.32 \cdot 10^{-2}$ and the coefficient of B^2 is $1.97 \cdot 10^{-5}$.

It is safe to conclude that the inferences made on the ordinary least squares estimates are valid in spite of the heteroscedasticity of the original variables.

APPENDIX 3B

SYMBOLS IN CHAPTER 3

B_i number of beds in hospital i

$c_{i.}$ average ward cost per case in hospital i

$\hat{c}_{i.}$ average ward cost per case predicted for hospital i

E_i total ward expenditure in hospital i

F_i case flow rate in hospital i; the number of cases treated per bed per year

n_i number of cases treated in hospital i

p_i vector of 9 case proportions in hospital i

P matrix of 9 case proportions in all hospitals

$\tilde{P}$ matrix of 8 case proportions in all hospitals

R_i proportional occupancy of beds in hospital i

S_i average duration of stay per case in hospital i

CHAPTER 4

A PRODUCTION FUNCTION FOR ACUTE HOSPITALS

4.1 Introduction

A production function for acute hospitals can be a useful tool for studying several practical problems: economies of scale, optimum input proportions, and the measurement of productive efficiency.

As a way of assessing the effects of hospital size, the production function is an alternative to the cost curve analysis of chapter 3. But the production function, unlike our cost curve, also includes the use of capital (measured by the number of beds) among the inputs. A further advantage of the production function for studying scale effects is that the results are not affected by differences in the efficiency with which hospitals of different size combine inputs: if large hospitals were (say) less efficient in combining inputs than smaller hospitals, the cost curve would underestimate potential economies of scale.

Second, from a production function we can infer input proportions that will achieve given output at minimum cost or, equivalently, maximum output for given cost.

Third, by relaxing the assumption that the parameters of the production function are constant, we can explore whether the elasticities of output with respect to particular inputs vary with hospital size. Allowing the coefficients to vary provides additional information about economies of scale, in particular non-neutral economies of scale. If the coefficients do vary substantially, the optimum input proportions are also likely to vary.

Finally, we may use the production function for evaluating the performance of individual hospitals. This has already been discussed in chapter 2.

Three problems arise in formulating an estimable production function. The output of the hospital must be specified in a way that recognizes its multiproduct character. Inputs must be measured appropriately and aggregated into useful categories. Finally, a mathematical model of hospital production must be selected. This requires specifying a form of the production function and a set of assumptions about the way that input quantities are determined. Because there have been no previous estimates of hospital production functions, these problems must be approached cautiously and with a willingness to experiment with alternative specifications.

Section 4.2 discusses some of these specification problems. Section 4.3 presents estimated production functions of the Cobb-Douglas form and examines the implied economies of scale and optimum input properties. More general production relations are developed and analyzed in sections 4.4 and 4.5. Alternative productivity measures are compared in the appendix of this chapter.

Ordinary least squares estimates are only appropriate if the explanatory variables are uncorrelated with the error term in the production function. MARSCHAK and ANDREWS (1944) showed that when inputs are jointly determined with output by the profit-maximizing firm, production functions estimated by ordinary least squares will be biased. The choice of an estimation method must depend on the assumptions about input determination. Two basic models underlie all past work: the profit-maximizing firm (MARSCHAK and ANDREWS, 1944; HOCH, 1955, 1958, 1962; MUNDLAK, 1961, 1963) and the regulated industry providing exogenously determined services at minimum cost (BORTS, 1952, 1960; KLEIN, 1953; NERLOVE, 1963; DHRYMES and KURZ, 1964). Neither of these models is appropriate to the hospital. The first requires no comment. The "regulated public utility" is unsatisfactory in two ways. The level of output of a hospital is not exogenously determined: the extensive interregional variation in hospital admissions dispells the idea that there is a given demand that a hospital must satisfy (see chapter 7, especially 7.2). Second, the hospital has only limited discretion about input levels. The number of beds in each hospital remains practically constant from year to year. Staffing rules set by the Ministry of Health determine the maximum numbers of medical and nursing staff that may be hired. Because all salaries and wages are based on national scales, hospitals in many areas are unable to obtain as much staff as they can afford to hire. Section 4.5 considers these problems and presents a production model that embodies some of the special characteristics of the hospital. Alternative approaches to the problem of simultaneous equations bias are also considered in section 4.3.

The studies in this chapter are based on the same 177 acute, general, non-teaching hospitals described in the previous chapters.

4.2 Specification of the production function

This section focuses on the specification of the production function and ignores the related input determination equations. The simplest stochastic assumption is therefore made: that the error in the equation is independent of each of the inputs. The form of the production function is discussed first (section 4.2.1). The specification of hospital output (section 4.2.2) and inputs (section 4.2.3) is then considered.

4.2.1. The form of the production function

Three production functions have been prominent in the econometric literature: the constant elasticity of substitution (C.E.S.) function, the Cobb-Douglas function, and the Leontief fixed-proportions function. In considering these we ignore for the moment the problem of specifying output and inputs, writing Q_i for the output of hospital i and X_{ri} for the quantity of the rth input used by hospital i.

In the C.E.S. production function the elasticity of input substitution is a parameter to be estimated; the Cobb-Douglas function is a special case with elasticity of substitution equal to one, while the Leontief function is the limiting case with elasticity of substitution equal to zero (ARROW et al. 1961). The C.E.S. function has therefore been advocated as a more general and more desirable hypothesis. Unfortunately, the parameters of the C.E.S. function must be estimated from the reduced from equation relating the net output per man to the wage rate. This estimation procedure cannot be applied to hospitals. First, it would be unwise to base estimates on the assumption (implicit in the reduced form equations) that hospitals use the input proportions which minimize total cost for given output, or more strictly, adjust inputs so that the wage rate and the marginal product of labour are equal. One of the reasons for studying the production function is to estimate the efficiency with which inputs have been combined. Second, because hospitals all face the same relative prices for variable inputs and because the capital input (number of beds) cannot be varied by the hospital, it would be impossible to estimate the C.E.S. parameters by the usual estimation procedure.[1]

The Cobb-Douglas production function (equation 4.1) poses none of these estimation difficulties.

$$Q_i = A \prod_{r=1}^{s} X_{ri}^{\alpha_r} U_i. \qquad (4.1)$$

If each X_{ri} is independent of the error term in the equation, we can estimate the α_r's by ordinary least squares regression in the logarithms of the original variables. Even if this assumption is not fulfilled, it is possible to obtain unbiased or consistent estimates; this is developed in section 4.3.5. Estimates of a Cobb-Douglas function, presented in section 4.3, indicate that this is a useful specification. However the implicit assumption that all inputs can be substituted for each other is questionable. We may, for example, doubt that a given output could be maintained by decreasing the number of doctors and increasing the expenditure on patients' food. The evidence of this chapter suggests that a production function that implies substitution among some, but not all, inputs may be best.

In the Leontief-fixed proportions production function (equation 4.2) no substitution among inputs is possible. In this extreme form the Leontief

$$Q_i = \min [f_1(X_{1i}), f_2(X_{2i}), \ldots, f_s(X_{si})] \qquad (4.2)$$

function seems untenable. By increasing the number of doctors, for example, a hospital may be able to shorten the length of patient stay and thus decrease the input of beds for a given output.

A mixed Leontief-Cobb-Douglas specification (equation 4.3) implies that substitution among some, but not all, inputs is possible. We shall find in section 4.4 and the appendix that although this is a useful hypothesis its predicted Q_i values for individual hospitals do not differ substantially from those predicted from an equation of form (4.1).

$$Q_i = \min [f_1(X_{1i}), f_2(X_{2i}), \ldots, f_k(X_{ki}), (A \prod_{r=k+1}^{s} X_{ri}^{\alpha_r})] \qquad (4.3)$$

Stating the relationship between output and inputs in the form of a production function suggests that the relations are purely technical rather

---

[1] After completing this chapter, I developed a two-stage procedure for the direct estimation of the parameters of the C.E.S. function (FELDSTEIN, 1968).

than a mixture of technical and behavioural. The statistical evidence presented below, as well as discussions with hospital administrators, suggests that a distinction should be made between those inputs that determine the level of the hospital's output and those housekeeping inputs that affect the standards of comfort but do not influence the number of cases treated. Both of these ideas are also developed in section 4.5.

4.2.2. *Specifying output*

Almost without exception, the "output" in econometric production functions is either a single homogeneous physical quantity or the market value of a set of heterogeneous outputs.[2] The inpatient department of an acute hospital produces a set of treated cases of various types that can neither be weighted equally in considering a hospital's output nor aggregated by any market prices. We experiment with two approaches to output specification: explicitly including a set of variables to describe casemix and deriving a weighted sum of individual cases as a single composite output measure.

In its most general form we may write the production relation as an implicit function of s inputs (X_{ri}), m outputs (C_{ji}) – the number of cases of type j in hospital i, and an error term (U_i):

$$\phi(X_{1i}, \ldots, X_{si}, C_{1i}, \ldots, C_{mi}, U_i) = 0 \tag{4.4}$$

One explicit form of this equation would make the number of cases of one type a function of the inputs and the other outputs:[3]

$$C_{1i} = \phi(X_{1i}, \ldots, X_{si}, C_{2i}, \ldots, C_{mi}, U_i) \tag{4.5}$$

However, even if the inputs are exogenously determined, the C_{ji}'s are obviously not; the lack of independence between the C_{ji}'s and U_i would make ordinary least squares estimates biased. Any attempt to define a complete system of m equations is almost certain to be abortive.

---

[2] Only recently have there been any attempts to specify methods for estimating production functions for the multiproduct firm. The "transcendental" production function defined for this purpose (MUNDLAK, 1963, 1964) is unsuitable for the hospital problem because it relies on the existence of varying market prices for the products.

[3] This was essentially the specification used by KLEIN (1953) for railway production of passenger miles and freight miles. Klein's estimation procedure assumed a Cobb-Douglas function and cost-minimizing input combinations.

An alternative to equation (4.4), containing the same information, is the implicit function of the s inputs, the total number of cases (C_i), the proportion of cases in $m-1$ categories (p_{ji}) and the error term:

$$\phi(X_{1i}, \ldots, X_{si}, C_i, p_{1i}, \ldots, p_{m-1,i}, U_i). \tag{4.6}$$

Rewriting this explicitly we obtain

$$C_i = \phi(X_{1i}, \ldots, X_{si}, p_{1i}, \ldots, p_{m-1,i}, U_i). \tag{4.7}$$

If we assume that the p_{ji}'s are exogenous, i.e., that the hospital's policy influences the number of cases treated but not the speciality composition of those cases, we are no longer precluded from using ordinary least squares regression estimates.

Writing a Cobb-Douglas form of equation (4.7) as:

$$C_i = (\prod_r X_{ri}^{\alpha_r})e^{p'_i\beta} \tag{4.8}$$

introduces casemix in a desirable way, implying that a change in any casetype proportion has a proportional effect on the total number of cases that will be produced. This is compatible with the assumption of chapters 2 and 3 that a change in casemix proportion has an additive effect on the average cost per case.

For the mixed Leontief-Cobb-Douglas form of equation (4.3) we may write:

$$C_i = \min\ [f_1(X_{1i}, p_{1i}, \ldots, p_{m-1,i}), \ldots, f_k(X_{ki}, p_{1i}, \ldots, p_{m-1,i}),$$

$$(\prod_{r=k+1}^{s} X_{ri}^{\alpha_r}e^{p'_i\beta})] \tag{4.9}$$

A useful form of the individual sub-functions of equation (4.9) would be (for input k)

$$C_i = X_{ki}^{\beta_{k0}}\ e^{p'_i\beta_k}V_{ki} \tag{4.10}$$

since the equation could be estimated easily in logarithms and provides a simple measure (β_{k0}) of the economies or diseconomies of scale.[4]

If we do not specify casemix explicitly in the production function, we must find an output measure that incorporates a description of casemix.

---

[4] This is similar to the approach of DHRYMES and KURZ (1964) who used a logarithmic Leontief function but assumed that output was an exogenous variable and therefore regressed cost on output.

When products are sold in a competitive market it is common to aggregate them with their prices as weights. As discussed in chapter 2, this would be a special case of weighting by relative marginal social values, i.e., selecting weights whose ratios are society's marginal rates of substitution between the corresponding products. We suggested there that although the relative social values "in use" of different case types cannot be measured, it might be a rough first approximation to accept their relative average costs as a measure of the relative values of additional treated cases. We may therefore define the weighted output ("work") of a hospital as:

$$W_i = \sum_j c_{.j} C_{ji} \tag{4.11}$$

where $c_{.j}$ is the average cost of treating a case of type j. These average costs were derived in chapter 2 from a regression of cost per case on the set of casemix proportions. The sections that follow present estimates of Cobb-Douglas and mixed Leontief-Cobb-Douglas functions with W as the measure of output.

Both methods of incorporating casemix make the coefficients of the inputs independent of the specific casemix being treated. This implies that the optimum input combination is also independent of the hospital casemix. This assumption may be unacceptable. We therefore investigate in section 4.3.4 a specification of the form:

$$C_i = A \prod_r X_{ri}^{p'_i \alpha_r} U_i. \tag{4.12}$$

For the studies in this chapter, cases are generally aggregated into the nine categories: general medicine, paediatrics, general surgery, E.N.T. surgery, traumatic and orthopaedic surgery, other surgery, gynaecology, obstetrics, and "others".

4.2.3. Specifying inputs

Although the theory of the production function requires that inputs be specified in physical terms, this is not always possible. Consider the simple classification of inputs into beds, nurses, doctors and other supplies. Beds could be measured in physical units. "Other supplies" must necessarily be measured in value terms. Although the input of nurses and doctors could be measured in nursing hours and doctors hours, an aggregation by wage rates would be preferable. There are several grades of nurses and doctors;

we must either include these explicitly as several variables, aggregate without weights to obtain crude total doctor hours and total nursing hours, or find an appropriate set of weights. The Cobb-Douglas or Leontief functions would be implausible if several grades of nurses and doctors were explicitly included; positive output does not, as would be implied by the production function, require some of each such input. Aggregation by wage rates seems the best compromise. Such aggregated cost data is readily available for each hospital.

Measuring inputs by costs has been common practice in estimating production functions. The uniformity of wage rates in the health service eliminates one important difficulty of this approach. Nevertheless, the aggregation by wage rates is almost certain to introduce some bias into the individual coefficients and their sum. In the analysis of this chapter, only the number of beds is expressed in physical terms.

Inputs are first classified into beds, doctors, nurses, and "other supplies". A more detailed specification identifying also drugs and dressings, catering, and "other housekeeping activities" is then presented.

4.3 Cobb-Douglas production functions

In this section we consider first (4.3.1) a Cobb-Douglas function with four inputs: nurses, doctors, beds, and other supplies. Alternative output specifications are shown to have little effect on the elasticities of the four inputs. The elasticities imply slight (but not significant) diseconomies of scale. A more suitable input specification, in which supplies are divided into drugs and dressings, catering, and other housekeeping is then presented.

Section 4.3.2 derives the optimum input proportions implied by this production function and compares these with proportions observed on average. Section 4.3.3 considers the implications of allowing the production function parameters to vary with size. In section 4.3.4 the parameters associated with each input are allowed to vary with casemix. Finally, a number of alternative estimation procedures are considered in section 4.3.5.

4.3.1. *Estimates of alternative functions with constant coefficients*

Production function coefficients for doctors (M), beds (B), nurses (N), and other supplies (S) were estimated by ordinary least squares regression on the logarithms of these variables. The inputs are assumed at this stage to be independent of the error in the equation. Such an assumption is justified if inputs are determined by central government rules, local supply conditions, and decisions of the distant past. For now this assumption provides a useful and plausible starting hypothesis.

TABLE 4.1

Coefficients of Cobb-Douglas production functions

Equation	α_M	α_B	α_N	α_S	$\Sigma_1^4 \, \alpha_i$	$\bar{R}^2$
(4.13)	0.476	0.414	0.074	−0.084	0.880	
	(0.080)	(0.110)	(0.108)	(0.124)	(0.029)	0.86
(4.14)	0.331	0.500	0.037	−0.010	0.858	
	(0.081)	(0.086)	(0.091)	(0.097)	(0.030)	0.91
(4.15)	0.387	0.465	0.047	0.069	0.968	
	(0.071)	(0.098)	(0.096)	(0.111)	(0.026)	0.90

Equation (4.13) $\quad C = A M^{\alpha_M} B^{\alpha_B} N^{\alpha_N} S^{\alpha_S}$

Equation (4.14) $\quad C = M^{\alpha_M} B^{\alpha_B} N^{\alpha_N} S^{\alpha_S} e^{p'_i \beta}$

Equation (4.15) $\quad W = A M^{\alpha_M} B^{\alpha_B} N^{\alpha_N} S^{\alpha_S}$

Table 4.1 presents estimates obtained with three different output specifications. It is clear that the relative orders of magnitude of the coefficients are nearly the same for all three equations. The coefficients of equation (4.13) are biased by the omission of a casemix description in the specification of the production relation. We shall therefore limit our attention to the other two equations. In these, the elasticity with respect to beds is highest, followed by the elasticity with respect to doctors. The other two coefficients are much lower in both equations and do not exceed their standard errors. We shall discuss the interpretation of these low coefficients below.[5]

The sum of the coefficients indicates that, on average, there are slightly

---

[5] Although heteroscedasticity was anticipated, examination of sample error variances indicates that it is not a problem. The four quartile error variances were not monotonically increasing (2.989; 2.633; 3.507; 2.696). The likelihood ratio (see explanation in the appendix of chapter 2) of 0.5620 is associated with a χ^2 value of 1.1526 which is not significantly different from zero at the 25 per cent level.

decreasing return to scale. The standard error of the sum of the coefficients is calculated as

$$S.E.(\sum_i \alpha_i) = [\sum_i var(\alpha_i) + \sum_i \sum_{\substack{j \\ i \neq j}} covar\ (\alpha_i \alpha_j)]^{\frac{1}{2}}\ i, j = M, B, N, S.$$

These standard errors indicate that the differences between the sum of the coefficients and 1.0 may be due to chance; for equation (4.14) the difference is "significant" at the five per cent level while for equation (4.15) this difference is only "significant" at the twenty per cent level. This accords well with the results of chapter 3 that hospital size has little effect on cost per case.

The low value of the elasticity with respect to "other inputs" suggests that it may be inappropriate to aggregate drugs and dressings, catering, and the remaining "housekeeping" expenditures into a single input category. This is confirmed by the parameter estimates for the more disaggregated inputs, presented in table 4.2. The dependent variable here is the weighted output of cases W.

TABLE 4.2

Coefficients of Cobb-Douglas production function with disaggregated supplies

Input	Symbol	Coefficient value	Standard error
Medical	α_M	0.306	0.073
Beds	α_B	0.409	0.096
Drugs and dressings	α_D	0.209	0.059
Nursing	α_N	0.023	0.094
Catering	α_C	0.040	0.097
Other expenditure	α_X	−0.022	0.107
Sum of coefficients		0.965	0.025

The previous low value of the supply coefficient ($\alpha_S = 0.069$) reflects the moderate value of α_D and the low values of α_C and α_X. The values of the other coefficients, and of the total, is affected very little by this disaggregation.

4.3.2. *Optimum input proportions*

The low values of some of the input coefficients presented in table 4.2 suggest that the Cobb-Douglas form may not be wholly appropriate. Alternative forms will therefore be considered in sections 4.4 and 4.5. But now we shall accept the Cobb-Douglas results and investigate the optimum input proportions implied by the estimated coefficients.

The problem of optimizing input proportions may be posed as either constrained cost minimizing or output maximizing: the same optimum proportions are obtained in both ways. Table 4.3 compares the average observed ratios of input quantities with the optimum ratios implied by the coefficients of table 4.2. No results are presented for "other supplies" (X) because α_X is negative. The optimum input-bed ratios are based on the assumption that the number of beds can be varied at a "capital cost" of k pounds per bed per year.

TABLE 4.3

Observed and optimum input ratios

Input ratio	Observed average	Optimum ratio
M/D	2.507	1.464
M/N	0.414	13.304
M/C	1.567	7.650
D/N	0.168	9.087
D/C	0.265	5.100
N/C	1.498	0.554
M/B	128.57	0.749k
D/B	53.08	0.511k
N/B	300.30	0.056k
C/B	204.26	0.100k

The optimum input ratios differ substantially from those observed. In the face of such large discrepancies, the reader may justifiably resist placing great confidence in the precise values of the estimated optimum ratios. But the table as a whole does indicate the directions in which budget allocations should probably be changed. Ignoring for the moment the possibility of altering the number of beds, we note that the current ratios of M/D and N/C are too high while M/N, M/C, D/N, and D/C are too low. In short, too much is being spent on nurses, catering and other supplies and not enough on doctors, drugs, and dressings. The government appears to have inappropriately limited the supply of doctors and at the same time used its monopsony power to keep medical salaries substantially below their relative marginal productivity in the hospital service. Two implications emerge from this. First, the number of doctors in hospital should be increased even if higher salaries were needed to attract them. Second, until hospital medical staffs are substantially increased, the opportunity cost of the doctor's time should be evaluated at a shadow price which is substantially higher than that implied by current salaries.

The optimum number of beds depends on the annual capital cost (k) at which beds can be obtained. For any plausible estimate of this,[6] the ratios of table 4.3 indicate that the N/B and C/B ratios are too high. A strict interpretation of these results would imply that expenditure on nursing, catering and other supplies should be decreased relative to the number of beds. But caution must be used in applying the results of a production function the form of which may not be wholly appropriate. We return to this in sections 4.4 and 4.5 where inputs are divided into those that contribute directly to the production of cases (doctors, beds, drugs and dressings) and those that are part of the general overhead required to maintain a number of occupied beds at a given standard of amenity (nursing, catering and other supplies).

For now, we continue our analysis in the context of the Cobb-Douglas function. Instead of contrasting average and optimum input ratios, we compare the expenditure in each category in the "average" hospital with the optimum expenditure for a hospital with that total budget. We then compare the actual output of the "average" hospital with the maximum possible output of a hospital with that budget and bed constraint. The average hospital has a total annual expenditure of £ 354 204; this is divided among the input categories in the way shown in column 2 of table 4.4. Because of the obviously inappropriate coefficients of catering, other supplies, and nursing, we shall not calculate an optimum allocation of the budget among all expenditure categories but rather limit the reallocation

---

[6] Construction and furnishing costs in even the most expensive hospitals currently being built do not exceed £ 5 000 per bed. A twenty-year life for these facilities would almost certainly be an underestimate. On this basis, and assuming an 8 per cent opportunity cost of capital, the annual cost of capital (including depreciation) would be £ 510. Adding to this an exaggerated annual opportunity cost of land of £ 240 per bed would bring the total "rent" to £ 750.

TABLE 4.4

Average and optimum inputs and outputs

Inputs and outputs	Average *	Optimum reallocation I	Optimum reallocation II
(1)	(2)	(3)	(4)
Medical ($\pounds$)	37 084	80 095	31 303
Drugs and dressings ($\pounds$)	15 599	54 707	21 380
Nursing ($\pounds$)	88 146	6 020	88 146**
Catering ($\pounds$)	59 587	59 587**	59 587**
Other supplies ($\pounds$)	153 788	153 788**	153 788**
Beds**	302.9	302.9	302.9
Weighted output (cases)	6 666	10 323	6 760

* Average inputs are unweighted averages of total expenditure in each input category among the 177 hospitals.

** Optimum inputs have not been calculated for these categories; current average inputs are assumed.

to fewer inputs. Two calculations are reported: Optimum reallocation I (presented in column 3 of table 4.4) is limited to expenditure for nursing, medical, and drugs and dressings; Optimum reallocation II (column 4) considers only medical staff and drugs and dressings.[7]

The amount to be allocated among the first three expenditure categories is $\pounds$ 140 829. An optimum allocation requires that $\pounds$ 140 829 $= N + M + D = N[1 + (\alpha_M/\alpha_N) + (\alpha_D/\alpha_N)]$. Using the coefficients presented in table 4.2 we obtain the values for N, M and D shown in column 3 of table 4.4. An analogous calculation yields the values shown in column 4. The "average" hospital, using the input quantities shown in column 2, produces a weighted output [8] of 6666 cases. If that hospital optimally reallocated its expenditure among N, M and D, the expected weighted output would increase to 10 323

---

[7] An explicit justification for this type of limitation will be developed in section 4.4. A similar analysis will be presented there for a production function which allows substitution only among those inputs that are considered to contribute directly to the production of cases.

[8] Since output (W) is defined as the weighted sum of cases, each case weighted by its average cost, we obtain a "weighted output of cases" by dividing W by the average cost per case, $\pounds$ 54.62.

cases; a reallocation of medical and drug expenditure would yield an expected weighted output of 6 760 cases. The ratios of the average weighted output (6 666) to the maximum possible outputs 10 323 or 6 760 provide measures of the absolute level of input efficiency: 65 per cent or 98 per cent. This low level of absolute input efficiency was referred to in chapter 2 where we noted that the relatively small variation in input efficiency values and their limited influence on costliness should not be construed as an indication of satisfactory absolute input efficiency.

Although one may feel that the indicated optimum expenditure pattern is an unrealistic extreme change from the present allocation, the desirable directions of change are clear.

Before developing alternative estimation procedures and different general forms of the production function, we consider the relations of production function coefficients to hospital size and casemix.

4.3.3. *Production functions for hospitals of different size*

The production function coefficients (input elasticities) vary with hospital size, implying differences in optimum input combinations and total returns to scale.

Table 4.5 presents input coefficients for hospitals in each of the four size quartiles and for all hospitals taken together. Catering expenditure and

TABLE 4.5

Input elasticities in hospitals of different size

Size quartile		Input coefficients					
Min.	Max.	Nursing (N)	Medical (M)	Beds (B)	Drugs and dressings (D)	House- keeping (H)	Total
72	167	0.09 (0.21)	0.05 (0.13)	0.42 (0.19)	0.25 (0.11)	0.05 (0.19)	0.86
168	251	−0.00 (0.18)	0.18 (0.17)	0.24 (0.31)	0.17 (0.12)	0.14 (0.22)	0.72
252	407	0.07 (0.02)	0.43 (0.15)	0.12 (0.24)	0.36 (0.16)	−0.04 (0.19)	0.95
408	1064	−0.07 (0.21)	0.48 (0.13)	0.08 (0.24)	0.18 (0.11)	0.26 (0.20)	0.93
All hospitals		0.03 (0.09)	0.31 (0.07)	0.41 (0.10)	0.21 (0.06)	0.01 (0.10)	0.97

"other supplies" are now included in the category "housekeeping". Each row of the table refers to a separately estimated equation. Later in this section we show that the estimates presented in this table are consistent with the results of other methods of studying the effects of hospital size on the input elasticities.

The coefficient of medical inputs rises substantially with hospital size. Additional expenditure on medical staff is very much more effective in large hospitals than in small ones. The reason for this is not clear. One possible explanation is that additional availability of medical staff raises the overall speed and efficiency of hospital operations and that the scope for doing this may increase with hospital size. This is consistent with the estimates of the effects of hospital scale presented in chapter 3 and is supported by further studies discussed in chapter 5, section 5.4. A second possible explanation is that the partial elasticity of output with respect to medical staff inputs is not independent of the ratio of output to medical staff as assumed by the Cobb-Douglas production function.[9] If this elasticity is an increasing function of the ratio of output to medical staff, the observed set of elasticities would imply that the output to medical staff ratio increases with hospital size. This does in fact occur,[10] primarily because medical staff per bed is lower in larger hospitals.[11] Each explanation is probably of some importance. In either case, the general policy implication of these results is clear: the increased expenditure on medical staff should be focused on hospitals of above average size. If the second explanation is valid, additional medical staff should also be allocated to those smaller hospitals which have high current output to medical staff ratios.[12]

The elasticity of output with respect to beds falls markedly with increased hospital size. Again we must seek an explanation outside the framework of the Cobb-Douglas production function. First, the partial elasticity with respect to beds may depend on the relative availability of other inputs.

---

[9] The Cobb-Douglas function assumes that $(\partial W/\partial M) \cdot (M/W) = \alpha_M$ or $(\partial W/\partial M) = \alpha_M (W/M)$. If in fact $(\partial W/\partial M) = \alpha_M (W/M)^\rho$ where $\rho > 1$, the elasticity rises with increasing values of W/M. More generally, if all partial elasticities are of the form $(\partial W/\partial X_i) = \alpha_i (W/X_i)^\rho$, the production function has constant elasticity of substitution of ρ^{-1}.

[10] The ratios of weighted output to medical staff (W/M) in the four quartiles of hospital size are (in cases per pound of medical staff expenditure): 9.47; 9.91; 10.12; and 10.36.

[11] The correlation between medical expenditure per bed and the number of beds is -0.343.

[12] Of course even with constant elasticity, a higher output: input ratio raises marginal productivity.

In smaller hospitals the more ample supply of medical staff may make the provision of additional beds relatively more productive. The second explanation is the same as that offered for the increasing elasticity with respect to medical staff: that the elasticity of output with respect to any input may be an increasing function of the ratio of output to that input. Since the output per bed falls with hospital size,[13] the elasticity with respect to beds also falls. Although this explanation may appear circular ("larger hospitals have lower output per bed, therefore have lower elasticity of output with respect to beds and therefore have lower output per bed . . ."), it is not. The lower output per bed in larger hospitals is only partly a reflection of lower output elasticity with respect to beds. Output per bed is also low because of the relatively smaller medical staff and the general tendency for the pace of a larger institution to decrease.

To the extent that the lower elasticity of beds in larger hospitals is due to lower medical staff expenditure per bed, its policy implications for the location of additional beds must depend on the ease with which doctors can be transferred from small to large hospitals. In general, the higher medical expenditure per bed in smaller hospitals cannot be altered by staff transfers. A hospital with only 150 available beds which has the average medical expenditure per bed (£ 129) would have a total medical staff budget of only £ 19 350 per year, or only enough for fewer than six consultants or ten senior medical officers.[14] The hospital must maintain medical staff in each broad speciality. In addition, its ratio of senior medical staff to junior medical staff must be higher; a consultant surgeon may supervise the work of several registrars but if only one surgeon is to be available he cannot be a registrar. Although it might be possible to use more part-time appointments in smaller hospitals, it would in general be difficult to reduce appreciably their medical staff expenditure. This implies that hospital expansion should be concentrated on smaller hospitals where the ratio of medical staff to beds is currently high. In effect, when medical staff expenditure is revalued at a proper shadow price, the cost per case of smaller hospitals is higher than indicated by ordinary accounting costs.

Although the elasticity with respect to drugs and dressings differs sub-

---

[13] The relation between output per bed (W/B) and hospital size (B) is given by (W/B) $= -0.357B + 1351.1$. More generally, see chapter 5, section 5.4.
  (0.093)

[14] The average pay in 1955–56 of a consultant was £ 3 391 and of a senior medical officer was £ 2 005. (Cmnd. 939, 1960).

stantially among size groups, there is no intelligible pattern. The same is true of nursing and "housekeeping".

The sum of the elasticities for the several inputs provides an estimate of the extent of decreasing or increasing returns to scale. In all size groups we find decreasing returns to scale but the results are closer to constant returns for the larger hospitals. The overall equation shows a higher value (0.98) than any of the individual equations, indicating that some of the returns to scale take the form of a shift in the entire production function as size increases.

The results which were presented in table 4.5 are supported by two alternative methods of estimating the effects of hospital size on production function coefficients. We consider first a production function in which each coefficient is itself a linear function of hospital size:

$$W = AN^{\alpha_N + \alpha'_N B} M^{\alpha_M + \alpha'_M B} B^{\alpha_B + \alpha'_B B} D^{\alpha_D + \alpha'_D B} H^{\alpha_H + \alpha'_H B} \qquad (4.16)$$

When we transform to logarithms and estimate the eleven parameters we obtain (with $B^* = 0.01B$):

$$w = [0.123 - 0.025B^*]n + [-0.035 + 0.116B^*]m + [0.460 - 0.053B^*]b$$
$$+ [0.240 - 0.010B^*]d + [0.117 - 0.041B^*]h + \text{constant term.} \qquad (4.17)$$

The output elasticity with respect to medical expenditure rises at the rate of 0.116 per 100 beds while the elasticity with respect to beds falls at 0.053 per 100 beds. The simplifying assumption of a linear relationship between size and each elasticity produces rates of change which are unrealistically high; the medical and bed elasticities assume values less than zero and greater than one within the observed range of hospital size. But the sign and general order of magnitude of the size effects do support the conclusion of table 4.5 about the changes in medical and bed elasticities with hospital size. For the other inputs the hospital size coefficients are relatively small and have large standard errors, indicating effects that are uncertain or unsubstantial.

To relax the assumption of a linear relationship between size and each elasticity while preserving a large number of degrees of freedom, we have estimated a set of single equations in each of which the elasticity with respect to a particular input is allowed to take a different value in each hospital size quartile. This is done by defining four variables (one for each size class) for the input being studied; each variable takes the value of the input if the observation is in the corresponding size class and the value zero otherwise. Separate constant terms are also calculated for each size class.[15] Equation (4.18) shows the result for medical staff; m_1 is the logarithm of medical expenditure in a hospital in the smallest size quartile. This agrees quite well with the pattern of medical staff elasticities presented

$$w = 0.19m_1 + 0.21m_2 + 0.36m_3 + 0.46m_4 + 0.01n$$
$$\quad (0.10) \quad (0.13) \quad (0.12) \quad (0.10)$$
$$\qquad\qquad + 0.26b + 0.22d + 0.06h + \text{constant terms.} \qquad (4.18)$$

in table 4.5 (0.05, 0.18, 0.43, and 0.48). The elasticities with respect to the number of beds are shown in equation (4.19). These are similar to the results of table 4.5 for all but the largest hospital class (0.42, 0.24, 0.12, and 0.08):

$$w = 0.33b_1 + 0.19b_2 + 0.07b_3 + 0.36b_4 + 0.01n$$
$$\quad (0.14) \quad (0.23) \quad (0.20) \quad (0.13)$$
$$\qquad\qquad + 0.21d + 0.09h + \text{constant terms.} \qquad (4.19)$$

Nursing elasticities varied unsystematically between -0.04 and $+0.11$ and had large standard errors. Elasticities of drugs and dressings showed a slight tendency to increase with size [0.196 (standard error $= 0.08$), 0.151 (0.107), 0.274 (0.111), 0.271 (0.090)]. Housekeeping elasticities showed no pattern.

Both alternative methods therefore confirm the important conclusion that the elasticity with respect to medical staff increases substantially with hospital size. The high value of the elasticity with respect to beds in the smallest hospital size group is also confirmed, although there is some doubt about the elasticity in the largest size group. The extremely low elasticity with respect to nursing staff is found for all size groups by each of the three methods. No important pattern emerges for drugs and dressings or house-keeping expenditure.

4.3.4. *A production function with coefficients varying with casemix*

The models considered above imply that the input elasticities are independent of the particular casemix being treated. A more general function would allow the individual elasticities to differ according to the mix of cases. For example, additional nursing expenditure may have a greater effect on output if the cases are surgical than if they are obstetric.

---

[15] For a more detailed description of this method, see chapter 3, section 3.4.5.

A particularly simple specification of this type makes the elasticity of each input a linear function of the casemix proportions. As stated in equation (4.12), such a production function is:

$$C_i = A \cdot \prod_{r=1}^{s} X_{ri}^{p'_i \alpha_r} U_i.$$

To make the estimation problem manageable, the casemix was reaggregated into six types: all medicine (including cases previously classified as "others"); paediatrics; ear, nose and throat; all surgery; gynaecology; and obstetrics. For each input (X_{ri}), there was substantial variation among the individual estimated case-type coefficients $(\alpha_{jr}\text{'s})$. The optimum input proportions for any particular hospital would therefore depend on its casemix. But for a hospital with average casemix proportions $(p_j\text{'s})$, the estimated weighted input elasticities $(\alpha_r = \sum_j \alpha_{rj} p_j.)$ are very similar to those obtained by our usual estimation procedure with dependent variable W: thus, $\alpha_B = 0.359$, $\alpha_M = 0.292$, $\alpha_D = 0.241$, $\alpha_N = -0.053$ and $\alpha_H = 0.072$.[16]

4.3.5. Alternative estimation methods

Although the Cobb-Douglas production function appears to provide useful information about the effects on output of variation in beds, drugs and dressings, and medical staff, the parameter estimates for nurses and housekeeping expenditure are obviously unsatisfactory. There are two possible explanations. First, a general Cobb-Douglas function relating output to all hospital inputs may be inappropriate. Other specifications and corresponding estimation methods will therefore be developed in sections 4.4 and 4.5. Second, the ordinary least squares estimation method applied to the Cobb-Douglas function may be improper. Three alternative estimation methods are therefore considered in this section: instrumental variables, mixed cross-section and time-series analysis, and indirect least squares.

Ordinary least squares may be inappropriate for three reasons. First, each of the inputs (except the number of beds) is a value aggregate instead of a physical quantity. Even if each observed expenditure differs from being proportional to the physical quantity by a random (multiplicative) error, ordinary least squares estimates will be biased and inconsistent. Second,

---

[16] When two alternative input specifications were used, the weighted average input elasticities were nearly the same.

each of the inputs except the number of beds and the medical staff may not be exogenously determined but set by the hospital in relation to its desired or expected output. Endogenous input variables are not independent of the error in the equation, making ordinary least squares inappropriate. Third, the production function specification may have omitted the input "good management" (GRILICHES, 1957). If this is correlated with size or with any of the other inputs, parameter estimates will be biased. In particular, if hospitals with good management also spend less on nursing and house-keeping, these coefficients will be biased downwards.

4.3.5.1. *Instrumental variables.* The method of instrumental variables provides consistent estimates in the presence of the first two conditions if the instrumental variables are uncorrelated with the error in the equation. The production function has been estimated with instrumental variables for all of the inputs except the number of beds; a quartile rank number for each variable was used as the instrument. The instrumental variable estimates are given in equation (4.20); the corresponding ordinary least squares estimates (originally presented in table 4.5) are shown in equation (4.21).

$$w = 0.245m + 0.511b + 0.125d + 0.066n + 0.051h + \text{constant}$$
$$(0.067) \quad (0.073) \quad (0.054) \quad (0.066) \quad (0.073) \tag{4.20}$$

$$w = 0.307m + 0.408b + 0.211d + 0.026n + 0.014h + \text{constant}$$
$$(0.072) \quad (0.096) \quad (0.058) \quad (0.093) \quad (0.101) \tag{4.21}$$

The instrumental variable coefficients are broadly similar to those obtained by ordinary least squares. The elasticity with respect to medical expenditure is lower in the instrumental variable equation and the elasticity with respect to beds is higher. More significantly, the elasticity with respect to drugs and dressings is substantially reduced. But although the elasticities with respect to nursing and housekeeping are slightly higher, they are still unacceptably low. An alternative method of estimation must therefore be considered.

4.3.5.2. *Pooled cross-section and time-series analysis.* The simultaneous use of data from cross-section samples for two different years provides an alternative way of dealing with some of the conditions that make ordinary least squares inappropriate. To see the reasons for this method, we examine in detail the specification of equation (4.22) which presents in logarithmic form the production function for hospital i in year t.

$$w_{it} = \alpha_0 + \alpha_1 m_{it} + \alpha_2 b_{it} + \alpha_3 d_{it} + \alpha_4 n_{it} + \alpha_5 h_{it} + u_{i.} + u_{.t} + \varepsilon_{it} \qquad (4.22)$$

Instead of the usual error term, u_{it}, the error has been specified as the sum of a year effect ($u_{.t}$), a hospital effect ($u_{i.}$), and a purely random term (ε_{it}). The year effect is the same for all hospitals; in any particular year $u_{.t}$ will not be zero but its expectation over the years is zero. Similarly, the hospital effect differs among hospitals but is the same for each hospital in all years. A value of $u_{i.}$ greater than zero indicates a hospital of above average efficiency. If $u_{i.}$ is correlated with any of the inputs – e.g., if larger hospitals tend to be more efficient than average – the coefficients of the input variables will be biased upwards. The differences in $u_{i.}$ values may reflect the omission of "management" in the specification of the production function, the third reason given above for the inappropriateness of ordinary least squares. The $u_{i.}$ term is also relevant to the second reason, the problem of simultaneous equations bias. Assume that the hospital determines some of its inputs as a function of the year's *planned* output. If the hospital decides these input levels before the year begins (as it may be forced to by the budgetary process), it will take into account the effect of $u_{i.}$ on output but not the effects of $u_{.t}$ or ε_{it}. The endogenously determined input variables are therefore independent of $u_{.t}$ and ε_{it} but not of $u_{i.}$. The simultaneous use of two observations on each hospital permits the estimation of the $u_{i.}$ term or, equivalently, its elimination.

More specifically, with more than one observation on each hospital we could estimate a coefficient for each input, a time term for each period, and an additive (in logarithms) "hospital effect" term for each of the hospitals. This would be a form of covariance analysis (WILKS, 1962; MUNDLAK, 1961, 1963; HOCH, 1962). A simpler procedure may be used when there are exactly two observations on each hospital (WALTERS, 1961). The estimated input parameters obtained in this way are the same as the covariance analysis estimates but the computational procedure is easier. By subtracting from equation (4.22) the corresponding equation for the previous period, we obtain (where $\dot{w}_i = w_{it} - w_{i,t-1}$):

$$\dot{w}_i = \alpha_1 \dot{m}_i + \alpha_2 \dot{b}_i + \alpha_3 \dot{d}_i + \alpha_4 \dot{n}_i + \alpha_5 \dot{h}_i + (u_{.t} - u_{.,t-1}) + \dot{\varepsilon}_i. \qquad (4.23)$$

Because $u_{i.}$ is assumed constant through time, it is eliminated when we take first differences. The term $(u_{.t} - u_{.,t-1})$ is a constant in the cross-section regression, representing the change in output due to differences in time period.

Pooled cross-section equations of this type were calculated using data for the financial years ending in 1960 and 1961. To simplify the preparation of data, we assumed that the proportional casemix composition remained the same in both years. The change in output could therefore be measured as the change in the number of cases treated.

The parameter estimates presented in equation (4.24) are generally similar to the corresponding coefficients of (4.15) with the exception that the medical staff elasticity (0.123) is lower than the previous value (0.387).[17] This lower value suggests

$$\dot{w} = 0.123\dot{m} + 0.497\dot{b} + 0.062\dot{n} + 0.094\dot{s} + 0.02$$
$$\phantom{\dot{w} =} (0.061) \quad (0.074) \quad (0.058) \quad (0.058) \qquad\qquad (4.24)$$

that good hospital management may be an omitted input that is closely correlated in cross section with larger medical staff. The coefficients of nursing and supplies are still extremely low. As a final attempt to investigate whether plausible elasticities for these inputs can be obtained in the Cobb-Douglas model, we consider indirect least squares estimation.

4.3.5.3. *Indirect least squares.* Under certain conditions, indirect least squares yield consistent estimates of a production function when inputs are endogenous. HOCH (1958) applied indirect least squares to estimate an agricultural production function for farms using the assumption that farm managers determined output and input levels in the way that maximized expected profits (see also HOCH, 1962; KMENTA and JOSEPH, 1963; KMENTA, 1964). Although it is unnecessary to use the profit maximizing assumption, we present the model in its original form and then discuss its application to the hospital.

A firm with a production function of Cobb-Douglas form will earn maximum profits if each of its inputs is proportional to the desired level of output, the constant of proportionality for each input reflecting the prices of the input and output, their price elasticities, and the elasticity of output with respect to that input. Writing Y for output and X_j for the level of input j,

---

[17] The separation of drugs and dressings from other housekeeping inputs was not possible because the two-period data was prepared before the importance of this distinction was recognized.

profit maximizing requires $X_j = \lambda_j Y$, where λ_j is the appropriate proportionality constant. Assume that the input equation is not satisfied exactly but that each firm differs from the optimum by a multiplicative error; interfirm differences in λ_j may also be included in this error. The production and input relations of the ith firm may therefore be written:

$$Y_i = A(\prod_{j=1}^{k} X_{ji}^{\alpha_j})U_i \tag{4.25}$$

$$X_{ji} = \lambda_j Y_i V_{ji} \tag{4.26}$$

or, in logarithms (with $\mu_j = \log \lambda_j$)

$$y_i = a + \sum_{j=1}^{k} \alpha_j x_{ji} + u_i \tag{4.27}$$

$$x_{ji} = \mu_j + y_i + v_{ji} \qquad j = 1, \ldots, k \tag{4.28}$$

Hoch assumed that the error terms in the input equations (the v_{ji}'s) are uncorrelated with the error term in the production equation (u_i), although they may be correlated among themselves. This is a very strong assumption, implying that the "technical efficiency" of an enterprise (u_i) is uncorrelated with its departure from average input-output ratios (v_{ji}'s).[18] The meaning of this assumption in the hospital model will be discussed below.

The specification of (4.27) and (4.28) indicates that ordinary least squares estimates of (4.27) would be inappropriate: the x_{ji}'s are dependent upon y_i and therefore u_i. But subtracting $y_i \sum_{j=1}^{k} \alpha_j$ from both sides yields:

$$y_i(1 - \sum_{j=1}^{k} \alpha_j) = a + \sum_{j=1}^{k} \alpha_j(x_{ji} - y_i) + u_i \tag{4.29}$$

or, using (4.28)

$$y_i(1 - \sum_{j=1}^{k} \alpha_j) = (a + \sum_{j=1}^{k} \alpha_j \mu_j) + \sum_{j=1}^{k} \alpha_j v_{ji} + u_i \tag{4.30}$$

If the regression of y_i on the $(x_{ji} - y_i)$'s is calculated, as in (4.31), the k

---

[18] The v_{ji}'s measure "economic efficiency" only if the λ_j do not vary among firms. This is Hoch's assumption. For an agricultural production function, u_i includes both "technical efficiency" and conditions of nature. If the latter are much more important than the former, Hoch's assumption may do little harm.

regression coefficients can be solved for estimates of the α_j's since $\beta_j = \alpha_j(1 - \sum_{s=1}^{k} \alpha_s)^{-1}$.

$$y_i = \beta_0 + \sum_{j=1}^{k} \beta_j(\langle_{ji} - y_i) + u_i \tag{4.31}$$

If the v_{ji}'s are uncorrelated with u_i, the b_j's are consistent and the desired estimates of the α_j's are therefore also consistent.

Two problems arise in applying this procedure. First, the method cannot be applied if there are exactly constant returns to scale ($\sum_{j=1}^{k} \alpha_j = 1$) because this would imply dividing all terms by zero in passing from (4.30) to (4.31). But even if returns to scale are not exactly constant, if the sum of the α_j's is close to one, the estimating equation will be ill-conditioned and the estimates unstable. Second, if each v_{ji} is not uncorrelated with u_i, the estimates will not be consistent. The independence of technical and economic efficiency is a sufficient condition to assure that the errors are uncorrelated, but it is not necessary. A lower than average level of technical efficiency implies $u_i < 0$; a lower than average level of economic efficiency does not imply the sign of v_{ji} (because all $v_{ji} \neq 0$ are inefficient if the λ_j are the same for all firms) but rather that the absolute value of v_{ji} is large. Since this may be either a large positive or large negative value, technical efficiency and input efficiency may be positively correlated while u_i and v_{ji} are independent. But if technical inefficiency is associated with a particular type of economic inefficiency, u_i and v_{ji} will not be uncorrelated, e.g., technically inefficient firms may use too much labour and too little capital, making $\mathscr{E}(u_i v_{i, \text{capital}}) > 0$ and $\mathscr{E}(u_i v_{i, \text{labour}}) < 0$.

To apply the indirect least squares method to estimating the hospital production function we must posit that each input is proportional to output and must find ways of dealing with the two problems discussed in the previous paragraph. Although profit maximizing behaviour is a convenient assumption for deriving a proportional input-output relation, it is not necessary. Similar results are obtained if hospitals are assumed to minimize costs. However it would be unwise to base parameter estimates on the assumption that hospitals are cost minimizers. But a model of proportional input-output relations, perhaps reflecting arbitrary norms that have developed in the hospital service, may nevertheless be plausible. It is therefore without any strong theoretical reason that we posit a proportional relation between inputs and output. This changes the interpretation of the v_{ji}'s. They are no longer measures of departure from efficiency but only from average input-output ratios. We return to this problem below. The problem of constant returns to scale is also deferred until after we have examined a preliminary set of estimates.

The basic set of estimates appears in equation (4.32). The parameters

$$w_i = 0.866(b_i - w_i) - 0.308(m_i - w_i) - 0.636(n_i - w_i)$$
$$(0.303) \qquad (0.232) \qquad (0.280)$$

$$+ 0.131(d_i - w_i) - 0.725(h_i - w_i)$$
$$(0.185) \qquad (0.305)$$

$$+ 17.238 \qquad (4.32)$$

of the production function [19] (the α_j's) are obtained from these coefficients by solving the six equations: $\beta_j = \alpha_j(1 - \sum_{s=1}^{k} \alpha_s)^{-1}$, $j = 1, \ldots, 6$. This is easily done if we note that each is equivalent to $\alpha_j = \beta_j(1 - \sum \alpha_s)$. Denoting by B a matrix each of whose columns is the vector β, we have $\alpha = \beta - B\alpha$ or $\alpha + B\alpha = \alpha(I + B) = \beta$. Thus, $\alpha = (I + B)^{-1}\beta$. The production function coefficients obtained in this way are presented in equation (4.33):

$$w_i = 2.642b_i - 0.940m_i - 1.939n_i + 0.399d_i - 2.213h_i + \text{constant} \quad (4.33)$$

The coefficient values are obviously unsatisfactory. Alternative estimates embodying several modifications of the original procedure were therefore made.

The assumption that all inputs are endogenous may be inappropriate for the hospital. The number of beds is historically determined and not chosen in relation to a desired output. One equation is therefore dropped from the hospital model. The first stage estimation equation includes the logarithm of the number of beds instead of $(w_i - b_i)$. The β_j's are now equal to $\alpha_j(1 - \sum_{s \neq \text{beds}} \alpha_s)^{-1}$. This procedure also eliminates the danger that $(1 - \sum \alpha_s)$ will be close to zero. The number of doctors may also be considered exogenous because it depends on staffing norms of the Ministry of Health (stated in terms of the approximate number of doctors per bed) and on conditions of local availability. Two partial indirect least squares equations were therefore estimated: in (4.34) the number of beds is treated as exogenous; in (4.35) the number of doctors is also exogenous. Only the

---

[19] Except the constant term $a = \log A$. The term $\beta_0 = (a + \Sigma\mu_j)(1 - \Sigma\alpha_j)^{-1}$ and, since the μ_j's are unknown, $\log A$ cannot be estimated.

final solved equations are presented (with asterisks indicating variables not directly included in the first stage):

$$w = 4.167b + 0.318m^* - 1.496n^* - 0.270d^* - 2.167h^* + \text{constant} \quad (4.34)$$

$$w = 2.695b + 1.512m - 1.281n^* - 0.410d^* - 1.742h^* + \text{constant} \quad (4.35)$$

Again, the estimated elasticities are unacceptable. This may reflect correlation between the v_{ji}'s and the u_i; for example, hospitals with below average technical efficiency ($u_i < 0$) may generally have more nurses relative to doctors than average. But a more fundamental misspecification of the production function may be involved. In the next two sections we therefore consider two alternative models of hospital production.

4.4 A mixed Cobb-Douglas Leontief production function

The strikingly low values of α_N and α_H presented in section 4.3 raised the question of whether the Cobb-Douglas specification is really appropriate for describing the production behaviour of a hospital. Substitution possibilities may be more limited than those implied by the Cobb-Douglas form; or, as suggested in section 4.2, nursing, catering and other supplies may constitute housekeeping activities that affect the amenity standards but not the medical output of the hospital. In this section we consider a production function embodying both Cobb-Douglas and Leontief characteristics, thus allowing the possibility of substitution among some but not all inputs. After discussing the specification and estimation of such a function (section 4.4.1), we investigate its implications for optimum input combinations (section 4.4.2). The observed input levels are again assumed to be exogenously determined. In the next section we consider a more general model of production relations.

4.4.1. *An estimated function with limited substitution*

The elasticity estimates of section 4.3 indicate that medical staff, drugs and dressings, and beds can be related to hospital output by a Cobb-Douglas production function. All three categories of inputs contribute directly to the treatment of additional cases and cases obtaining greater weight in the output index. It is also reasonable to believe that a substantial amount of substitution may be possible.

In contrast, nursing and the other housekeeping inputs cannot be related to output in the Cobb-Douglas function. Instead, we may view these inputs as providing a background of patient care, facilities and hospital maintenance which is necessary but which cannot be substituted for direct health inputs (doctors, drugs, dressings, and beds) in the production of cases.

This hypothesis may be expressed in the form:

$$W = \min [f_1(N), f_2(H), A M^\alpha B^\beta D^\gamma] \qquad (4.36)$$

The general form of this function corresponds to the Leontief non-substitution case in which a minimum level of each "input" is required for any given output level. But the third "input" takes the form of the input mix of a Cobb-Douglas production function – a type of weighted geometric average of the three health-care inputs.[20] For simplicity, catering and "other supplies" are taken together in the second input category.

More specifically, we assume that the relationships between output and nursing, and between output and housekeeping inputs can be estimated by a log-log function, e.g., $\log W = \alpha_0 + \alpha_1 (\log N)$. Although this departs from the strict constant-proportion assumption of the usual Leontief model (unless $\alpha_1 = 1$), it provides a more general homogeneous function that indicates directly whether there are decreasing ($\alpha_1 < 1$) or increasing ($\alpha_1 > 1$) returns to scale in nursing and housekeeping inputs.

The simplest method of calculating the parameters of equation (4.36) is to estimate three separate equations by ordinary least squares.[21] But this method offers only an approximation because, in estimating each equation the information about the other variables is ignored. In particular, the separate estimates make no allowance for the constraint on output that may be imposed by the other input categories. Each equation is actually relevant only when it provides a binding constraint – i.e., only in those hospitals in which its predicted output is less than the minimum imposed by the other inputs. This principle can be used as the basis for an iterative process for improving the separate-equations estimates presented in equations (4.37.a) to (4.37.c):

---

[20] In the general Cobb-Douglas function the weights (coefficients) need not sum to one.
[21] This was the procedure followed by DHRYMES and KURZ (1964) who used a C.E.S. function in place of the Cobb-Douglas one.

$$w = 0.318m + 0.432b + 0.213d + 4.94 \qquad (4.37.a)$$
$$(0.065) \quad (0.062) \quad (0.058)$$

$$w = 0.949n + 1.99 \qquad (4.37.b)$$
$$(0.031)$$

$$w = 0.957h + 0.98 \qquad (4.37.c)$$
$$(0.029)$$

All three equations show slight and almost identical decreasing returns to scale; (4.37.a) and (4.37.c) are homogeneous of degree 0.96 and (4.37.b) is of degree 0.95. In contrast to the results obtained in section 4.3 where nursing and housekeeping expenditure were incorporated into the Cobb-Douglas function, equations (4.37.b) and (4.37.c) indicate a close relationship between output and these inputs.

We can use the coefficients of equations (4.37) as a starting point for obtaining estimates of the parameters of (4.36) by a method that incorporates the underlying assumption that an input determines output only when it acts as a binding constraint. For each hospital in the sample, equations (4.37) indicate three predicted values of log W. We divide hospitals into three groups according to which of the three predicted values of log W is least, i.e., which of the three input categories is the binding constraint. Each subgroup is then the sample for re-estimating the corresponding equation. The process can be repeated until a stable set of coefficients is found.

Such a method of dividing the hospitals places great weight on the precise values of the original set of estimated coefficients. A less restrictive method of defining subsamples would admit a hospital to a subsample for a given constraint if none of the other constraints were ten per cent below it.

Both methods have been applied. The results obtained by the first method (equations (4.38)) differ somewhat from the original estimates of equations (4.37). The less restrictive method of grouping (equation (4.39)) produced values very similar to the original estimates. In the analysis of section 4.4.2 the original estimates will therefore be used.

$$w = 0.227m + 0.422b + 0.292d + 5.23 \qquad (4.38.a)$$
$$(0.148) \quad (0.199) \quad (0.134) \qquad N = 32$$

$$w = 0.894n + 2.73 \qquad (4.38.b)$$
$$(0.086) \qquad N = 40$$

$$w = 0.983h + 0.80 \tag{4.38.c}$$
$$(0.033) \qquad N = 105$$

$$w = 0.321m + 0.398b + 0.229d + 4.94 \tag{4.39.a}$$
$$(0.091) \quad (0.087) \quad (0.081) \qquad N = 90$$

$$w = 0.994n + 1.57 \tag{4.39.b}$$
$$(0.046) \qquad N = 89$$

$$w = 0.992h + 0.66 \tag{4.39.c}$$
$$(0.029) \qquad N = 141$$

4.4.2. *Optimum input proportions*

We return now to the problem posed in section 4.3.2: given a limited budget (E) and a fixed number of beds (B_0), how should a hospital allocate its funds among medical staff (M), drugs and dressings (D), nursing staff (N), and other housekeeping inputs ($H = C + X$) to obtain maximum output (W).

Our new production function may be written as:

$$w = \min \left[(\alpha_0 + \alpha_1 n), (\beta_0 + \beta_1 h), (\gamma_0 + \gamma_1 m + \gamma_2 b + \gamma_3 d) \right] \tag{4.40}$$

The optimizing problem is now more complicated than it was for the Cobb-Douglas production function. The optimum budget allocation must satisfy the following conditions:

$$\alpha_0 + \alpha_1 n = \beta_0 + \beta_1 h \tag{4.41.a}$$

$$\alpha_0 + \alpha_1 n = \gamma_0 + \gamma_1 m + \gamma_2 b + \gamma_3 d \tag{4.41.b}$$

$$D = (\gamma_3/\gamma_1)M \quad \text{or} \quad d = m + \log \gamma_3 - \log \gamma_1 \tag{4.41.c}$$

$$N + H + D + M = E \tag{4.41.d}$$

$$b = \log B_0. \tag{4.41.e}$$

If equation (4.41.a) and (4.41.b) are not both satisfied the hospital will have purchased slack (completely unproductive) quantities of at least one input. Equation (4.41.c) is analogous to the optimum conditions for the Cobb-Douglas function. Equations (4.41.d) and (4.41.e) express the budget and available bed constraints.

Estimates of the α's, β's, and γ's have been obtained in equations (4.37). To solve for the optimum values of N, H, M and D we note first that, from equation (4.41.a):

$$h = \frac{\alpha_0 - \beta_0}{\beta_1} + \left(\frac{\alpha_1}{\beta_1}\right) n. \tag{4.42}$$

Similarly, from equations (4.41.b) and (4.41.c):

$$\gamma_1 m + \gamma_3 (m + \log \gamma_3 - \log \gamma_1) = \alpha_0 - \gamma_0 - \gamma_2 b + \alpha_1 n, \tag{4.43}$$

or

$$m = \frac{\alpha_0 - \gamma_0 - \gamma_2 b - \gamma_3 (\log \gamma_3 - \log \gamma_1)}{\gamma_1 + \gamma_3} + \left(\frac{\alpha_1}{\gamma_1 + \gamma_3}\right) n.$$

Using (4.41.c), the budget constraint may be stated as:

$$N + H + \left(1 + \frac{\gamma_3}{\gamma_1}\right) M = E \tag{4.44}$$

But since $\alpha_1, \beta_1, \gamma_1$ and γ_3 are all positive, equations (4.42) and (4.43) show that H and M are increasing functions of N. We may find the optimum values of the four variable inputs by the following simple computer procedure:

(i) select a low value of N (e.g., $N = 1\,000$).

(ii) calculate the corresponding values of H and M, using the optimum conditions indicated in equations (4.42) and (4.43).

(iii) find $N + H + (1 + \gamma_3/\gamma_1)M$.

(iv) if this sum is less than the budget constraint (E), increase the value of N and repeat from (ii). If the sum exceeds E, the optimum value of N lies in the interval between the current and immediately previous trial value of N.

When a rough interval containing the optimum value of N has been found, N can be located as precisely as desired by considering sufficiently fine subintervals in the same way.

An application of this method with the coefficients of equations (4.37) indicates that a hospital with the average total budget ($E = £\,354\,200$) and 300 beds should allocate £ 85 000 for nursing. Equation (4.42) indicates that the optimum expenditure on housekeeping activity is therefore £ 221 500. The remainder, £ 47 700 is to be spent on medical staff and drugs and dressings in the ratio of 0.318 to 0.213, or £ 28 038 for medical staff and £ 18 779 for drugs and dressings.

The optimum allocation calculated in this way is (as one might expect on a basis of the underlying estimation equations) generally not very different from the average observed allocation shown in table 4.4. The ratio of optimal nursing to other housekeeping expenditure (0.384) is very close to the observed ratio (0.413). The expenditure in these categories is 86.5 per cent of the total, slightly more than the observed 85.1 per cent. Expenditure on medical staff and drugs and dressings of course does not change. As before, the optimum drugs and dressings expenditure increases in relation to medical staff. But this increase now more than doubles expenditure on drugs and dressings. More disconcerting, it results in an absolute decrease in medical staff expenditure.

This surprising conclusion may reflect the fact that the production function used in this section is not a completely satisfactory description of the technical relations determining hospital output. Although it is possible that the hospital's output would be limited if nursing staff and other housekeeping expenditures were reduced sufficiently, in practice it is unlikely that either of these is ever a binding constraint. As suggested in the analysis of 4.3, it is more probable that the supplies of both are so ample that changes in them do not affect output. If this is so, the specified production function yields misleading results.

A related difficulty is the assumption made throughout this section that all inputs are exogenous. As discussed in 4.3.5, if this assumption is incorrect the parameter estimates will be biased.

An alternative more general model, developed in the next section, relaxes both of these assumptions.

4.5 A more general model of production relations

The current model (described formally below) assumes that the hospital's output is not constrained by exogenously determined levels of nursing and housekeeping expenditures. Instead, output depends on the number of beds (B), medical staff (M), and drugs and dressings (D). Within their observed ranges, N and H do not affect output. Beds and medical staff are exogenously determined; drug and dressing expenditure is related to them and the proportional mix of cases. Nursing and housekeeping expenditure are determined by the hospital in relation to the scale and intensity of its operation.[22]

---

[22] The exact characteristics of the model were decided after a number of alternative sets of estimates were made. The results of chapter 5 also influenced the choice of specification.

There is no need to justify the assumption that the number of beds in a hospital is exogenous. Medical expenditure reflects both Ministry rules that relate maximum staff size to the number of hospital beds and the local conditions that determine the supply of medical staff. Medical staff in any hospital is also largely inherited from the past. It therefore seems appropriate to assume that M as well as B is exogenous. The proportional composition of case types, p will also be assumed to be exogenous.

The model contains five equations that determine D, N, H, W and R (the percentage occupancy of available beds). Although the behavioural system is recursive (WOLD, 1964), the estimation procedure makes no assumptions about error covariances. All relations are of constant elasticity.[23]

Expenditure on drugs and dressings is assumed to reflect the number of beds, the size of the medical staff, and the casemix proportions. Writing lower-case letters for the logarithms of the corresponding upper-case variables, the estimated relation is:

$$d = 0.506b + 0.514m + p'\hat{\gamma} \qquad (4.45)$$
$$(0.085) \quad (0.090)$$

Hospital output depends on B, M and D. The production function is therefore the second equation of the recursive model. A consistent estimate is obtained by replacing the drugs and dressings observation by an estimate $(\hat{d})$ from equation (4.45).

$$w = 0.400b + 0.517m + 0.046\hat{d} + 5.202 \qquad (4.46)$$
$$(0.152) \quad (0.154) \quad (0.283)$$

The proportional occupancy of available beds was found to depend on B, M and p.

$$r = -0.110b + 0.126m + p'\hat{\gamma} \qquad (4.47)$$
$$(0.022) \quad (0.023)$$

Finally, nursing and housekeeping expenditure depend on the size and intensity of use of the hospital and on the desired standard of amenity. The investigation of several alternatives indicated that the best measure of size and intensity of use are B, R, and p. No measure is available for the standard of amenity. But if it is assumed to be independent of B, R, p and

---

[23] Except with respect to casemix proportions; because these are frequently zero, the logarithmic transformation is not possible.

the error in each input equation, these equations will indicate the inputs of N and H required for an amenity level of one (i.e., with logarithm zero); the units in which the amenity level is measured can be defined so that this is the average.

$$n = 0.864b + 3.248\hat{r} + p'\hat{\gamma} \qquad (4.48)$$
$$\quad (0.021) \quad (0.425)$$

$$h = 0.893b + 3.035\hat{r} + p'\hat{\gamma} \qquad (4.49)$$
$$\quad (0.020) \quad (0.408)$$

The parameter estimates in each of the five structural equations are quite plausible. The production relation (equation 4.46) implies slightly decreasing returns to scale. It also indicates that the optimum allocation of expenditure between medical staff and drugs and dressings would be in the ratio 517 : 46 or 11.2 to one. This is a substantially higher ratio than obtained in previous ordinary least squares estimates. One explanation of this is suggested by equation (4.45) which shows that high expenditure on drugs and dressings is generally associated with more amply available medical staff. Equation (4.47) indicates that percentage occupancy also rises with more medical staff. Finally, equations (4.48) and (4.49) show that nursing, and housekeeping expenditure rise less than proportionately with hospital size but are very sensitive to increased percentage occupancy of available beds.

By substituting equation (4.45) into equation (4.46) we obtain the reduced form equation

$$w = 0.423b + 0.541m + p'\hat{\gamma} \qquad (4.50)$$

This supports the conclusion that there are slightly decreasing returns to scale.

Substitution of equation (4.47) into (4.48) and (4.49) yields the reduced form equations:

$$n = 0.497b + 0.409m + p'\hat{\gamma} \qquad (4.51)$$

$$h = 0.459b + 0.382m + p'\hat{\gamma} \qquad (4.52)$$

Equal proportional increases in beds and medical staff yield slightly less than proportionate increases in nursing and housekeeping expenditure. More intensive medical staffing increases utilization of capacity and thus creates greater demands for nursing staff and housekeeping expenditure.

For given values of D, M and p, equations (4.45), (4.51), and (4.52) determine the values of D, N and H of a hospital with an average amenity level. If the sum of M, D, N and H determined in this way exceeds the hospital's budget (E), the amenity standard will have to be below average. Stated in this way, the possibility of increasing hospital output by decreasing the amenity standard becomes clear. A decrease in the proportion of total expenditure devoted to N and H permits an increase in expenditure for M and D. If we replace equation (4.45) by the optimum condition $D = 0.089 M$, we obtain from (4.46) that $W = B^{0.400}M^{0.517}(0.089M)^{0.046} e^{p'\hat{\gamma}}$ or $W = (0.089)^{0.046}B^{0.400}M^{0.563}e^{p'\hat{\gamma}}$ where $M(1.089) = E - N - H$. It is clear from this that a proportional increase in M has a greater impact the larger the hospital (i.e., the greater is B). Because the ratio of W to M is higher in larger hospitals, a given absolute increase in M will also have a greater effect the larger the hospital.

4.6 Conclusion

Three approaches to estimating a production function for acute hospitals have been investigated. A general Cobb-Douglas production function relating output to all inputs did not yield satisfactory parameter values with any of the several estimation methods used. A mixed Cobb-Douglas/Leontief function, although it did have plausible coefficients, was tentatively rejected as an inaccurate specification of the technical and stochastic properties of hospital production. A more general model, with beds and medical staff the only exogenous inputs, was finally adopted.

Too little is known about the behavioural characteristics of hospital production for us to be certain that any particular stochastic specification is the correct one. Fortunately, all three approaches supported the same answers to the general substantive questions posed in section 4.1. First, there are slight but unimportant decreasing returns to scale. Second, output would increase if a greater proportion of total expenditure were devoted to medical staff and less to nursing and housekeeping activities. Third, this effect of increased medical staff is more substantial in larger hospitals. A general expansion of medical staff and a reallocation in favour of larger hospitals seems warranted. Finally, as shown in the appendix, the productivity index values obtained by all three methods are very highly correlated.

The recursive model that was finally adopted (section 4.5) provides a greater justification for the estimation of cost functions in chapters 2, 3 and 5. If the only expenditure that is exogenous is for medical staff, it is legitimate to treat total cost as a dependent variable. Even the output of the hospital (or number of cases treated) becomes stochastically prior to the vast majority of total cost; only some 15 per cent of expenditure is for medical staff, drugs and dressings. But it would be unwise to be dogmatic about the "proper" specification of a model of hospital production. It is reassuring that the results of this chapter agree with those of chapter 3. The next chapter looks at the utilization of hospital capacity from several slightly different viewpoints. Again the estimates are compatible with each other and with those of the current chapter.

Comparison of alternative productivity measures

The different production function models discussed in this chapter imply productivity values that are highly correlated with each other. Table 4A-1 presents the correlation matrix of predicted outputs and table 4A-2 presents the correlation matrix of the productivity values. Numbers I through IX refer to the following equations:

Cobb-Douglas:

  I Equation (4.15) $w = \phi(m, b, n, s)$
  II Equation of table 4.2 $w = \phi(m, b, d, n, c, x)$
  III Equation of table 4.5 $w = \phi(m, b, d, n, h)$

Mixed Cobb-Douglas Leontief:

  IV Equation (4.38.a) $w = \phi(m, b, d)$
  V Equation (4.38.b) $w = \phi(n)$
  VI Equation (4.38.c) $w = \phi(h)$
  VII Equation (4.39) $w = \min\,[\phi_1(m, b, d), \phi_2(n), \phi_3(h)]$
                            (Estimates based on binding constraint only)
  VIII Equation (4.40) $w = \min\,[\phi_1(m, b, d), \phi_2(n), \phi_3(h)]$
                            (Estimates based on values within ten per cent of binding constraint)

More general production model

  IX Equation (4.47) $w = \phi(m, b, d)$

The only specification that yields output and productivity values that are not highly correlated with the others is number VII, the equation based on estimates for binding constraints only.

TABLE 4A-1

Correlations of predicted hospital output*

	II	III	IV	V	VI	VII	VIII	IX
I	0.996	0.996	0.996	0.969	0.972	0.552	0.991	0.998
II		1.000	1.000	0.965	0.964	0.529	0.992	0.995
III			1.000	0.965	0.964	0.529	0.992	0.995
IV				0.965	0.963	0.528	0.991	0.995
V					0.926	0.504	0.952	0.981
VI						0.662	0.977	0.963
VII							0.573	0.539
VIII								0.986

* Numbers I through IX refer to hospital output (W) predicted by the corresponding equation. See previous page for identification of these equations.

TABLE 4A-2

Correlations of hospital productivity values*

	II	III	IV	V	VI	VII	VIII	IX
I	0.963	0.963	0.962	0.813	0.799	0.189	0.895	0.984
II		0.999	0.999	0.777	0.756	0.112	0.896	0.947
III			0.999	0.776	0.753	0.110	0.896	0.948
IV				0.777	0.747	0.106	0.888	0.948
V					0.546	−0.013	0.673	0.897
VI						0.520	0.859	0.732
VII							0.239	0.121
VIII								0.852

* Numbers I through IX refer to hospital productivity values ($P*$) based on the corresponding equation. See previous page for identification of these equations.

SYMBOLS IN CHAPTER 4

A lower case letter shown in brackets refers to the logarithm of the corresponding upper case variable.

B (b) number of beds in a hospital
C (c) total catering expenditure of a hospital
C_{ji} number of cases of type j in hospital i
C_i total number of cases in hospital i
$c_{.j}$ average cost of treating a case of type j
D (d) total drugs and dressing expenditure of a hospital
E total ward expenditure of a hospital
H (h) total "housekeeping" expenditure of a hospital $(H = E - M - N - D)$
k capital cost of a hospital bed year
M (m) total medical staff expenditure of a hospital
N (n) total nursing staff expenditure of a hospital
p_{ji} proportion of cases of type j in hospital i
$\mathbf{p}_i$ vector of proportions of case types in hospital i
Q_i output of hospital i (as used in general formulation); see also W
R percentage occupancy of available beds in a hospital
S (s) total "other supplies" expenditure of a hospital $(S = E - M - N)$
W (w) weighted output of a hospital
X (x) total "other expenditure" of a hospital $(X = E - M - N - D - C)$
X_{ri} quantity of rth input used by hospital i
α_r elasticity of output with respect to X_r

CHAPTER 5

DIFFERENCES IN THE INTENSITY OF UTILIZATION
OF CAPACITY

5.1 Introduction

Chapter 3 showed that there is substantial interhospital variation in the intensity with which bed capacity is used. The case-flow rate ranges between 9.41 and 40.48 cases per bed-year; a standard deviation of 5.33 is associated with the mean of 23.18. We now study the implications and causes of this variation.

Section 5.2 examines the cost implications of differences in intensity of utilization by studying the behaviour of the hospital's "short-run" average cost function. For the purpose of these studies, the "short-run" cost function does not refer to the changes in costs through time but rather to the effect on costs of changes in output with a given capacity or, more precisely, changes in the intensity of capacity utilization.[1] Because we have separate measures of output and capacity, we are able to estimate these "short-run" average cost functions from cross-section data. The estimated functions show that although cost per patient-week would rise if capacity were used more intensely than at present, substantial savings could be made in cost per case.

Section 5.3 discusses the implications of more intense utilization from a different point of view: the marginal cost of treating an additional case. Once the hospital is maintaining a given number of beds, the cost of an additional case [2] is substantially less than the average cost. This is particularly

---

[1] For discussion of the effects of short-run changes in output on hospital costs, see P. J. FELDSTEIN (1961), LONG (1964).

[2] More precisely, the additional annual expenditure if one more case is treated per year.

true for some cost components. The estimated marginal costs of treating patients in different categories, which should be relevant to the doctors' problem of allocating patients between in-patient and out-patient care, are also estimated.

Because costs are so very much affected by intensity of utilization, it is worth examining what factors influence case-flow rates, average durations of patient stay, and percentage utilization of capacity. This is done in section 5.4.

5.2 Cost implications of differences in intensity of utilization

The short-run average cost function of economic theory relates average cost and output when the size of plant is fixed. In practice, econometric estimates of short-run cost functions have been made with time-series data for an individual firm (e.g., DEAN, 1941; DEAN, 1951; JOHNSTON, 1960). Although a measure of capacity is not introduced explicitly in such studies, observations are confined to a period that is short enough to warrant the assumption that capacity remains constant.

The studies presented in this section depart from the traditional method of estimation and use cross-section analyses.[3] The data has already been described in chapters 2 and 3. Because we have separate measures of capacity (the number of beds, B) and output (the number of cases, n, with an adjustment for casemix), we are able to study the way in which unit costs respond to changes in output with "given" capacity, or, equivalently, changes in the intensity of capacity utilization.

The case-flow rate (i.e., the case-bed ratio, F), is the basic measure of the intensity with which hospital capacity is used. The case-flow rate affects unit costs in two ways. If the cost per patient week were not affected by F, an increase in F would obviously decrease cost per case. But for most hospitals, an increase in F would increase cost per patient week and thus offset some of the potential decrease in cost per case. Nevertheless, until F is substantially above its current average level, the elasticity of cost per week with respect to F is of absolute value less than one and cost per case is a decreasing function of F.

---

[3] WALTERS (1963) suggests cross-sectional estimation of short-run cost curves but his proposed estimation equation requires *a priori* knowledge of the minimum cost output level for each plant.

5.2.1. *Estimated short-run average cost function*

Equation (5.1) presents the short-run cost curve as a simple quadratic function relating cost per case directly to the intensity of capacity utilization.

$$c_{i.} = -6.647F_i + 0.103F_i^2 + p_i'\hat{\gamma} \qquad (5.1)$$
$$(0.668) \quad (0.014)$$

The vector p_i again represents the proportion of cases in each of the nine categories.[4]

From this equation we can calculate that $c_{i.}$ is at a minimum when the case-flow rate is 32.1 cases per bed-year. This should be compared with the average of only 23.2 cases. For hospitals with the average F value, the elasticity of cost per case with respect to F is -0.81. By increasing F from 23.2 cases to 32.1 cases, a hospital decreases its expected cost from £ 54.62 to £ 46.30. Only seven hospitals (3.95 per cent) have case-flow rates exceeding 32.1 cases; the short-run cost function is therefore decreasing throughout most of the observed range of F values. Before considering alternative estimates of this function, we will briefly note the characteristics of the corresponding cost-per-patient-week function.

Equation (5.2) presents a quadratic short-run cost-per-patient-week function $(c_i^w. = 7c_{i.}/s_i)$:

$$c_i^w. = -0.272F_i + 0.011F_i^2 + p_i'\hat{\gamma} \qquad (5.2)$$
$$(0.279) \quad (0.006)$$

This curve appears to have a minimum at $F = 12.3$. Cost-per-patient-week rises from this minimum of £ 27.13 to £ 28.42 at the average $F = 23.2$, and to £ 31.61 at $F = 32.1$ where cost per case appears to reach a minimum. The average hospital is therefore operating on the rising section of the short-run cost-per-week curve; at $F = 23.2$ the elasticity of cost-per-week with respect to F is $+0.196$. When F reaches 32.1, the elasticity is $+0.243$. To study whether this cost curve is actually U-shaped rather than monotonically increasing, we have examined the residuals from equation (5.2) for the seven hospitals in which $F \leq 12.3$. If the appropriate function were actually monotonically increasing, these residuals would tend to be negative. In fact, only four were negative; the average of the residuals was 0.61 with

---

[4] See above, chapter 3, sections 3.4.2 and 3.4.3. Casemix specification is discussed again below, pp. 131-132.

a standard error of 4.50. Although a null hypothesis that the curve was U-shaped would formally be maintained, there is too little evidence for a clear decision either way.

Hospital size has so far been ignored in considering the short-run cost curves. As shown in chapter 3 and developed in section 5.4 below, hospital size does influence the intensity with which hospital capacity is used. Nevertheless, as shown by equations (5.3) and (5.4), including a measure of hospital size in the short-run function does not substantially affect its shape.

$$c_{i.} = -7.1428F_i + 0.1092F_i^2 - 3.5414 \cdot 10^{-2}B_i + 1.9574 \cdot 10^{-5}B_i^2 + \mathbf{p}_i'\hat{\gamma}$$
$$\quad\;\;(0.6391)\quad(0.0131)\quad(1.0800)\qquad\qquad(1.0738)$$

$$(5.3)$$

$$c_i^w. = -0.5196F_i + 0.0143F_i^2 - 1.8864 \cdot 10^{-2}B_i + 1.093 \cdot 10^{-5}B_i^2 + \mathbf{p}_i'\hat{\gamma}$$
$$\quad\;\;(0.2569)\quad(0.0053)\quad(0.4342)\qquad\qquad(0.4317)$$

$$(5.4)$$

These functions imply that the minimum cost per case would be achieved at $F = 32.7$ and minimum cost per week at $F = 18.2$; these minima may be compared with the previously calculated values of $F = 32.1$ and $F = 12.3$. Although the estimated average short-run cost curve for all hospitals is not substantially affected by the hospital-size terms, it is not true that the same short-run curve is necessarily appropriate for hospitals in every size group. This is considered in section 5.2.4.

Because casemix has a substantial effect on both cost per case and case-flow, it might be feared that the short-run cost curve estimates would be sensitive to differences in casemix specification. Chapter 2 showed that casemix (specified as a vector of nine case proportions) can explain 30.8 per cent of the variation in cost per case; in the same way we may show that casemix can explain 35.2 per cent of the variation in F. Nevertheless, experimenting with casemix specification indicates that the coefficients (and implied minimum cost value of F) are influenced little by omitting casemix from the cost function or by changing its specification. Equations (5.5) and (5.6) correspond to (5.1) and (5.3) but casemix is now omitted; numbers in square brackets beneath the standard errors are the coefficients of the original equations.

$$c_{i.} = -6.7479F_i + 0.1012F_i^2 + \hat{\alpha} \qquad (5.5)$$
$$\phantom{c_{i.} = -6.} (0.6518) \quad (0.0136)$$
$$\phantom{c_{i.} = -6.} [6.6473] \quad [0.1033]$$

$$c_{i.} = -7.1861F_i + 0.1060F_i^2 - 0.0242B_i + 1.2169 \cdot 10^{-5}B_i^2 + \hat{\alpha} \quad (5.6)$$
$$\phantom{c_{i.} = -7.} (0.6398) \quad (0.0132)$$
$$\phantom{c_{i.} = -7.} [7.1428] \quad [0.1092]$$

In equation (5.7) the casemix ($\tilde{p}_i'$) is specified by classifying cases into four groups: general medicine, general surgery, obstetrics, and "others".

$$c_{i.} = -7.0873F_i + 0.1058F_i^2 - 0.0257B_i + 1.2552 \cdot 10^{-5}B_i^2 + \tilde{p}_i'\hat{\gamma} \quad (5.7)$$
$$\phantom{c_{i.} = -7.} (0.6508) \quad (0.0143)$$
$$\phantom{c_{i.} = -7.} [7.1428] \quad [0.1092]$$

It is clear from these equations that the form of casemix specification will not influence the estimated shape of the short-run cost curve.

The use of ordinary least squares to estimate these short-run cost curves tacitly implies that F is independent of the error in the equation. We have already met this problem in chapter 3, section 3.5.6. We then argued that consistent estimates would be obtained by using instrumental variables for F and F^2, with a rank group number serving as the instrument.

TABLE 5.1

*Comparison of ordinary least squares and instrumental variable estimates of short-run average cost functions**

Adjustment for hospital size	Estimation method**	Coefficient of		Elasticity of cost per case with respect to F at $F = 23.2$
		F	F^2	
None	O.L.S.	-6.6473 (0.6684)	0.1033 (0.0138)	0.81
None	I.V.	-0.3538 (0.4726)	-0.0269 (0.0099)	0.70
B, B^2	O.L.S.	-7.1428 (0.6391	0.1092 (0.0131)	0.89
B, B^2	I.V.	-0.4485 (0.4765)	-0.0276 (0.0099)	0.75

* All equations include a vector of nine case proportions.
** O.L.S. = Ordinary least squares; I.V. = Instrumental variable.

Table 5.1 compares the properties of the short-run average cost curves estimated by ordinary least squares with ones estimated with instrumental variables. Hospitals were divided into four and six groups by rank order and the group numbers used as instruments.

The coefficients of F and F^2 obtained by the instrumental variable estimation procedure differ substantially from the ordinary least squares estimates. Both instrumental variable equations imply a monotonically decreasing average cost curve. But the exact general form of the function is unimportant. All four estimates indicate similar elasticities of cost per case with respect to case-flow rate when calculated at the current average rate ($F = 23.2$). The instrumental variable estimates are only slightly lower than those obtained by ordinary least squares.

5.2.2. Alternative forms

Because only seven hospitals have F values exceeding the implied turning point of the short-run average-cost-per-case curve, it is difficult to infer from their residuals from equation (5.3) whether the U-shaped curve is a better hypothesis than a curve that is monotonically decreasing with a positive second derivative. Of the seven residuals, three are positive and the average value is -0.854. This would suggest that the quadratic form is not inappropriate at these extreme values.

Nevertheless, comparing the quadratic function (equation (5.3), repeated below) with the semilogarithmic form (5.8) and the inverse form (5.9) shows that the latter has slightly greater explanatory power than the others.

$$c_{i.} = -7.1428F_i + 0.1092F_i^2 - 0.0354B_i + 1.9574 \cdot 10^{-5}B_i^2 + p_i'\hat{\gamma}$$
$$\quad (0.6391) \quad (0.0131) \quad (0.0108) \quad (1.0738)$$
$$R^2 = 0.74 \quad (5.3)$$

$$c_{i.} = -47.1736(\log F_i) - 0.0397B_i + 2.5106 \cdot 10^{-5}B_i^2 + p_i'\hat{\gamma}$$
$$\quad (3.0649) \quad (0.0113) \quad (1.1233)$$
$$R^2 = 0.72 \quad (5.8)$$

$$c_{i.} = 951.2F_i^{-1} - 0.0394B_i + 2.4152 \cdot 10^{-5}B_i^2 + p_i'\hat{\gamma}$$
$$\quad (53.7) \quad (0.0103) \quad (1.0277)$$
$$R^2 = 0.76 \quad (5.9)$$

This would favour the hypothesis that the average cost-per-case curve is monotonically decreasing. Against this must be weighted the evidence that cost-per-patient-week in this range is increasing at an increasing rate. At some point the cost-per-case curve would therefore begin to turn upward.

But the choice between these two forms is not of great importance to us. We are concerned not about the theoretical shape of this cost curve but rather about its shape in the range relevant for current decisions. All three forms indicate that the elasticity of cost per case with respect to F is significantly negative at the current average case-flow rate; the three elasticities are -0.89, -0.86 and -0.75. The conclusion is therefore clear that substantial savings in cost per case could be achieved by increasing case-flow rates.

5.2.3. *Short-run cost functions in hospitals of different size*

The characteristics of short-run cost functions of hospitals in different size groups are also quite similar. The analysis of this section considers divisions of hospitals into two groups (above and below the mean) and four groups (with divisions at the one standard deviation point). As in section 3.5.3 of chapter 3, we consider three hypotheses. Hypothesis one, that all coefficients differ among size groups, requires estimating a separate cost function (of the type used in (5.3)) for each size group. Hypothesis two, that the coefficients of the casemix variables remain constant, uses an analysis of covariance (dummy variable) equation of the type discussed in section 3.4.5 and 3.5.3. Hypothesis three uses a similar formulation to allow only the coefficients of F and F^2 to vary among size groups.

Table 5.2 presents the coefficients of F and F^2, the value of F at which average case cost would reach a minimum, and the elasticity of cost per case with respect to F evaluated at the current average value of F (23.2). The results suggest that cost per week rises less rapidly as F increases in smaller hospitals than in larger ones. As a result the elasticity of cost per case with respect to F is of greater absolute value in smaller hospitals and the minimum cost value of F is higher. But the differences are less important than the similarities: cost per case would fall substantially if F increased and would continue to fall until the number of cases per bed was approximately thirty per cent greater than now.

5.2.4. *Individual input categories*

Changes in the case-flow rate need not have the same effect in all input categories. The response of cost per patient week to changes in F is greater

TABLE 5.2

Short-run cost functions in hospital size groups

No. of groups	Min. Max.	No. of hosp.	Hypothesis One Coefficients F	F^2 (10^{-2})	Min.*	Elas.**	Hypothesis Two Coefficients F	F^2 (10^{-2})	Min.*	Elas.**	Hypothesis Three Coefficients F	F^2 (10^{-2})	Min.*	Elas.**
One	72–1064	177	−7.143 (0.639)	10.918 (1.312)	32.7	−0.88	—	—	—	—	—	—	—	—
Two	72–302	111	−6.354 (0.970)	9.260 (1.873)	34.3	−0.87	−6.430 (1.045)	9.450 (2.023)	34.0	−0.87	−6.624 (1.023)	9.857 (1.975)	33.6	−0.87
	303–1064	66	−9.241 (1.292)	15.676 (1.971)	29.5	−0.84	−8.282 (0.980)	13.604 (2.201)	30.4	−0.84	−8.249 (0.977)	13.487 (2.195)	30.6	−0.85
Four	72–117	15	−5.464 (3.001)	6.149 (4.722)	44.4	−1.11	−1.889 (3.196)	1.380 (5.161)	68.4	−0.53	−1.749 (2.792)	1.260 (4.686)	69.4	−0.49
	118–302	96	−8.466 (1.434)	13.698 (2.962)	30.9	−0.90	−8.695 (1.559)	14.121 (3.224)	30.8	−0.91	−8.621 (1.530)	14.018 (3.173)	30.7	−0.90
	303–488	40	−8.896 (1.448)	14.866 (3.126)	29.9	−0.85	−8.647 (1.188)	14.124 (2.578)	30.6	−0.89	−8.760 (1.158)	14.375 (2.496)	30.5	−0.89
	489–1064	26	−12.827 (3.550)	23.197 (7.927)	27.6	−0.88	−7.341 (2.274)	11.796 (5.615)	31.1	−0.79	−7.462 (2.209)	12.116 (5.467)	30.8	−0.78

* Value of F at which c_i is minimum.

** Elasticity of c_i with respect to F calculated at $\bar{F} = 23.2$.

for some inputs than for others. While there is little reason for catering costs per week to rise with F, medical costs are likely to increase. Differences in the shape of estimated individual short-run cost curves also reflect any input substitution which is related to F. If hospitals substitute nurses for domestics as F increases, the costs of the former would rise more quickly than those of the latter. It is not possible to separate the cost-curve effect from the substitution effect. The possibility that both influences are at work must therefore be borne in mind in interpretating any empirical results.

The values of F at which costs would be at their minima are shown in the fifth column of table 5.3. The final column indicates the percentage reduction in costs from their current mean to their minimum value.

Although the minimum-cost value of F is approximately the same in all categories, the percentage reductions in costs differ substantially. As expected, direct costs fall less than indirect costs. Nursing and domestic costs behave more like indirect costs than like medical care costs (medical staff, drugs, dressings, etc.).[5]

5.3 Marginal costs of treating additional cases

An alternative way of studying the cost implications of differences in the intensity of use of hospital capacity is to examine the marginal costs of treating additional cases.

The marginal cost analysis presented below shows the way in which a hospital's annual expenditure in different categories is affected by increasing the number of cases treated per year. Separate marginal costs for cases of different types have also been estimated. These results should be of direct relevance in determining optimum policies of hospital care. Although doctors at present appear to show little interest in cost when choosing between in-patient and out-patient care for a particular patient, to the extent that they do consider costs, their attention focuses on *average* rather than *marginal* cost. If the simple fact that long-run marginal cost per case is substantially less than average cost per case were properly appreciated by doctors and hospital administrators, admission rates and the intensity of use of hospital capacity might be substantially higher.

---

[5] This supports the classification used in the production function specification of chapter 4, sections 4.4 and 4.5.

TABLE 5.3

Short-run average cost curve by input type

Cost type	Average cost per case £	Coefficients* of		Min. cost F	Min. cost per case	Percentage reduction
		F	$F^2 \cdot 10^{-2}$			
Medical	5.71 (1.43)	−0.461 (0.085)	0.71 (0.18)	32.46	5.11	10.5
Nursing	13.54 (3.47)	−1.506 (0.182)	2.13 (0.37)	35.35	10.39	23.2
Domestics	3.40 (2.39)	−0.902 (0.169)	1.44 (3.47)	31.32	2.45	27.9
Nursing and domestics	16.93 (5.22)	−2.408 (0.268)	3.57 (0.55)	33.73	12.60	25.6
Ward staff	22.64 (6.18)	−2.869 (0.311)	4.28 (0.64)	33.52	18.06	20.2
Drugs	1.77 (0.49)	−0.100 (0.036)	0.13 (0.07)	38.13	1.48	16.4
Dressings	0.60 (0.20)	−0.037 (0.016)	0.06 (0.03)	32.80	0.54	9.4
Clothing and linen	1.68 (0.55)	−0.974 (0.046)	0.16 (0.09)	31.22	1.58	6.1
Med. and surg. appliances	0.45 (0.19)	−0.042 (0.015)	0.05 (0.03)	38.67	0.32	28.3
Total direct	30.44 (7.61)	−3.520 (0.382)	5.30 (0.78)	33.21	25.10	17.5
Laundry	1.76 (0.61)	−0.256 (0.042)	0.41 (0.09)	30.92	1.51	14.3
Catering	9.24 (2.69)	−1.215 (0.152)	1.83 (0.31)	33.20	7.40	19.9
Total indirect	24.14 (6.96)	−3.625 (0.368)	5.66 (0.76)	32.02	19.06	21.0

* Coefficients are based on equations of the form:

$$c = \beta_1 F + \beta_2 F^2 + \beta_3 B + \beta_4 B^2 + p'\gamma$$

5.3.1. *Estimation of marginal costs*

Although the marginal cost of treating an additional case could be derived from the average cost curves discussed in section 5.2, we have chosen the easier and more direct procedure of estimating total cost curves and finding their first derivatives with respect to cases.

As the simplest example of this consider equation (5.10):

$$E_i = 813.09B_i + 11.43n_i + p_i'\hat{\gamma} \qquad (5.10)$$
$$(45.86) \quad (2.30)$$

where E_i = total annual ward cost in hospital i ($\bar{E} = £\,354\,204$). Despite the high correlation between B_i and n_i, the standard errors of their coefficients are relatively small. From the first derivative of E_i with respect to n_i we find that the marginal cost of treating an additional case with a fixed number of beds is $£\,11.43$ with a standard error of $£\,2.30$; this should be compared with the average cost per case of $£\,54.62$.

Increasing the number of cases treated with a given number of available beds occurs in two ways: increasing the percentage occupancy of the available beds (i.e., increasing the number of patient-days or "occupied beds" [6]) and increasing the number of cases treated in a given number of patient days (i.e., decreasing the average duration of stay per case). We may compare two types of marginal cost: the cost of an additional case with a fixed number of available beds (MC1) and the lower cost of an additional case with a fixed number of occupied beds (MC2).

In equation (5.11) we have replaced the number of available beds (B) by the number of occupied beds (BO). The first derivative of E_i with respect to n_i ($£\,6.43$) is therefore MC2, the marginal cost of treating additional cases with given occupancy.[7]

$$E_i = 1094.24(BO)_i + 6.43n_i + v_i'\hat{\gamma} \qquad (5.11)$$
$$(54.09) \qquad (2.26)$$

---

[6] An "occupied bed" is defined as 365 patient days.

[7] Although we are concerned only with the marginal cost of treating additional *cases*, equations (5.10) and (5.11) indicate the marginal cost of additional bed-years: $£\,813.09$ for the "variable" costs of an additional *available* bed with a given case output and $£\,1094.24$ for an additional occupied bed. This latter figure implies that for a given number of cases an additional patient-day costs $£\,2.99$, or $£\,1.07$ less than the average cost per patient-day ($£\,4.06$).

To summarize, the simple linear total cost functions imply that a hospital could treat an additional case for £ 6.43 by reducing the duration of stay of other cases in a way which kept the total number of bed days constant. By increasing percentage occupancy, a smaller reduction in durations of stay is required but money costs rise to an average marginal case cost of £ 11.43. In using marginal costs for deciding resource allocations (in this context, the number of cases to be admitted), the appropriate marginal cost estimate must answer the question: what costs would be avoided if this were not done.[8] The estimated marginal cost of £ 11.43 per case is the long-run avoidable cost of an extra case in a "fully operating" hospital when the adjustment in percentage occupancy is of average magnitude. For changes that required re-opening a previously closed ward or actually expanding the size of the hospital by building, the avoidable costs would be substantially higher.

5.3.2. *Four problems in estimating marginal cost*

In the first part of this section we made four assumptions that now must be explored: (1) a linear total cost function is an acceptable approximation; (2) marginal costs are the same in hospitals of different size; (3) the errors are sufficiently homoscedastic so that there would be little difference in the results if generalized least squares estimation were used; and (4) the possibility of correlation between the error term and the number of cases treated does not invalidate these single-equation ordinary least squares estimates. The evidence to be presented indicates that these assumptions are not wholly satisfactory. If marginal cost estimates are to be applied to making decisions for particular hospitals or departments, it would be better to specify the cost function in a way which takes into account the size of the hospital and the current number of cases being treated. But the estimates based on single linear equations presented above and in sections 5.3.3 and 5.3.4 are adequate for describing the general relationship between average cost and the various measures of marginal costs, both for costs and cases in general and when considered by input category and individual case types.

5.3.2.1. *Linearity.* In place of the linear equations of 5.2.1 we now consider the quadratic functions:

---

[8] For a discussion of "avoidable costs", see MEYER and KRAFT (1958).

$$E_i = 17.382n_i - 2.828 \cdot 10^{-4}n_i^2 + 728.32B_i + 7.637 \cdot 10^{-2}B_i^2 + p'_i\hat{\gamma} \qquad (5.14)$$
$$(5.985)\quad(2.627)\qquad\qquad(115.32)\quad(9.633)$$

$$E_i = 11.564n_i - 2.843 \cdot 10^{-4}n_i^2 + 1104.02(BO)_i - 0.891 \cdot 10^{-2}(BO)_i^2 + p'_i\gamma$$
$$(5.736)\quad(2.530)\qquad\qquad(134.04)\qquad(13.551)\qquad\qquad(5.15)$$

Both equations indicate that marginal cost decreases slightly as the number of cases increases. Evaluating marginal cost at the average number of cases ($n = 6594$) we find that the total marginal cost is £ 13.65 (linear estimate: £ 11.43) and the marginal cost with a fixed number of patient days is £ 7.87 (linear estimate: £ 6.43). The results are thus generally similar to those obtained by the linear approximation: marginal cost is very much lower than average and reduced by nearly one half if the number of occupied beds is constant. When a cubic term in the number of cases is added to the total cost equations we find in both equations that its coefficient is negative and less than its standard error.

5.3.2.2. *Hospital size.* Table 5.4 shows that marginal cost per case is higher in hospitals of greater than mean size and that this is concentrated

TABLE 5.4

Marginal cost per case by hospital size

Hospital size*	Number of hospitals	Hypothesis One** MC1***	Hypothesis One** MC2***	Hypothesis Two** MC1***	Hypothesis Two** MC2***
≦ 302	111	7.27 (3.93)	1.91 (3.71)	9.81 (5.82)	4.78 (5.52)
≧ 303	66	13.06 (4.44)	7.59 (4.37)	11.58 (2.52)	6.08 (2.48)
All hospitals	177	—	—	11.43 (2.30)	6.43 (2.26)

  * Number of available beds.
  ** Hypothesis One estimates obtained from separate equations for small and large hospitals. Hypothesis Two estimates obtained from single equations using all data but allowing coefficients of B and n to vary.
***MC1 is the cost of treating an additional case when the number of *available* beds is constant. MC2 is the cost of treating an additional case when the number of *occupied* beds is constant.

primarily in the marginal cost of increasing the number of cases treated with a given number of occupied beds (MC2). Estimates were obtained from separate equations for hospitals above and below mean size, thus allowing all coefficients to vary between size groups. These are presented under hypothesis one. Under the second hypothesis, only the coefficients of n and B are allowed to vary; these estimates are obtained with all observations used in estimating each equation.

The hypothesis two estimates agree quite well with the set of coefficients obtained for all hospitals. When all coefficients are allowed to vary (hypothesis one), the marginal cost estimates differ more between size groups. Although in actual application it may be worthwhile to recognize that size influences marginal cost, for the purpose of studying the general pattern of marginal costs the estimates obtained when size is ignored are not likely to be misleading.

5.3.2.3. *Homoscedasticity.* To assess the homoscedasticity of the general total cost function (5.14), we ordered the hospitals by size and calculated the error variance in each quartile. These error variances differed substantially. The likelihood ratio [9] was $8.913 \cdot 10^{-14}$. The generalized least squares regression based on these estimated error variances had much more homoscedastic residuals. The likelihood ratio, 0.822, was not different from one at the fifty per cent level.

The parameter estimates obtained in the generalized least squares regression (equation (5.16)) were quite similar to the ordinary least squares results presented in (5.14).

$$E_i = 15.602n_i - 2.175 \cdot 10^{-4}n_i^2 + 782.32B_i + 4.010 \cdot 10^{-2}B_i^2 + p_i'\hat{\gamma}$$
$$ (5.566) \quad (2.617) \qquad\quad (109.65) \quad (9.819) \qquad\qquad\qquad\qquad (5.16)$$

The implied marginal cost per case at $\bar{n} = 6594$ is £ 14.17 in equation (5.16) and £ 13.65 in equation (5.14). The unbiased estimates of the standard errors are very similar to the ordinary least squares estimates. It seems likely that disregarding heteroscedasticity elsewhere in this chapter will not have important effects on our results.

5.3.2.4. *Instrumental variables estimates.* Because the number of cases treated is an endogenous variable in a system of production relations, it could be correlated with the error in the total cost function. Ordinary

---

[9] For a full description of this method, see Appendix 2A.

least squares estimates would be biased but instrumental variable estimates will be consistent if the instrument is uncorrelated with the error. To define instruments, the hospitals were ranked by n_i and divided into four and six groups, the group numbers serving as the instruments. The group into which a hospital falls will almost always be determined by its size (number of beds) and will thus be independent of the error term.

The instrumental variable estimates, presented in equation (5.17), imply

$$E_i = 3.010n_i + 6.334 \cdot 10^{-4}n_i^2 + 745.70B_i + 0.122B_i^2 + p_i'\hat{\gamma}$$

$$(4.342) \quad (2.924) \qquad (110.63) \quad (0.086) \qquad (5.17)$$

a marginal cost of £ 11.36 at $\bar{n}$ = 6594, very similar to the marginal cost of £ 11.43 in the basic linear equation (5.10) and only somewhat less than the £ 13.65 of the ordinary least squares quadratic function.

If the production model of chapter 4, section 4.5, is correct, there is little reason to fear a substantial interdependence between the number of cases treated and the error in the total cost equation. The instrumental variable estimate lends support to this.

5.3.3. *Marginal cost by input category*

If marginal cost analysis is to be used in estimating the expenditure effects and staff requirements entailed by increased utilization of available beds, it is important to recognize that the relationship between average and marginal costs will not be the same in all expenditure categories. Similarly, the relative size of the two separate marginal costs (MC1 and MC2) will differ between input categories.

The additive nature of linear regression allows us to disaggregate costs into their individual components and estimate marginal costs that sum to the overall MC1 and MC2 values. Table 5.5 presents the separate marginal costs for doctors, nurses, drugs and dressings, and all other purchasables. The average cost per case is shown for comparison.

The average incremental cost per case is, in effect, the marginal cost of treating an additional case when the number of beds is not constant. This is derived from a regression equations of the form, $E_i = \beta n_i + p_i'\gamma$. As expected, these values are close to the average cost per case.

The total marginal cost per case (£ 11.43) is concentrated most heavily

TABLE 5.5

Marginal cost by input category

Input category	Average cost per case	Average incremental cost*	MC1*	MC2*
Doctors	5.71	5.00 (0.17)	2.85 (0.31)	2.49 (0.32)
Nurses	13.52	11.97 (0.56)	1.63 (0.73)	0.19 (0.72)
Drugs and dressings	2.31	2.19 (0.95)	1.00 (0.17)	0.90 (0.18)
Other purchasables (Total ward cost except doctors, nurses, drugs and dressings)	33.08	28.13 (1.23)	5.95 (1.67)	2.85 (1.69)
Total ward cost	54.62	47.29 (1.87)	11.43 (2.30)	6.43 (2.26)

* *Average incremental cost* is the increase in total ward cost of treating an additional case. MC1 is the cost of treating an additional case when the number of *available* beds is constant.

MC2 is the cost of treating an additional case in the same number of total patient days, i.e., it is the marginal case cost when the number of *occupied* beds is constant.

in the expenditure for doctors (£ 2.85) and other purchasables (£ 5.95). The ratio of total marginal costs to the corresponding average costs is highest for doctors (0.50) and lowest for nurses (0.12). The most significant impact of an increase in utilization of available beds would be in the demand for doctors' services.

For doctors, the cost of an additional case is the same whether or not average stay is decreased; doctors treat cases, not patient days. Drugs and dressings are affected in the same way. In contrast, almost no additional nursing cost is involved in increasing the number of cases treated if the number of occupied beds is kept constant. Nursing staff again appears to be a fixed overhead. Additional expenditure on other purchasables is only partly reduced if the number of occupied beds remains constant.

These marginal cost relations support some of the conclusions reached in chapter 4's discussion of the hospital production function. In particular, the high marginal cost for doctors and the low marginal cost for nurses is consistent with the relative output elasticities.

5.3.4. *Marginal costs of individual case types*

Until now we have estimated marginal costs on the assumption that the casemix proportions remain unchanged. In this section we consider the marginal costs of individual case types.

Chapter 2 showed that the average cost per case varies substantially among the major case types. In estimating the marginal costs of individual case types we cannot assume that the ratio of marginal cost to average cost is the same for all case types. Similarly, the relation between MC1 and MC2 may differ.

These relations could in principle be investigated, both for total ward cost and for each of its components, by explicitly specifying the total cost function in terms of the numbers of cases of each type. For example, the total marginal cost for each case type can be estimated from the equation

$$E_i = \alpha + \beta B_i + \sum_j \gamma_j n_{ij} + u_i \qquad (5.18)$$

where each γ_j is the total marginal cost of that case type. The precision with which the γ_j's can be estimated is limited by the multicollinearity of the n_{ij}'s. The large standard errors of the estimates presented in tables 5.8 and 5.9 reflect this problem.

Table 5.6 presents the marginal costs per case for seven case types [10]. For comparison, the average costs per case (derived in chapter 2 from a linear average cost curve) and the average incremental costs (derived from an equation similar to (5.18) but without a B term) are shown.[11] Marginal costs, like average costs, are highest for medical and "other" cases. Also noteworthy is the high ratio of marginal to average costs for obstetrics. But, in general, the individual marginal cost estimates cannot be accepted with any confidence. For nearly half the estimates, the standard error exceeds the coefficient. If it were considered important to find accurate marginal cost estimates for individual case types, two sets of estimates, based on different years' data, should be compared.

---

[10] General surgery, traumatic and orthopaedic surgery and other surgery have been combined in reducing the number of case types from nine to seven.

[11] For a further analysis of the similarity of average cost per case and average incremental cost, see Appendix 5A.

TABLE 5.6

Marginal costs of individual case types

Case type	Average cost per case*	Average incremental cost**	MC1***	MC2
General medicine	114.82	107.736	19.433	3.861
	(18.88)	(11.775)	(8.648)	(8.185)
Paediatrics	24.97	33.902	6.591	9.899
	(28.51)	(21.021)	(12.639)	(11.438)
Surgery	41.55	29.929	8.646	5.109
	(16.25)	(5.310)	(3.393)	(3.125)
E.N.T.	15.25	26.668	7.174	1.370
	(16.52)	(8.223)	(5.031)	(4.623)
Gynaecology	58.72	47.157	−1.593	−8.602
	(21.47)	(16.683)	(10.336)	(9.440)
Obstetrics	34.88	28.426	16.289	11.029
	(16.34)	(8.958)	(5.390)	(4.924)
Others	69.51	100.673	27.894	30.189
	(−)	(14.154)	(9.412)	(8.415)

 * *Average cost per case* as derived from average cost function; see chapter 2.
 ** *Average incremental cost* is the increase in total ward cost incurred by treating an additional case. The number of beds is not assumed constant. Estimates are derived from a total linear cost function for comparison with estimates obtained from average cost function, see Appendix 5A, table 5A-1.
 *** MC1 and MC2 are defined in the notes to table 5.5.

In spite of the difficulties encountered in estimating the marginal total ward cost for cases of different types, it was considered worthwhile to try estimating such individual marginal costs for the various input categories. The estimates are presented in table 5.7. Again the total marginal costs are more accurate than their components. The marginal cost of doctors' services is highest for surgery, gynaecology and obstetrics. Nursing marginal costs are highest for obstetrics, paediatrics and general medicine. While these features and certain other characteristics of the results appear reasonable, estimates capable of warranting our confidence would require combining more than one year's results.

5.4 Factors affecting use intensity

Section 5.2 showed that increased utilization of capacity (F) decreases cost per case. The substantial excess of average cost over marginal cost is

TABLE 5.7

Marginal costs of individual cost types for selected input categories

Input category	Marginal cost*	Case types						
		General medicine	Paediatric	E.N.T.	Surgery	Gynaecology	Obstetrics	Other
Doctors	MC1	0.986	0.998	2.340	4.031	3.246	0.667	1.514
		(1.349)	(1.972)	(0.785)	(0.529)	(1.613)	(0.841)	(1.469)
	MC2	−0.346	1.213	1.864	3.727	2.634	0.243	1.583
		(1.365)	(1.907)	(0.771)	(0.521)	(1.574)	(0.821)	(1.403)
Nursing	MC1	4.003	5.553	2.560	−0.187	−2.191	6.571	2.683
		(2.650)	(3.872)	(1.542)	(1.040)	(3.167)	(1.651)	(2.884)
	MC2	−0.336	6.487	0.939	−1.172	−4.142	5.100	3.347
		(2.556)	(3.572)	(1.444)	(0.976)	(2.948)	(1.538)	(2.628)
Drugs and dressings	MC1	0.270	1.891	−0.025	1.518	0.384	0.791	0.198
		(0.640)	(0.935)	(0.372)	(0.251)	(0.765)	(0.398)	(0.696)
	MC2	−0.162	2.049	−0.205	1.421	0.203	0.620	0.385
		(0.665)	(0.930)	(0.376)	(0.254)	(0.767)	(0.400)	(0.684)
All except doctors nursing drugs and dressings	MC1	14.445	0.040	2.274	4.802	−2.648	9.051	23.697
		(6.279)	(9.176)	(3.653)	(2.464)	(7.504)	(3.913)	(6.834)
	MC2	4.705	0.150	−1.228	1.133	−7.296	5.066	24.875
		(5.988)	(8.367)	(3.382)	(2.286)	(6.906)	(3.602)	(6.156)
All ward costs	MC1	19.433	6.591	7.174	8.646	−1.593	16.289	27.894
		(8.648)	(12.639)	(5.031)	(3.393)	(10.336)	(5.390)	(9.412)
	MC2	3.861	9.899	1.370	5.109	−8.602	11.029	30.189
		(8.185)	(11.438)	(4.623)	(3.125)	(9.440)	(4.924)	(8.415)

* MC1 is the cost of treating an additional case when the number of *available* beds is constant.
MC2 is the marginal case cost when the number of *occupied* beds is constant.

another manifestation of the advantage of higher case-flow rates. In this section we therefore explore the reasons why some hospitals obtain substantially higher F values than others. We consider not only the case-flow rate but also its components, duration of stay and percentage occupancy of available beds.

The hospital's casemix composition has a substantial influence on the number of cases treated per bed. A regression of F on nine case proportions accounts for 35.2 per cent of the variation in F. In sections 5.4.1 to 5.4.5 we shall, wherever relevant, estimate relations that are "net" of this casemix effect by including a vector of casemix proportions in the regression equations.

5.4.1. *Hospital size*

We have already shown (3.5.1) that the hospital's case-bed ratio decreases as hospital size increases. The utilization of capacity can also be measured by the average duration of stay and the percentage occupancy of available beds. We shall first examine the relation of these three variables to hospital size. We then consider the way in which utilization of capacity within each department is affected by hospital size and department size.

To facilitate the comparison of these relations, the results will be expressed as elasticities. Relations have been estimated by linear equations and the elasticities calculated for the mean value of the utilization and size variables.

From equation (5.19) we estimate that the elasticity of F with respect to B, when casemix is taken into account, is -0.110.

$$F_i = -0.836 \cdot 10^{-2} B_i + p_i' \hat{\gamma} \qquad (5.19)$$
$$(0.202)$$

The standard error of this elasticity (with F and B treated as non-random variables) is 0.026. The use of a linear approximation for this relation has little effect on the estimated elasticity; a quadratic function yields an elasticity of -0.145 while a log-log regression indicates an elasticity of -0.133. Similar calculations show that the elasticity of length of stay with respect to B is 0.125 (standard error: 0.029) and of percentage occupancy is -0.002 (standard error: 0.009). The effect of hospital size on F therefore acts almost entirely through the increase in average duration of stay.

The elasticity values indicate the extent to which utilization rates respond to hospital size. We can also study how much of the observed variation in F is explained by hospital size differences. The correlation between F and B is -0.43; thus 18.5 per cent of the variation in F can be explained by a linear relation in B. To measure the explanatory effect of B when casemix is taken into account we compared the R^2 value of the regression of F on the casemix proportions ($R^2 = 0.352$) with the R^2 value when a term in B is added to that regression ($R^2 = 0.412$); here B explains an additional 6 per cent of the variation of F. We cannot do more than indicate that the explanatory effect of B lies in the range between 6 per cent and 18.5 per cent. The effect of B on F is thus economically significant and a small but important proportion of the variation in F is due to hospital size differences.

Table 5.8 presents elasticities that show the effects of hospital size on the utilization of beds in five major departments. Elasticities were estimated from simple two-variable regressions such as (5.20), relating utilization in an individual department (here $F_{(m)}$ equals the number of medical cases treated divided by the number of beds in the medical department) to the

TABLE 5.8

Effect of hospital size on capacity utilization in individual departments

Department**		Elasticity with respect to total number of beds in hospital*		
		Case-flow rate	Length of stay	Percentage occupancy
Gen. medicine	(169)	−0.106 (0.036)	0.156 (0.032)	0.011 (0.027)
Gen. surgery	(173)	−0.143 (0.034)	0.132 (0.027)	−0.020 (0.022)
E.N.T.	(129)	−0.100 (0.075)	0.083 (0.044)	0.051 (0.684)
Gynaecology	(131)	−0.040 (0.053)	0.007 (0.044)	−0.083 (0.298)
Obstetrics	(82)	−0.011 (0.045)	0.013 (0.030)	−0.026 (0.047)

* Elasticities at the mean values are estimated from regressions relating capacity utilization to number of beds available and casemix proportions. An observation is omitted if there are no beds in the relevant department.

** The number of observations is indicated in parentheses.

total bed size of the hospital. In estimating each equation any observation was omitted if the hospital had no beds in the relevant department. Each

$$F_{(m)i} = -0.647 \cdot 10^{-2} B_i + 20.733 \qquad (5.20)$$
$$(0.221)$$

elasticity was calculated at the mean values of the two variables and its approximate standard error obtained from the standard error of the regression coefficient by assuming that the mean values of the two variables were not random variables. The data on the availability and use of beds in each department was obtained from the annual reports of the individual hospitals (S.H.3 forms) made available by the Ministry of Health.

Although hospital size decreases case-flow rate in all departments, the magnitude of the effect varies substantially. Surgery, medicine and E.N.T. are most responsive. In the first two departments the response is due to an increased duration of stay.

To assess the extent to which hospital size explains the variation in each utilization rate, we examined the correlation between the two variables.[12] Although very little of the variation in the general medicine case-flow rate can be explained by hospital size (only 4.9 per cent), approximately 12 per cent of general medicine length of stay variation can be explained in this way. For general surgery, more than nine per cent of case-flow rate variation and twelve per cent of length of stay variation can be explained. The evidence for individual departments thus supports the conclusion noted above for the hospital as a whole: size has an adverse effect on utilization (as measured by the elasticities) and explains a small but sometimes important proportion of the variation in utilization rates.

Table 5.9 shows the effect of department size on capacity utilization. A comparison of tables 5.8 and 5.9 indicates that a department's case-flow rate and length of stay is influenced more by the size of that department than by the size of the hospital. Both the elasticity values and the implied correlations are larger in absolute value in table 5.9 than in 5.8.

---

[12] An estimate of the correlation between B and any utilization variable may be obtained directly from table 5.8. Because the elasticities are derived from linear 2-variable regressions, for a given number of observations (T) there is a one-to-one correspondence between the r^2 value of that equation and the ratio of the elasticity to its standard error. Denoting that ratio as t (for obvious reasons), we have $r^2 = t^2/(T-2+t^2)$. The value of T is indicated in parentheses in the first column of the table.

TABLE 5.9

Effect of department size on capacity utilization

Department**		Elasticity with respect to numbers of beds in department*		
		Case-flow rate	Length of stay	Percentage occupancy
Gen. medicine	(169)	−0.130 (0.026)	0.150 (0.022)	−0.011 (0.020)
Gen. surgery	(173)	−0.160 (0.042)	0.107 (0.035)	−0.054 (0.027)
E.N.T.	(129)	−0.145 (0.075)	0.052 (0.045)	−0.083 (0.072)
Gynaecology	(131)	−0.048 (0.049)	0.001 (0.033)	−0.021 (0.028)
Obstetrics	(82)	−0.012 (0.037)	−0.010 (0.024)	0.026 (0.024)

* Elasticities at the mean values are estimated from regressions relating capacity utilization to number of department beds and casemix proportions. An observation is omitted if there are no beds in the relevant department.

** The number of observations is indicated in parentheses.

The percentage occupancy of obstetrics beds increases with the size of the department. This reflects the smaller proportion of beds that need be kept empty in preparation for emergency admissions.[13] It is surprising that the percentage occupancy of general surgery beds decreases with department size. Since some 50 per cent of surgical cases are emergency admissions, a reduction in the proportion of empty reserve beds would be expected.

In summary, larger hospitals have lower case-flow rates, both overall and in each of the major departments. These lower case-flow rates are almost exclusively a reflection of longer lengths of stay. The correlations between utilization rates and hospital size indicate that a small but occasionally important proportion of the variation in utilization can be explained by hospital size. The effects of department size on utilization rates are greater than the effects of hospital size.

---

[13] Approximately 15 per cent of obstetrics admissions are on an emergency (unbooked) basis. On the theoretical relation of department size to percentage occupancy, see BAILEY (1956) and NEWELL (1964a).

5.4.2. *Waiting-list pressure*

The intensity with which available capacity is utilized may be responsive to the pressure of demand for admission. The length of the waiting list is the most direct way in which the unmet demand for admission is brought to the attention of hospital administrative and medical staff. That it is in fact a bad measure of the potential demand for hospital admissions [14] is irrelevant at this point; it is a useful variable for explaining utilization rates because it is accepted as a relevant measure of demand by those who influence hospital performance.

We consider the response of the three utilization variables for each department to the total waiting list per bed available in the hospital and to the waiting list per bed available in the same department. The interpretation of the estimated elasticities is not so clear as it was when hospital size was the explanatory variable. Longer waiting lists may increase the utilization of capacity; at the same time, more intense utilization of capacity will tend to decrease waiting lists. In general, the simultaneity of this relationship will cause an underestimate of the effect of demand pressure on capacity utilization. This will be less of a problem when we consider the relation between departmental utilization and the overall waiting-list pressure in the hospital.

As in 5.4.1, each elasticity was estimated from a linear regression and calculated for the mean values of the two variables. Data was derived from the annual hospital reports (form S.H.3). An observation was omitted if the hospital had no beds in the relevant department.

Table 5.10 shows the effects of overall hospital waiting-list pressure on the utilization of beds in particular departments. All but one of the elasticities (percentage occupancy in general medicine) have the expected sign. General medicine, general surgery and gynaecology are the departments most responsive to waiting list pressure. Increased case-flow rates are due primarily to shorter stays. For some departments, overall waiting-list pressure explains a substantial proportion of the variation in case-flow rate and length of stay. For general medicine, more than 22 per cent of the variation in duration of stay and nearly 8 per cent of the variation in case-flow rate can be explained by linear relations with hospital waiting-list pressure. The corresponding figures for general surgery are 14 per cent and 10 per

---

[14] See chapter 7, especially section 7.3.

TABLE 5.10

Effect of hospital waiting-list pressure* on capacity utilization in individual departments

Department***		Elasticity** with respect to waiting-list pressure in hospital		
		Case-flow rate	Length of stay	Percentage occupancy
Gen. medicine	(169)	0.104	−0.165	−0.021
		(0.027)	(0.023)	(0.021)
Gen. surgery	(173)	0.115	−0.112	0.016
		(0.026)	(0.021)	(0.017)
E.N.T.	(129)	0.021	−0.021	0.029
		(0.059)	(0.034)	(0.056)
Gynaecology	(131)	0.128	−0.049	0.041
		(0.035)	(0.031)	(0.021)
Obstetrics	(82)	0.047	−0.030	0.017
		(0.033)	(0.022)	(0.022)

* Hospital waiting-list pressure is defined as the total waiting list divided by the total number of available beds.

** Elasticities at the mean values are estimated from linear regressions relating capacity utilization to number of beds available and casemix proportions. An observation is omitted if there are no beds in the relevant department.

*** The number of observations is indicated in parentheses.

cent. The hospital waiting list, even if it is a bad measure of unsatisfied potential demand, does influence hospital behaviour.

Table 5.11 shows that the absolute values of the elasticities with respect to department waiting list pressure are lower than the corresponding elasticities of table 5.10. As already noted, this is likely to be due to the fact that a department's more intense use of its beds tends to decrease the length of its waiting list.[15] In general, the pattern of elasticities is very much the same as in table 5.10. One striking exception is the substantial effect of the departmental waiting list on the percentage occupancy of ear, nose and throat beds.

---

[15] The importance of this should not be exaggerated. As discussed in chapter 7, the waiting list is affected very little by the number of cases treated. Although more intense use of beds may decrease the waiting list somewhat, more patients are likely to join the waiting list because of the reduced delay before admission. This will be particularly true when patients (or their general practitioner) can choose at which of several hospitals to seek care.

TABLE 5.11

Effect of department waiting-list pressure* on capacity utilization

Department***		Elasticity** with respect to waiting-list pressure in department		
		Case-flow rate	Length of stay	Percentage occupancy
Gen. medicine	(169)	0.095	−0.060	0.083
		(0.020)	(0.019)	(0.014)
Gen. surgery	(173)	0.108	−0.079	0.037
		(0.023)	(0.019)	(0.015)
E.N.T.	(129)	0.134	0.011	0.196
		(0.056)	(0.035)	(0.050)
Gynaecology	(131)	0.049	−0.011	0.027
		(0.018)	(0.015)	(0.012)

* Department waiting-list pressure is defined as the department waiting-list divided by the number of available beds in the department.

** Elasticities at the mean values are estimated from linear regressions relating capacity utilization to number of beds available and casemix proportions. An observation is omitted if there are no beds in the relevant department.

*** The number of observations is indicated in parentheses.

The general conclusion is clear: the perceived unsatisfied demands for admission, measured by the waiting list pressure of the hospital and the department, have some substantial effects on length of stay and occasional effects on percentage occupancy. A not insignificant proportion of inter-hospital variation in utilization can be explained in this way.

5.4.3. *Interdepartment similarity of utilization behaviour*

Some writers on hospital behaviour have stressed that the hospital has a "character" of its own, a spirit or morale which affects all departments and all aspects of hospital performance (REVANS, 1964). If this hypothesis is correct, we would expect high positive interdepartment correlations of the utilization variables.

Table 5.12 presents interdepartment correlations of case-flow rate, length of stay, and percentage occupancy of available beds. In general, the correlations are positive, but of quite low value. Half of the ten correlations among case-flow rates are less than 0.3; there are three correlations greater than 0.3 for length of stay and none for percentage occupancy. The cor-

TABLE 5.12

Interdepartment correlations* of capacity utilization

Case-flow rate

Department	General surgery	E.N.T.	Gynaecology	Obstetrics
General medicine	0.464	0.067	0.333	0.382
General surgery		0.102	0.406	0.267
E.N.T.			−0.019	0.069
Gynaecology				0.431

Length of stay

Department	General surgery	E.N.T.	Gynaecology	Obstetrics
General medicine	0.511	0.238	0.366	0.168
General surgery		0.290	0.231	0.169
E.N.T.			0.201	−0.030
Gynaecology				0.374

Percentage occupancy of available beds

Department	General surgery	E.N.T.	Gynaecology	Obstetrics
General medicine	0.103	−0.066	0.114	0.259
General surgery		−0.137	0.201	0.070
E.N.T.			0.024	−0.042
Gynaecology				0.048

* First order correlations. Observations omitted if either department has no beds.

relation is greatest between the two largest departments, medicine and surgery.

Some part of the positive interdepartment correlations may be due to the influence of the hospital size and hospital waiting-list pressure that is common to all departments in the same hospital. As table 5.13 shows, department sizes and department waiting-list pressures are also positively intercorrelated. It is therefore worthwhile to estimate the extent to which there are correlations among hospital utilization rates that are not due to size and waiting-list pressure. To do this, we first estimated, for each of the five departments, equations of the form:

$$F_{ij} = \alpha_j + \beta_{j1} \left(\frac{WL_j}{B_j} \right)_i + \beta_{j2} \left(\frac{WL}{B} \right)_i + \beta_{j3}(B_j)_i + \beta_{j4}(B)_i + u_{ij} \quad (5.21)$$

TABLE 5.13

Interdepartment correlations* of size and waiting-list pressure

Department size

Department	General surgery	E.N.T.	Gynaecology	Obstetrics
General medicine	0.735	0.127	0.644	0.607
General surgery		0.397	0.675	0.622
E.N.T.			0.235	0.052
Gynaecology				0.630

Department waiting list pressure**

Department	General surgery	E.N.T.	Gynaecology
General medicine	0.254	−0.147	0.064
General surgery		0.145	0.427
E.N.T.			0.168

* First order correlations. Observations omitted if either department has no beds.

** There are no waiting lists in obstetrics departments.

where F_{ij} is the case-flow rate in department j of hospital i, WL_j is the waiting list in department j, and B_j is the number of beds available in department j. (For obstetrics, the first two terms were omitted.) The correlation between the residuals of the equations for F_{ij} and F_{ik} is a measure of the extent to which there is some factor uncorrelated with the influence of size and waiting-list pressure but common to different departments (j and k) of the same hospital, that influence utilization rates. Table 5.14 presents these correlations for caseflow rates and for lengths of stay.

It is clear that "correcting" for size and waiting-list pressure has little effect on the estimated measures of utilization similarity. On balance, the evidence appears to provide some rather weak support for the theory of an underlying "hospital morale" that influences intensity of utilization in all departments.

5.4.4. *Availability of medical staff*

Although size and waiting-list pressure have been shown to affect intensity of utilization, there is substantial unexplained variation in utilization rates. We turn now to an explanation suggested by our study of the hospital production function. The studies presented in chapter 4 indicated that differences in input proportions could substantially affect hospital output. In particular, it was shown that an increase in the number of doctors will generally yield a substantial increase in hospital output. We now examine a related question: what are the effects of increased medical staff expenditure per bed on the intensity with which capacity is utilized?

TABLE 5.14

Interdepartment correlations of adjusted utilization rates

Case-flow rate residuals

Department	General surgery	E.N.T.	Gynaecology	Obstetrics
General medicine	0.437	0.019	0.321	0.413
General surgery		0.072	0.328	0.278
E.N.T.			−0.076	0.105
Gynaecology				0.386

Length of stay residuals

Department	General surgery	E.N.T.	Gynaecology	Obstetrics
General medicine	0.384	0.207	0.407	0.290
General surgery		0.287	0.285	0.171
E.N.T.			0.148	−0.037
Gynaecology				0.437

Medical staffing per bed varies substantially. A standard deviation of £ 29.14 is associated with a mean value of £ 128.57 per bed per year. Part of this variation is associated with casemix differences; 25.4 per cent of the variance can be explained by a regression on nine case proportions. Some of the remaining variation is due to differences in local policy with respect to desired medical staffing. The rest reflects a large number of factors – hospital location, past staffing ratios, etc. – that influence the hospital's current availability of medical staff.

Equation (5.22) implies that the partial elasticity of the case-flow rate

$$F_i = 0.096 \left(\frac{M}{B} \right)_i + p_i' \hat{\gamma} \qquad (5.22)$$
$$(0.011)$$

with respect to the intensity of medical staffing (M/B, medical expenditure per available bed), calculated at the mean values of the two variables, is 0.535 (standard error: 0.062). Similar calculations for length of stay and percentage occupancy yield elasticities of -0.446 (standard error: 0.062) and 0.103 (standard error: 0.022).

Before considering the policy implications of these high elasticities, we must consider two objections to this analysis: first, that equation (5.20) is misspecified and the estimated elasticity therefore misleading; second, that the intensity of medical staffing should not be treated as an explanatory variable.

It would be quite reasonable to argue that the coefficient of (M/B) in equation (5.22) is seriously biased by misspecification. A hospital with a high medical expenditure per bed might tend to be one in which other expenditure per bed was also high. If these other expenditures also increase the intensity with which capacity is utilized, their omission would cause the elasticity to be seriously biased upwards (except in the unlikely event that there was a more than compensating correlation between the omitted variables and the casemix proportions p_i). Although it might be reasonable to expect this bias, it does not in fact occur. Equation (5.23) relates case-flow rate to the intensity of medical staffing, the intensity of nursing (N/B) and the other expenditure per bed (S/B). In the log-log regression, the coefficients are estimates of constant elasticities.

$$\log F_i = 0.556 \log\left(\frac{M}{B}\right)_i + 0.013 \log\left(\frac{N}{B}\right)_i + 0.008\left(\frac{S}{B}\right)_i + p_i'\hat{\gamma} \qquad (5.23)$$
$$ (0.087) \qquad\qquad (0.100) \qquad\qquad (0.112)$$

As an alternative to measuring capacity utilization as a case-flow rate adjusted for casemix, we consider the ratio of hospital output [16] (W) per available bed. The results of the two equations are very similar. Both

$$\log\left(\frac{W}{B}\right)_i = 0.399 \log\left(\frac{M}{B}\right)_i + 0.067 \log\left(\frac{N}{B}\right)_i + 0.093 \log\left(\frac{S}{B}\right)_i + \hat{\alpha} \qquad (5.24)$$
$$\phantom{\log\left(\frac{W}{B}\right)_i =} (0.071) \qquad\qquad (0.095) \qquad\qquad (0.109)$$

estimates indicate that the elasticity of F with respect to (M/B), presented above on the basis of equation (5.22), was not seriously biased upward

---

[16] For a full definition, see chapter 4.

and that the influence of medical staffing on the utilization of capacity is not shared by nursing expenditures or "other" expenditures.[17]

It would be useful to investigate whether this effect held equally in hospitals of all size. In addition, the study of individual institutions to determine the reason for the effect of medical staff on utilization would also be helpful. But the implication of these results for medical staffing policy is clear: an increase in medical expenditure per bed can be expected to increase the intensity of utilization and decrease cost per case substantially.

5.4.5. *The budget constraint*

In section 5.2.1 we have shown that cost per patient week increases with the number of cases treated per bed. The converse of this statement is an interesting proposition in its own right: the number of cases per bed increases with the expenditure per patient week.[18]

The first statement implies a causal relation that is appropriate if higher authorities adjust the hospital's budget to meet whatever costs are implied by the hospital's chosen intensity of utilization. The second interpretation is important if we view the hospital as adjusting its behaviour to a budget determined for it by higher authorities. In reality, neither description is completely accurate. The system by which budgets and operational patterns gradually adapt through time lies somewhere between these two extremes.

If we do assume that each hospital's authorities adjust the intensity of utilization in response to a budget which is exogenously determined, we can describe this process of choice as a maximizing of a utility function subject to constraints on the number of available beds and the total expenditure.[19] When certain conditions are satisfied, such a process of utility maximization implies that the number of cases treated per bed will increase, and the average duration of stay decrease, in response to an increase in the available budget per bed.

Let the hospital's management select the number of cases to be treated per year (N), the average duration of stay per case (S), and the quality of

---

[17] As would be expected on a basis of chapter 4, when S is disaggregated into "drugs and dressings" and "other purchasables", we find a substantial positive elasticity for the first of these, although one that is lower than that for medical staff.

[18] If we disregard differences in percentage occupancy of available beds, the expenditure per patient week is proportional to the budget per available bed.

[19] This model may be contrasted with that used in chapter 4, section 4.5. Note that some symbols are given a different meaning in this section than elsewhere in the current chapter.

care [20] (Q) to maximize a utility function $U = U(N, S, Q)$ subject to constraints imposed by the number of available beds (B) and the total expenditure (E) allowed by the budget. Although some results can be obtained even if the utility function is only ordinal, the analysis is both simpler and more interesting if we assume the utility function is cardinal and is separable by a logarithmic transformation. Thus if u, n, s, and q are the logarithms of the corresponding upper case variables, the separability assumption is that $\partial^2 u/\partial n\,\partial s = \partial^2 u/\partial n\,\partial q = \partial^2 u/\partial s\,\partial q = 0$. This assumption does *not* imply, for example, that the marginal utility with respect to the number of cases is unaffected by the duration of stay ($U_{NS} = 0$). Such an assumption would be unwarranted; it would be more plausible to assume $U_{NS} > 0$, an increased duration of stay making each case more desirable. But $u_{ns} = 0$ implies only that the elasticity of utility with respect to the number of cases is unaffected by duration of stay; i.e., that a longer stay increases both the level of utility and the marginal utility with respect to more cases in the same proportion. Similar interpretations may be given to $u_{nq} = u_{sq} = 0$.

The constraints may be stated as $B = NS/365R$ and $E = NSD$ where R is the proportion of beds occupied and D is the average cost per day. Let us assume that R is constant and that D is a constant-elasticity function of S and Q but is not a function of N: $D = AS^{\alpha}Q^{\beta}$, where A, α and β are constants. Formally stated, the hospital management seeks to maximize:

$$U^* = U(N, S, Q) + \lambda_1(NS/365R - B) + \lambda_2(NS^{\alpha+1}Q^{\beta}A - E). \quad (5.25)$$

The analysis is obviously simplified by working in the logarithms of these variables. Writing lower case letters for the logarithms of the corresponding uppercase variables, we may restate the problem as maximizing the logarithm of utility subject to the same constraints:

$$u^* = u[n, s, q] + \mu_1[n+s-r-\log 365 - b] + \mu_2[n+(\alpha+1)s+\beta q+a-e]. \quad (5.26)$$

The five first-order conditions for a maximum are (writing u_n for $\partial u/\partial n$, etc.):

$$
\begin{aligned}
u_n + \mu_1 + \mu_2 &= 0 \\
u_s + \mu_1 + (1+\alpha)\mu_2 &= 0 \\
u_q + \mu_2\beta &= 0 \qquad\qquad (5.27) \\
n+s-r-\log 365 - b &= 0 \\
n+(\alpha+1)s+\beta q+a-e &= 0.
\end{aligned}
$$

---

[20] Quality is a catch-all term to denote the general level of amenities provided to patients as well as additional expenditure on professional staff.

In the usual way (SAMUELSON, 1947, Chapters II and III) we now disturb this system of equations, allowing n, s, q, μ_1, μ_2, b and e to vary. The second-order relations obtained in this way are (writing u_{ns} for $\partial^2 u/\partial n\, \partial s$):

$$\begin{bmatrix} u_{nn} & 0 & 0 & 1 & 1 \\ 0 & u_{ss} & 0 & 1 & 1+\alpha \\ 0 & 0 & u_{qq} & 0 & \beta \\ 1 & 1 & 0 & 0 & 0 \\ 1 & 1+\alpha & \beta & 0 & 0 \end{bmatrix} \begin{bmatrix} dn \\ ds \\ dq \\ d\mu_1 \\ d\mu_2 \end{bmatrix} = \begin{bmatrix} 0 \\ 0 \\ 0 \\ db \\ de \end{bmatrix}. \qquad (5.28)$$

Denoting the bordered Hessian matrix by H, and element i, j of its inverse by H^{ij} we obtain:

$$\begin{bmatrix} dn \\ ds \\ dq \\ d\mu_1 \\ d\mu_2 \end{bmatrix} = H^{-1} \begin{bmatrix} 0 \\ 0 \\ 0 \\ db \\ de \end{bmatrix} \quad \text{or} \qquad (5.29)$$

$$dn = H^{14}db + H^{15}de \qquad (5.30)$$

and

$$ds = H^{24}db + H^{25}de. \qquad (5.31)$$

In this section we are interested in the effects of a changed budget on a hospital with a fixed number of beds. We therefore assume $db = 0$; in chapter 7 we shall return to this model and investigate the implications of $db > 0$.

Evaluating H^{15} and H^{25} we obtain

$$H^{15} = -H^{25} = [-\alpha u_{qq}]|H|^{-1}. \qquad (5.32)$$

$|H|$ may be assumed negative since this is the sufficient second order condition for a constrained maximum (GILLESPIE, 1951, pp. 97–98) and is necessary for a regular constrained maximum. Since cost per patient day decreases as duration of stay increases,[21] α is less than zero.

The sign of H^{15} and therefore of dn/de and ds/de will depend on u_{qq}. If the

---

[21] A value for α of -0.192 was obtained from the equation:

$$d = -0.192s + p'\hat{\gamma}.$$
$$(0.047).$$

elasticity of utility with respect to quality of care decreases as quality increases ($u_{qq} < 0$), an increase in the budget causes an increase in the number of cases treated and a decrease in the average duration of stay.

This conclusion agrees well with observed behaviour. Two types of estimates were made. In the first, the number of beds was statistically "held constant" by relating the number of cases treated per bed and the average duration of stay to the total budget available per bed:

$$(n-b) = 0.618(e-b)+p'\hat{\gamma} \qquad (5.33)$$
$$(0.103)$$

$$s = -0.390(e-b)+p'\hat{\gamma} \qquad (5.34)$$
$$(0.103)$$

Thus the estimated value of dn/de is positive (0.618) and the estimated value of ds/de is negative (-0.390). An alternative and less restricted pair of estimates were obtained from the equations

$$n = 0.512e+0.418b+p'\gamma \qquad (5.35)$$
$$(0.113) \quad (0.103)$$

$$s = -0.249e+0.343b+p'\hat{\gamma} \qquad (5.36)$$
$$(0.110) \quad (0.101)$$

Again, the elasticities are of the correct signs.

The actual values of the coefficients, however, do not agree with the theory. The estimated absolute value of dn/de is greater than that of ds/de; the theory requires that they be equal. But the theory as presented in highly simplified and it is not surprising that there are these discrepancies between theoretical prediction and actual observation. A more complete theory would have to include additional constraints (e.g., medical staff), a variable elasticity of cost per case to duration of stay, and changes is percentage occupancy of available beds. Even then, the estimation of reaction elasticities from cross-section data might not be appropriate; much of the interhospital variation in the intensity of utilization could reflect the relative availability of beds in the local area.[22]

But the broad qualitative conclusion of the theoretical analysis, which is supported by the observed elasticities, appears convincing: an increase

---

[22] See chapter 7, especially section 7.4.

in the available budget per bed induces hospital authorities to substitute more cases for longer stays. Liberalizing the budget constraints will increase the intensity of utilization of available beds.

5.5 Conclusion

The intensity of capacity utilization is an extremely important characteristic of hospital operations. Section 5.2 has shown that although more intensive utilization increases cost per patient week, the cost per case is substantially reduced. At the current average number of cases per bed per year (23.2), the elasticity of cost per case with respect to the case-flow rate is -0.81; the minimum cost per case occurs at a case-flow rate of more than 30. Although substantial savings in cost per case would occur in all input categories, the response of cost per case to increases in case-flow rate is greater for some inputs than for others.

Marginal cost estimates also indicate that it would be desirable to increase the intensity with which available beds are used. The marginal cost of treating an additional case with a fixed supply of beds is substantially less than the average cost per case. About half of the additional cost per case is incurred if the percentage occupancy of available beds remains constant and average duration of stay is decreased. The general conclusion that average costs are much greater than marginal costs is applicable to all case types and input categories, although there is a good deal of variation among these. Specific marginal cost estimates, for example the high marginal nursing cost of additional obstetrics cases or the high marginal medical staff costs of additional surgical cases, may be useful in planning staff.

When the doctor decides whether to admit an additional case or to offer treatment on an out-patient basis, the marginal cost should be the relevant measure of the additional financial costs. Additional admissions also reduce the average duration of stay of current cases as well as increasing percentage occupancy. The total incremental "cost" of an additional case is therefore the marginal financial cost and the reduced duration of stay of cases already in hospital. Because percentage occupancy will tend to rise with the number of cases treated, a given percentage increase in the number of cases treated will require a decrease of less than that percent in the average duration of stay. If the size of this effect on duration of stay and the low level of marginal costs were recognized by doctors who are currently selecting between in-patient care and out-patient care, the balance might be toward more hospitalization.[23]

Section 5.4 discussed several factors that may affect use intensity. Larger hospitals and larger departments tend to use capacity less intensively. Greater waiting list pressure tends to increase intensity of use, particularly on a departmental basis. There is some weak evidence to support the theory that an underlying spirit or morale affects the intensity of use in all departments of each hospital. The most important single factor influencing the case-flow rate appears to be the availability of medical staff. Inputs of nursing and other purchasables have little effect. Finally, a simple behavioural model implies that the hospital's management may react to tight budgets by increasing average duration of stay and decreasing the number of cases treated. Estimates of the effects of differences in the available budget per bed support this conclusion.

The investigations indicate several ways of obtaining more intense utilization of available beds. First, medical staff should be made more aware of the true total "cost" of increasing the number of cases treated – the smaller proportional reduction in average duration of stay and the low marginal financial costs. Similarly, hospital administrators should recognize that average cost per case would be substantially reduced if intensity of utilization increased. Second, medical staff must be motivated to recognize that current durations of stay are preventing other cases from obtaining admission.[24] The observed response to departmental waiting list pressure suggests that medical staff should be made more aware of the extent to which individuals who could benefit from hospital treatment are currently unable to obtain admissions. This refers not only to persons on waiting lists but to those who are deterred by waiting list length from ever seeking care. Finally, an increase in hospital budgets and in the size of medical staff should increase substantially the intensity with which available beds are used.

---

[23] For a discussion of some of the reasons why doctors do not prefer shorter stays and more cases, see chapter 7, section 7.4.

[24] To the economist this point may seem trivial and hardly worth mentioning. The doctor, however, does not see his decision-making as choosing between alternative uses of scarce resources. Rather his criterion is: what is best for the patient currently in my care? The nature of this decision, and its implications for the way in which resources are currently being allocated, is developed below in chapter 7, section 7.4.

Incremental costs and costliness weights

The two tables in this appendix compare the average cost per case estimates derived from the linear total cost function with those derived from the average cost function used in the costliness calculations of chapter 2.

Table 5A-1 presents the values for total ward costs for nine case types. The estimates derived from the average cost function show less extreme values. In particular, the estimate for general surgery is far more satisfactory.

TABLE 5A-1

Costs of treating additional cases

Case type	Linear total cost function		Average cost function*	
Medical	125.33	(10.85)	114.82	(18.88)
Paediatric	46.34	(18.81)	24.97	(28.51)
General surgery	1.76	(7.24)	32.70	(14.88)
E.N.T.	19.70	(7.56)	15.25	(16.52)
T and Orthop. S.	19.12	(11.61)	39.69	(17.18)
Other surgery	85.90	(9.85)	98.02	(20.27)
Gynaecology	44.68	(14.92)	58.72	(21.47)
Obstetrics	29.39	(8.07)	34.87	(16.34)
Others	79.51	(12.98)	69.51	(0.89)

* These costs were used in calculating the costliness index; see chapter 2.

Table 5A-2 presents values for medical and nursing costs as well. Case types have been aggregated into seven categories. There is generally close agreement between the two types of estimates.

TABLE 5A-2

Costs of treating additional cases in selected input categories

Case type	Total cost		Medical cost		Nursing cost	
	I*	II*	I*	II*	I*	II*
Medical	107.74	114.82	7.663	8.833	28.77	27.70
	(11.78)	(18.88)	(1.306)	(1.811)	(3.41)	(4.91)
Paediatrics	33.90	24.97	3.063	4.066	13.21	13.18
	(21.02)	(28.51)	(2.332)	(2.735)	(6.09)	(7.41)
Surgical	29.93	41.55	5.640	5.946	5.78	10.14
	(5.31)	(16.25)	(0.589)	(1.551)	(1.54)	(4.20)
E.N.T.	26.67	15.25	3.814	2.469	8.03	3.87
	(8.22)	(16.52)	(0.912)	(1.585)	(2.38)	(4.30)
Gynaecology	47.16	58.72	6.933	7.452	11.48	16.28
	(16.68)	(21.47)	(1.851)	(2.059)	(4.84)	(5.58)
Obstetrics	28.43	34.87	1.585	1.847	9.97	11.37
	(8.96)	(16.34)	(0.994)	(1.567)	(2.60)	(4.25)
Others	100.67	69.51	7.017	3.015	23.10	13.41
	(14.15)	(0.89)	(1.570)	(0.085)	(4.10)	(0.25)

I* indicates estimates derived from linear total cost function

II* indicates estimates derived from average cost functions; surgical cost is a weighted average of costs for general surgery, traumatic and orthopaedic surgery, and "other surgery".

SYMBOLS IN CHAPTER 5

A special list on symbols used in section 5-4.5 is given after the main list.

B_i number of available beds in hospital i

BO_i number of occupied beds in hospital i

$c_{i.}$ average ward cost per case in hospital i

$c_{i.}^w$ average ward cost per week in hospital i

E_i total ward expenditure in hospital i

F_i case-flow rate in hospital i; the number of cases treated per bed per year

M_i total medical staff expenditure in hospital i

n_i number of cases treated in hospital i

n_{ij} number of cases of type j treated in hospital i

N_i total nursing staff expenditure in hospital i

p_i vector of 9 case proportions in hospital i

s_i average duration of stay per case in hospital i

W_i output of hospital i

Section 5.4.5 Notation

Lower case letters correspond to the logarithm of the corresponding upper case variable

B number of available beds in hospital

D average cost per patient day

E total available budget

N number of cases treated per year

Q "quality" of patient care

R proportional rate of occupancy of available beds

S average duration of stay per case

U utility of hospital "decision-maker"

α elasticity of average cost per patient day with respect to duration of stay per case

β elasticity of average cost per patient day with respect to quality of care

CHAPTER 6

AN EXPERIMENTAL APPLICATION OF LINEAR PROGRAMMING TO CASEMIX PLANNING

6.1 Introduction

Linear programming is a mathematical algorithm for maximizing (or minimizing) the value of a linear form subject to a set of linear inequalities. Successful applications to problems in industry, agriculture, and transportation have become increasingly common in recent years. This chapter develops an experimental application of linear programming to the problem of determining the combination of cases that should be treated by an individual hospital or a hospital system.

The attempt to apply linear programming to the hospital is itself novel. In addition, we consider three problems of more general relevance to the application of linear programming: (1) testing the assumed production relations; (2) estimating the elements of the technology matrix by statistical analysis of interplant data; and (3) replacing the constant weights of the linear form with a set of simple step functions.

Section 6.2 describes the economic model of hospital production that underlies the application of linear programming and discusses the formal structure of the optimizing problem. The statistical estimation of the elements of the technology matrix and the validation of the linearity assumptions are treated in section 6.3. Section 6.4 considers the specification of the objective function. Results are presented and discussed in section 6.5. A final section suggests the directions in which improvements must be made if linear programming is to make a useful contribution in this field.

6.2 The linear programming model of hospital production

A hospital's outputs are measured as the numbers of cases treated in each of several categories. Although we shall use the previously described classification of nine specialities, a specification of casemix in terms of *diagnostic* categories would have been preferable. A speciality classification is most appropriate for estimating and comparing costs but it would be easier to assign values to the outputs in the objective function if cases were classified by diagnosis. Unfortunately, the necessary diagnostic data, which has been collected in the Hospital In-patient Enquiry, could not be made available in time for this study.

Outputs and inputs are here assumed to be related in production by a set of *linear* functions. More explicitly, we posit that there is a fixed quantity (a_{ij}) of input of type i required per case treated of type j; this quantity is the same in all hospitals.[1] The total set of production relations of a hospital may therefore be represented by a technology matrix, A, with elements a_{ij}. If n is the vector of cases actually produced by the hospital and x is the vector of inputs used, the production process may be represented as:

$$An = x. \tag{6.1}$$

We shall consider a four by nine technology matrix, relating four inputs (nurses, doctors, bed days and "purchasables") to nine outputs (the nine case types). The next section discusses the estimation of the a_{ij}'s and the evaluation of the linearity hypothesis.

In framing the optimization problem we shall assume that only a limited number of doctors, of nurses, and of bed-days are available during the period for which the hospital is planning. In contrast, there is no need to distinguish between different "purchasables" since, subject to the overall budget limitation, these may be obtained without any specific restrictions. The problem is therefore to maximize a weighted sum of the number of cases treated subject to the input constraints. Formally, if the vector of value weights is w and the vector of maximum inputs is x_0, the problem is to find that output vector, n, such that $V = w'n$ is maximized subject to $An \leq x_0$.

---

[1] The notation in this chapter differs somewhat from that used previously. In particular, subscript i denotes the input type and subscript t the hospital.

The simplex method provides a convergent iterative process for solving for *n* (HADLEY, 1963).

A simple illustration with two case types (medical and surgical) and three inputs (doctors, nurses, and bed-days) will clarify the nature of this maximization. In figure 6.1 the solid line marked doctors indicates that the hospital has enough doctors to treat 550 medical cases and zero surgical cases, or 350 surgical cases and zero medical cases, or any other combination along the line. The broken line indicates that although there are enough nurses

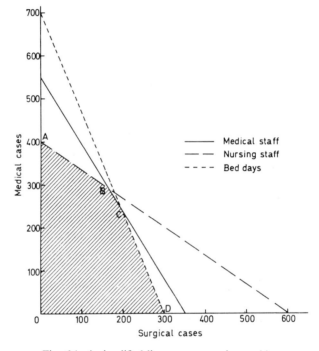

Fig. 6.1. A simplified linear programming problem.

to treat 600 surgical cases, they are sufficient for only 400 medical cases. Taking both medical and nursing availability into account, the hospital cannot produce more than 400 medical or 350 surgical cases. When bed-days (the dotted line) are considered, the maximum number of medical cases is unchanged but the maximum number of surgical cases is reduced to 300. But more important than these maxima is the shaded convex area which marks off the combinations of medical and surgical cases that are possible in view of the hospital's supply of the three inputs. The optimum production point will lie somewhere on the line ABCD. The exact point will depend on the relative values of the two outputs. For example, if the surgical cases are twice as "valuable" as medical ones an equal-value line joining 635 medical cases and 317.5 surgical cases would just touch the ABCD line at point C, where 241 medical cases and 197 surgical cases are produced.[2] This is the optimum output combination at the specified relative prices.

Although we have discussed the planning problem in terms of an individual hospital, the constant returns to scale implicit in the linear production relation make it unnecessary to specify the scale of the optimizing unit. If the constraints are all multiplied by a common value the solution vector will be similarly rescaled. For the calculations reported below we have chosen the "average" hospital, i.e., the constraints are equal to the averages over the 177 hospitals of the values of the various inputs. We have also chosen to state all constraints and outputs on a "per year" basis, although this too is simply a matter of scale and any other period of time could be used.[3]

Before discussing the difficult problem of defining the objective function, we consider the method of estimating the technology matrix and evaluating the linearity assumptions.

6.3 Estimating the technology matrix and evaluating the linearity assumptions

The elements a_{ij} of the technology matrix A indicate the quantity of input i required per case treated of type j. Although we shall measure the required number of bed-days in physical units, the other input requirements will be measured in money terms, e.g., the expenditure on nursing care required per obstetric case.

If we assume that the technology matrix is the same for all hospitals, we can obtain approximate estimates of the coefficients from a set of cross-

---

[2] The solution is only approximate. The approximation occurs because the linear programming formulation does not necessarily give integer answers. The exact results are: medical, $240\frac{5}{8}$; surgical, $196\frac{7}{8}$.

[3] The actual constraints were: nursing, £ 88 147; medical, £ 37 084; total expenditure, £ 354 204; and 90 235 bed days.

section regressions. Writing x_{it} as the quantity of input i used in hospital t, we obtain

$$x_{it} = \sum_{j=1}^{9} a_{ij} n_{jt} \qquad (6.2)$$

This relation, and thus the a_{ij}'s could be estimated directly by a regression in which the constant term is constrained to be zero. A simpler estimation procedure, and one in which the errors are likely to be more homoscedastic, is achieved by dividing all terms by $n_t = \sum_j n_{jt}$ to obtain:

$$\frac{x_{it}}{n_t} = \sum_{j=1}^{9} a_{ij} \frac{n_{jt}}{n_t} \qquad (6.3)$$

This is the same linear cost model already used in chapter 2 to estimate the various costliness values. Approximate estimates of the coefficients of (6.3) and their standard errors can be obtained by ordinary least squares. If we rewrite equation (6.3) and introduce an error term we will recognize the estimated coefficients are only approximations of the theoretical values and are in fact over-estimates. In the stochastic model underlying the regression estimates,

$$\frac{x_{it}}{n_t} = \sum_{j=1}^{9} a_{ij} \frac{n_{jt}}{n_t} + u_t, \qquad (6.4)$$

we assume $\mathscr{E}(u_t) = 0$. But for the economic model we require that if (6.3) does not hold exactly the relationship must be:

$$\frac{x_{it}}{n_t} \geq \sum_{j=1}^{9} a_{ij} \frac{n_{jt}}{n_t} \qquad (6.5)$$

If the linear economic model is correct, a hospital cannot have less than the required amount of a given input but may have an excess because one or more of the other inputs imposes a binding constraint on output. Thus the stochastic element must be non-negative and cannot have expectation zero. The result of the regressions is to overestimate on average the coefficients of the technology matrix; this bias will be greater for those inputs for which excess availability is greatest and most frequent. Of course, this bias is no different from that which we have already encountered in the estimation of cost and production functions; observed values are necessarily not less than the theoretical cost curve values and, similarly, not greater than the theoretical output values of the production function.

The technology matrix was estimated on the basis of four input categories: nurses, doctors, bed-days, other purchasables. The specification and estimation of the first three is straightforward but a word should be said about the specification of "other purchasables". If $\tilde{a}_{3j}$ is the amount of "other purchasables" required per case of type j, we may state this constraint as

$$\sum_j \tilde{a}_{3j} n_{jt} \leqq E_t - N_t^* - M_t^* \qquad (6.6)$$

where E_t is the total budget available to the hospital, N_t^* is the expenditure on nursing *required* for treating the optimum set of cases and M_t^* is the corresponding *required* expenditure on doctors.[4] Stated in this form the constraint could not be incorporated into the specification of the linear programming problem because N_t^* and M_t^* are themselves dependent on the solution to the problem. To resolve this problem we reformulate the constraint and the technical coefficients in terms of the total budget. Letting a_{1j} and a_{2j} be the amounts of nursing and medical expenditure required per case of type j, we may write $N^* = \sum_j a_{1j} n_{jt}$ and $M^* = \sum_j a_{2j} n_{jt}$. Adding N_t^* and M_t^* to both sides of (6.6) we obtain:

$$\sum_j (\tilde{a}_{3j} + a_{1j} + a_{2j}) n_{jt} \leqq E_t \qquad (6.7)$$

We therefore replace "other purchasables" $(\tilde{a}_{3j})$ by "total expenditure" $(a_{3j} = \tilde{a}_{3j} + a_{1j} + a_{2j})$ and use the total budget as the corresponding constraint.

Table 6.1 presents the technology matrix. The standard errors which appear in parentheses below each coefficient indicate that (subject to the reservations about bias noted above) the coefficients have been obtained with a high degree of accuracy.

JOHNSTON (1953) has proposed a method of testing whether a particular set of observations satisfies the programming model's assumptions of linearity and separability.[5] His method is most suitable when the coefficients

---

[4] This implies that the hospital may purchase any quantity of nurses and doctors less than or equal to the amounts specified by the constraints. An alternative would be to assume that they must purchase the "constrained" amounts but may use less. In this case the difficulty in the specifying of the general budget constraint disappears.

[5] The data to which Johnston applied this method referred to a set of products of a wholesale food processor. The cost data was prepared by the firm on a product-by-product basis so that the a_{ij}'s did not have to be estimated by multiple regression but could each be obtained by a time-series regression relating the output of that product to the costs allocated to it in the accounts. Johnston did not use the resulting estimates as the basis for a linear programming calculation.

TABLE 6.1

*Technology matrix**

Case type Input	Medical	Paediatric	General surgery	E.N.T.	Traumatic and orthopaedic surgery	Other surgery	Gynaecology	Obstetrics	Others
Nurses	27.364 (4.910)	14.452 (7.413)	8.272 (3.867)	2.992 (4.296)	8.972 (4.466)	22.620 (5.269)	9.400 (5.582)	10.864 (4.248)	12.748 (0.230)
Doctors	8.834 (1.811)	4.066 (2.735)	4.470 (1.427)	2.470 (1.585)	3.832 (1.647)	16.316 (1.944)	7.452 (2.059)	1.846 (1.567)	3.016 (0.085)
Total expenditure	114.482 (18.884)	24.967 (28.514)	32.702 (14.875)	15.247 (16.524)	39.703 (17.178)	98.020 (20.267)	58.721 (21.471)	34.878 (16.338)	69.509 (0.885)
Bed-days	30.676 (4.598)	7.432 (6.942)	5.968 (3.622)	4.168 (4.024)	12.056 (4.183)	23.536 (4.935)	16.396 (5.228)	8.944 (3.978)	16.364 (0.216)

* Each element shows the amount of the corresponding input required to produce a single case of the specified type. Amounts are shown in pounds except for bed-days. Standard errors appear in parentheses.

for each process (i.e., product) have been obtained separately. But it still provides some measure of reassurance in the present situation when all the coefficients relating to a single input have been obtained simultaneously by multiple regression. Johnston's method is to regress the actual amount of each input on the total quantity of that input "required" for the product vector on the basis of the technology matrix. If the linear programming assumptions are fulfilled, the constant term will not be different from zero and the regression coefficient will not be different from one. Writing $z_{it} = \sum_j a_{ij} n_{jt}$, Johnston proposes (in our notation) the regression:

$$x_{it} = c_0 + c_1 z_{it} + \varepsilon_t. \tag{6.8}$$

The results of these regressions, presented in table 6.2, show that the c_0 terms are positive but small in relation to the means of the dependent

TABLE 6.2

The linearity assumptions

Input	Mean value*	Regression coefficients**	
		c_0	c_1
Nursing ($\pounds$)	88 147	6 091	0.952
		(21 856)	(0.033)
Medical ($\pounds$)	37 084	2 975	0.898
		(6 827)	(0.023)
Total expenditure ($\pounds$)	354 204	31 831	0.886
		(72 159)	(0.025)
Bed days	90 172	402	0.987
		(19 798)	(0.028)

* Mean of annual total values for 177 hospitals.
** Coefficients refer to the regression $x_{it} = c_0 + c_1 z_{it} + \varepsilon_t$; see text for explanation. Standard errors are shown in parentheses.

variables and to their own standard errors. The c_1 values are less than one, but the differences are small and exceed their standard errors in only two of the equations.

6.4 Specifying the objective function

The maximand in the linear programming problem is a weighted sum of the elements of the output vector. Applying this formulation to the hospital requires assigning a unique value (weight) to each type of case.[6]

It is immediately clear that such a simple objective function would not be suitable. In general, the value of the cases of any type is not a constant but decreases as a function of the number of cases of that type that have already been treated.[7] For example, some obstetrical cases may benefit greatly from hospitalization while others will benefit much less; an obvious limit to the number of hospital obstetrical cases is the number of babies born. This suggests that a more appropriate formulation of the problem would be: maximize the value of a quadratic form ($V = w'n + n'Wn$) subject to the linear inequalities imposed by the technology matrix and constraint vector. This is the quadratic programming problem and can be solved by an iterative computational procedure (HADLEY, 1964). Unfortunately a computer programme was not available and it was felt that, in view of the difficulty of specifying the elements of W (even if it were assumed to be diagonal), the required programming effort would not be repaid by the results obtained in the current experimental application.

The assumption that the value of each type of case remained constant would be appropriate only if we were considering one of a number of hospitals sharing a single catchment area so that the number of cases treated by the optimizing hospital would be small in comparison to the total number of cases treated by the hospitals in the area. Even this would be inappropriate if every hospital performed the optimizing calculation.

A further problem arises if the simple specification of the objective function is retained. The number of non-zero case types in the output vector will be equal to the number of binding constraints. Since we have specified nine case types but only four input constraints, the solution will contain at least five case types in which no cases are treated.

The approach adopted has been to replace each constant weight in the objective function with a monotonically decreasing step function. This better represents the decreasing marginal value of additional cases and precludes any zero elements in the final output vector. More specifically, we place an infinite value of the first $\tilde{n}_j$ cases and a zero value on all cases after $\hat{n}_j$. This is equivalent to requiring that the hospital treat at least $\tilde{n}_j$

---

[6] As we have noted above, it would have been better for this purpose if the casemix could have been described by diagnostic category rather than hospital speciality.

[7] Recall that the number of cases, as all other variables, are on a "per year" basis.

cases of type j but not more than $\hat{n}_j$ cases. In practice we have used one-half the current average number of cases of each type as the minimum and two and a half times the current average as the maximum.

The minimum constraints $(n^* \geq \tilde{n})$ are introduced into the optimising problem by: (1) reducing the input constraints by the amounts that would be used if $\tilde{n}$ were produced; (2) maximizing the value of the objective function subject to the new input constraints; and (3) adding $\tilde{n}$ to the solution vector. Thus we find the optimum output vector $n^* = \tilde{n} + n^{**}$ where n^{**} maximizes $V = w'n^{**}$ subject to $An^{**} \leq (x_0 - A\tilde{n})$.

The maximum constraints are added to the problem in the same way that additional input constraints would be added. Each maximum output constraint requires one additional inequality; the lesser side of each inequality has a single non-zero element that is identically equal to the corresponding n^{**} while the greater side of the inequality is the difference between maximum and minimum outputs, $\hat{n}_j - \tilde{n}_j$. Thus the total problem may now be stated as:

$$\text{Max } V = w'n^{**}$$

subject to:

$$\begin{bmatrix} A \\ I \end{bmatrix} n^{**} \leq \begin{bmatrix} x_0 - A\tilde{n} \\ \hat{n} - \tilde{n} \end{bmatrix}$$

where I is an identity matrix of order nine.

The relative values (w) to be assigned to the cases produced, as well as the limits to be used for $\tilde{n}$ and $\hat{n}$, are a matter more for medical judgement and public policy than for economic analysis. In the calculations reported here, which must be regarded as only experimental and illustrative, three sets of weights have been used. First, the weights were defined as proportional [8] to the average total expenditure per case of each type. These are the same relative weights that were used to define hospital output in the production function calculations of chapters 2, 4 and 5. One rationale of this is that if average and marginal costs are the same, the ratios of average costs should equal society's marginal rates of substitution. A second possible justification, also referred to above, is that the production of a case of type j in one hospital might be thought of as reducing the required expenditure elsewhere in the system by an expected amount equal to the

---

[8] Because of the linearity of the model, the solution vector depends only on *relative* weights.

average cost of treating such a case. Neither reason is meant to do more than make weighting in proportion to average costs seem a plausible and interesting possibility in this experimental application. For a second set of weights, the relative average lengths of stay were used. Finally, a calculation was made in which all cases were given equal weight. The three sets of weights are presented in table 6.3; each is scaled in a way which makes the weight of medical cases equal 100.

6.5 Some results

Four sets of results are presented in table 6.4.[9] In addition to indicating the optimum number of cases treated in each category (expressed as proportions of the current average numbers of cases), the table shows the "slack quantity of each input" and the "input shadow prices". The slack quantity of each input is the difference between the quantity of inputs used and the maximum available quantity of that input. The input shadow prices may be interpreted in two ways. It is easiest to think in terms of the hospital "selling" its outputs at prices equal to the weights of the objective function. We may then ask of each input: what price could be paid by the hospital for an additional unit of the input so that the increased output made possible would have a value equal to that input price? For those inputs for which slack exists, the price would be zero but for non-slack inputs a positive price could be paid. A second interpretation of the shadow prices would be the prices that could be paid for the non-slack inputs so that the total "shadow" cost just equalled the output value.

When all cases are given equal weight in the objective function (the first row of table 6.4), only minimum quantities are produced in three categories (medical; other surgery; and gynaecology) and maximum quantities are produced in three categories (ear, nose and throat; traumatic and orthopaedic surgery; and obstetrics). The limited availability of nurses, doctors, and "budget" are all binding constraints. The number of slack bed days, 2 448, is only 2.7 per cent of total supply. The input shadow prices show that additional expenditure on doctors is very much more productive than expenditure on nurses or general "purchasables".

---

[9] The calculations were made by the Mercury computer using a programme titled SIMPAK-E. I am grateful to Mr. David Mayers of the Oxford University Computing Laboratory for his help with this work.

TABLE 6.3

Alternative weights for linear programming calculation

					Case types				
	Medical	Paediatrics	General surgery	E.N.T.	Traumatic and orthopaedic surgery	Other surgery	Gynaecology	Obstetrics	Others
Equal	100	100	100	100	100	100	100	100	100
Cost per case	100	21.8	28.6	13.3	34.7	85.6	51.3	30.5	60.7
Length of stay	100	24.2	19.5	13.6	39.3	76.7	53·4	29.2	53.3

TABLE 6.4

Summary of linear programming solutions

Objective function weights	Optimum number of cases treated*									Slack quantity of inputs				Input shadow prices**			
	Med.	Paed.	Gen. Surg.	E.N.T.	T and O.S.	O. Surg.	Gyn.	Obst.	Other	Nurses	Doctors	Bud-get	Bed-days	Nurses	Doc-tors	Bud-get	Bed-days
Equal weights	0.50	1.90	1.23	2.50	2.50	0.50	0.50	2.50	0.94	0	0	0	2 448	4	37	1	0
Equal weights (No case maxima)	0.50	0.50	0.50	2.71	0.50	0.50	0.50	5.62	0.50	985	0	0	21	0	91	1	0
Average duration of stay	1.81	0.50	0.50	0.50	0.50	0.50	0.50	0.50	0.50	4 459	5 078	2 084	0	0	0	0	1
Average cost per case	1.77	0.50	0.59	0.50	0.50	0.50	0.50	0.50	0.50	3 870	4 528	0	0	0	0	1	0
Current average values***	1 146	222	2 134	582	628	432	540	506	404	88 147	37 084	354 204	90 235	Not applicable			

* Expressed as proportion of current average values shown in bottom row.

** Each set of shadow prices is standardized so that lowest positive shadow price equals 1.

*** Input uses are unweighted averages over 177 hospitals. Numbers of cases treated are calculated from average total number of cases and average proportion in each category.

Removing the maximum limits on the number of cases treated in each category produces the results shown in the second row of table 6.4. All output above the minimum is concentrated in E.N.T. and obstetrics. The supply of doctors and the budget are binding constraints but the slack of the other two inputs is extremely low. Again the productivity of expenditure on doctors is very much the highest.

Substantially different results are obtained when relative average durations of stay are used as weights (third row). All output above minimum levels is concentrated in medical cases. The only effectively constrained resource is bed days. Weighting by average cost per case produces similar results. There is some production of general surgical cases and both budget and bed-days are binding constraints. The shadow-prices in these two solutions reflect the fact that in each calculation a row of the technology matrix is being used as the set of weights in the objective function; only the input corresponding to that row has a non-zero shadow price.

The results are presented only for illustration. They show that the optimal hospital output mix is quite sensitive to the weights used in the objective function. If the programming approach is to be of practical use, the specification and weighting of the outputs must be done in a way which more realistically reflects the medical characteristics of the case. Some approaches to this problem are discussed in the next section.

6.6 Improving the objective function

The process of assigning the weights to be used in the objective function is inevitably a matter of policy and value judgement. But if medical and lay administrators are to be able to make this difficult selection of weights, the specification of the mix of cases must satisfy two criteria. First, the categories into which cases are divided should be medically meaningful, and not merely administratively convenient. Second, all cases within each category should be of approximately equal value.

The specification of cases used in this chapter is unsatisfactory from both points of view. The division of cases into specialities is probably less useful than a division into diagnostic categories. Although specialities like E.N.T. and obstetrics are medically meaningful, categories such as "medical" are too heterogeneous. As already noted above, it would be possible to re-formulate the description of cases in terms of broad diagnostic categories and use information collected in the Hospital In-Patient Enquiry to estimate the associated technology matrix.

The three severity groups into which cases within each speciality were divided in the objective function were too large to permit a reasonable degree of intragroup homogeneity. A more acceptable procedure might be to divide each diagnostic category into several severity groups and assign a value to the cases in each group. The result would be a step-function for each diagnostic category with a larger number of value levels. If severity differences do not affect input requirements, the expanded technology matrix would only require repeating columns of the original matrix. If it were believed that more severe cases require longer or more intensive treatment, the columns of the original matrix would require modification.

The use of quadratic programming is an alternative to this more disaggregated step function. But policy makers are unlikely to be able to describe their preference weights in terms of the parameters of a quadratic function. Instead it would be necessary to estimate these parameters from the relative values placed on different groups in a step-function framework. Regardless of the final form in which the optimization is stated, the next stage in this work would be to obtain the casemix specification and relative weights that describe policy-makers' and medical administrators' preferences.

SYMBOLS IN CHAPTER 6

a_{ij} quantity of input type i required per case of type j

A technology matrix with elements a_{ij}

E_t total available budget in hospital t

M_t^* optimum expenditure on medical staff in hospital t

N_t^* optimum expenditure on nursing staff in hospital t

n_t total number of cases treated in hospital t

$\boldsymbol{n}$ vector of cases treated in each speciality; typical element n_{jt}

$\boldsymbol{n}^*$ vector of optimum numbers of cases in each speciality

$\tilde{\boldsymbol{n}}$ vector of minimum numbers of cases in each speciality

$\hat{\boldsymbol{n}}$ vector of maximum numbers of cases in each speciality

$\boldsymbol{n}^{**}$ vector of optimum numbers of cases in each speciality in excess of minimum ($\tilde{\boldsymbol{n}}$)

V value of objective function

$\boldsymbol{w}$ vector of objective function weights

$\boldsymbol{x}$ vector of inputs actually used; typical element x_{it}

$\boldsymbol{x}_0$ vector of maximum inputs

PART TWO

PLANNING THE SUPPLY AND USE OF HEALTH CARE RESOURCES

CHAPTER 7

THE SUPPLY AND USE OF HOSPITAL IN-PATIENT CARE

7.1 Introduction

Before the National Health Service came into operation, the number of hospital beds in each area was determined by the activities of voluntary charitable organizations, by the intensity of interest of local government officials, and by the market forces that affected both proprietary institutions and voluntary hospitals with limited ability to subsidize operating losses.[1] Now the supply of hospital beds is a matter of government policy. In January 1962, the government announced a fifteen-year construction programme (*The Hospital Plan for England and Wales*, Cmnd. 1604) to cost more than £ 700 million; subsequent revisions have indicated that the total cost will be very much higher.

The policy of hospital bed supply should be part of a general government programme for the provision of health care facilities, including out-patient departments, nursing homes, local authority clinics, domiciliary health workers, and general practitioners. In planning such a programme, central government authorities have *direct* influence on only some of the health facilities. Although the Ministry of Health can determine the detailed structure of the hospital system, under the current organization of the National Health Service it can only place inequality constraints on general practitioner and local authority services. But it is important for the policy-makers to recognize that central government actions in the health field will

---

[1] On the development of the English hospital system, see ABEL-SMITH (1964) and ECK-STEIN (1958). For a general discussion of the economics of voluntary provision of hospital beds see REDER (1965).

have *indirect* influences on the availability of other health care facilities. For example, a relative increase in the number of hospital beds (a directly controlled facility) may encourage more doctors to practice in an area (an indirectly controlled facility) and may cause the local authority to decrease its own expenditure on health care (also an indirectly controlled facility). The interdependence between directly and indirectly controlled facilities should be taken into account in central government planning.

More generally, associated with each possible government provision policy are: (1) a set of *available facilities* – both those directly and indirectly controlled; (2) the associated *costs* – both those incurred by the government and those paid by others; (3) a pattern of *utilization* of facilities (e.g.: hospital admission and length of stay by diagnosis; the mix of services provided by general practitioners); and (4) the ultimate effect of this care on the *health* of the community. In principle, the government's policy should be formulated by selecting the intensities (i.e., levels of provision) of the directly controlled facilities that maximize a social welfare function (the arguments of which are the measures of community health, the cost to the central government, and other costs) subject to the constraints imposed by the relations between government provision, total availabilities, costs, utilization, and health.[2] Equivalently, the government should ask of any proposed programme: is there any change in this programme that will either (1) cause an improvement in the community's health that more than justifies the increase (if any) in *total* expenditure on health or (2) causes a decrease in total health care costs that more than compensates for the reduction (if any) in the community health standard. Only when the answer to this equation is "no" has the government found an optimum health policy.

Although in principle this is surely the correct approach, we are far from being able to achieve it in practice. The conditional prediction relations required at each stage are still completely unknown. There has been no attempt to analyze the effects of government provision policy on the total pattern of available health facilities or to measure the influences of availability differences on the way that health resources are used. The link between the use of health facilities and the community's level of health is more difficult to study. There is no agreement on the dimensions in which

---

[2] This corresponds to Theil's general description of the optimum decision problem. See THEIL (1964), chapter 2.

the community's health should be measured .[3] The medical profession has not, in general, been interested in estimating the effects of alternative types of health care on the (probability distributions of) disabilities, impairments and mortality associated with different health conditions. Medical decision-makers are usually only interested in answering an ordinal question: will treatment X improve the health of this patient more than any other available treatment? The cardinal information necessary for comparing costs and benefits has not been sought because doctors have viewed their problems as unconstrained maximizations (FELDSTEIN, 1963a). With time it may be possible to educate medical authorities to recognize the importance of opportunity costs and therefore to obtain cardinal measures of the efficacy of alternative methods of care. But for the foreseeable future, the information of this type that accumulates would be more useful for piecemeal cost-benefit studies (see chapter 8) than for inclusion in a general policy model for the health sector.

We will therefore limit our attention to a more feasible proposal for conditional prediction planning. We may seek to associate with any proposed government supply programme an expected pattern of utilization, a government budget, and a total cost. The policy maker may then consider a number of possible supply programmes and select the one with the utilization-cost mix that he prefers. The problem may be formalized further by specifying a function of the various utilization rates and costs to be maximized subject to the constraints imposed by the estimated behavioural relations. The current chapter explores this approach in a preliminary way; it is developed more fully in chapter 9.

Unfortunately, government officials and researchers in this field do not consider the policy problem in this framework. Instead, they focus on supplying beds to satisfy the "need" for health care or to meet a presumed exogenous "demand" for hospitalization. This current approach is examined in the next two sections of this chapter (7.2 and 7.3). We show that any attempt to base supply policy on manifest demand is necessarily misleading (7.3).

We then examine in detail the (partial) effects of differences in the availability of hospital beds on their pattern of use (7.4). The effects that certain other factors have on use and on the relations of availability to use

---

[3] See, for example, the report of the World Health Organization on the measurement of health levels. (World Health Organization, 1957).

are briefly studied. In chapter 9 a more general model of the relations between facilities and utilization, corresponding to the conditional prediction planning process outlined above, is developed.

In this chapter we also consider a related problem: improving the allocation of available hospital facilities among competing uses. The process by which hospital beds are distributed among types of patients and diagnoses, as well as between more admissions and longer average stays, is very different from the allocation of resources in the production of other consumer goods and services. The observed pattern of use cannot be regarded as the result of an optimizing process involving consumers' preference functions and the associated production possibility frontier. Although the patients are the consumers of hospital care, it is primarily the doctors who allocate hospital resources. The patient decides whether he will seek medical advice, may have some influence on whether the doctor refers him to hospital, and may effect his exact length of stay. But the decisions about hospital admission and length of stay reflect medical judgement much more than patient preferences. Moreover, neither the patient nor the doctor is required to consider the financial or opportunity costs associated with a particular decision to consume hospital resources. Although a hospitalized person must bear some opportunity and inconvenience costs, he does not incur the hospital's cost of providing care. The doctor, in deciding to admit a particular patient or keep him longer in hospital, need not consider what other type of patient is being excluded from hospital care or forced to have a shorter stay.

Under such conditions, the resulting allocation of hospital resources need not be optimal. The government therefore has an obligation to try to improve the use of hospital facilities. In a system that precludes the rationing of health care by the price mechanism and that values the doctor's professional freedom in the belief that medical care will be best when the doctor's personal judgement is the final determinant of the treatment of each case, the government's action to influence doctors' use of available facilities is limited to providing them with appropriate "monitoring information". If doctors were made aware of the opportunity costs of particular decisions, they might act differently. Similarly, if doctors knew the way in which differences in the local availability of beds influenced the provision of care, they might wish to alter these patterns of use.

Several studies of the way in which hospital care is currently allocated are presented in chapters 7, 8 and 9. In section 7.4 and in chapter 9 we consider the way in which differences in the availability of hospital beds influence their use. Chapter 8 considers the process of hospital bed allocation in more detail, with special reference to maternity care.

7.2 Current approaches to supply planning

The Ministry of Health report, *Development of Consultant Services* (Ministry of Health, 1950), was the first attempt to plan hospital bed supply in the National Health Service. On the basis of the expert advice of prominent clinicians, it recommended uniform national bed-population ratios for each major speciality. These ratios were soon thought to be excessive. The authorities also began to believe that the appropriate number of beds for an area should reflect local conditions and population characteristics. Although no hospital building was done during the early years of the National Health Service, the current hospital building programme (Cmnd. 1604) is based on a revised set of bed-population ratios modified on an individual basis in local areas.[4]

Since 1950, a number of authors have discussed methods of planning hospital supply on the basis of local demand. A committee of the Royal Statistical Society suggested that potential demand be investigated by field research to discover the medical and social conditions of possible hospital patients as assessed by their general practitioners (Royal Statistical Society Working Group, 1955). All of the other studies have taken manifest demand – the number of hospital admissions plus the change in the waiting list – as the basis for planning.

The manifest demand approach was pioneered in England by BAILEY (1956) and other researchers associated with the Nuffield Provincial Hospitals Trust (Nuffield Provincial Hospitals Trust, 1955; FORSYTH and LOGAN, 1960; AIRTH and NEWELL, 1962).[5] Bailey suggested that the appropriate supply of beds was equal to the number required to keep pace with expected demand, plus twice the appropriate standard error ("for safety"), plus one or two more to allow the waiting list to decrease. He proposed that the

---

[4] United States hospital building policy is also based on optimum bed-population ratios. The Hill-Burton programme of federal government subsidies for hospital construction varies its bed-population ratios only with respect to differences in population density. See PALMER (1956) and ROSENTHAL (1964a).

[5] The use of similar methods in various European countries is discussed in World Health Organization (1965). BLUMBERG (1961) has advocated its use in the United States.

number required to "keep pace with expected demand" (which he called the "critical number") could be calculated as the number of hospital admissions during the previous period (A) plus the increase in waiting list (ΔW) multiplied by the average or desired duration of stay (S) and adjusted for the proportional rate of occupancy of available beds (P): thus the critical number of beds in an area equals $(A+\Delta W)S/365P$. The critical number plus twice its standard error plus one (or more) is referred to as the "actual number" of beds needed. For Bailey, this application of queuing theory was a method of reducing and limiting waiting-list length. It was adopted by a number of clinicians and hospital planners as a measure of "medically needed" services or of the beds required for "the number of patients who would have been admitted had beds been readily available" (FORSYTH and LOGAN, 1960, p. 44). Before discussing the reason why the "critical number" method is inappropriate, we describe a related type of demand-oriented planning.

ROSENTHAL (1962; 1964a) has proposed that United States hospital planning should aim to achieve an "identical pressure" on hospital beds in all areas, "a uniform probability of full utilization for a given percentage of the time". (ROSENTHAL, 1964a, p. 46.) He suggests that a supply pattern that would accomplish this should be determined by estimating the demand for patient days in each areas as a function of the demographic and economic characteristics of the population. The number of beds required to provide these patient days would depend upon the desired time and probability of full utilization and the hospital's size. He estimates the "demand function" by a cross-section regression with each state serving as one observation. Finally, as a modification of this method, designed to estimate "needed" hospital care rather than the economic demand for care, Rosenthal uses the regression equation to estimate the number of patient days that would be demanded if income, insurance and hospital charges were the same in all states.

All manifest demand methods are subject to the same criticism: they ignore the effect of available bed supply on the demand for hospital admission and on the average duration of stay per case. Where beds are scarce and waiting lists long, more work is done on an out-patient basis and the length of stay is relatively short; if the number of beds is increased, the hospitalization rate and the length of stay also increase.[6]

---

[6] The subsequent sections of this chapter establish this and examine this relation in detail.

The basic queuing theory model is inappropriate because demand is not an independent variable but a function of the supply and the length of the queue. Calculation of the critical number will therefore generally show that the current number of beds in an area is the correct number for the current period, an unwarranted reassurance of the wisdom of previous decisions. After a detailed study of the number of beds needed in the Barrow-in-Furness area, FORSYTH and LOGAN (1960, p. 10) concluded with apparent surprise, "*It appears that the number of beds used is the number available!*" (their italics). NEWELL (1964), reviewing the seven British studies done by that date, found that although the critical number varied substantially among the areas it was in each case approximately equal to the number already available.

Rosenthal's method is inappropriate for the same reason: it seeks to plan supply with reference to an assumed exogenous demand. If the level of supply in each of the states were increased, the parameters of the demand equation would change, indicating higher levels of predicted demand. Moreover, his use of the regression equations to study the influence of social and economic factors on the demand for hospital care is questionable. The omission of bed supply from the bed use ("demand") equations is a serious misspecification that is likely to have sizeable effects on each of the other coefficients.[7]

7.3 Inadequacy of the manifest demand approach

This section considers some evidence that shows why the number of hospital beds to be provided in an area cannot be determined on the basis of manifest demand. The study is based on the relation between demand and available beds in the hospital regions of England and Wales.

---

[7] For a discussion of specification bias, see chapter 3, section 3.4 or, more generally, THEIL (1961), p. 326. Rosenthal recognizes that including bed supply among the explanatory variables raises statistical difficulties and problems of interpretation because the supply of beds is itself changing and must be regarded as endogenous in the United States. See his reply (ROSENTHAL, 1964b) to a paper by DURBIN and ANTELMAN (1964) in which bed supply is treated as an exogenous variable in a single-equation ordinary least squares estimate of the influence of social and economic factors on hospital use. For a more general discussion of the correct treatment of bed supply in the context of a model of the American health sector, see my "An Aggregate Policy Model of the Health Care Sector" (forthcoming).

The hospital service is divided into fifteen administrative regions. Regions of this size provide natural catchment areas; that is, it is safe to assume that virtually all patients coming to a hospital are resident in the region in which the hospital is located. Because of the many incomparabilities between medical care in urban London and in the rest of the country, the four metropolitan London regions have been eliminated from the study. Data about hospital bed use is derived from the *Hospital In-Patient Enquiry for 1960* (Ministry of Health and General Registry Office, 1963). This continuous statistical collection programme provides tabulations of data for one patient in every ten who is discharged from or dies in hospital. All non-psychiatric hospitals in the National Health Service in England and Wales are covered by the enquiry. The analysis extends to all patients except those in psychiatric departments of general hospitals, in preconvalescent and convalescent units or hospitals, and in staff or private beds. Information about waiting lists and hospital bed availability was provided by the Ministry of Health (Ministry of Health, Statistics Branch (1961), and personal communication). All data is for 1960.

Per capita demand can be measured in three different ways: (1) the number of admissions per year; (2) the number of admissions plus the net increase in hospital waiting lists; or (3) the number of hospital beds used during the year. This information is presented in table 7.1; the numbers of persons on waiting lists and the numbers of available beds are also shown. Each of the three measures indicates substantial inter-regional variation in demand; table 7.2 presents the ranges and coefficients of variation.

The results of this section show that although there is substantial inter-regional variation in per capita demand for beds, the levels of regional demand do not provide a basis for planning the appropriate bed supply. First, observed demand cannot be taken as a measure of an area's relative "need" or "intrinsic demand" for hospital care because manifest demand is very much influenced by the exogenous available supply. Second, the demand for bed days rises *proportionately* with available supply; the evidence does not indicate that there is a level of supply at which the demand for beds would be satiated. Third, although the demand for admissions rises less than proportionately, the data again does not suggest a level of supply beyond which demand no longer rises. Finally, although unsatisfied demand (persons on waiting lists per 1 000 population) is less in regions where beds are more amply available, the effect of supply is too small to make the reduction of waiting lists a reasonable criterion for bed provision policy.

TABLE 7.1

Regional demands for hospital care

Region (1)	Admissions* (2)	Discharges + increases in waiting lists* (3)	Beds used* (4)	Waiting list* (5)	Beds available* (6)
Birmingham	71.26	71.41	3.73	9.65	5.02
East Anglia	63.56	63.55	3.66	9.29	5.06
Leeds	79.37	78.33	3.98	6.06	5.94
Liverpool	90.66	91.03	5.33	7.44	6.79
Manchester	78.14	78.02	4.03	13.41	4.89
Newcastle	85.16	84.88	3.96	9.62	5.15
Oxford	83.73	83.26	4.46	11.45	5.35
Sheffield	67.85	67.73	3.24	10.96	4.61
South Western	77.81	77.85	4.37	11.59	5.95
Wales	81.50	81.22	4.56	9.98	5.87
Wessex	79.46	79.28	4.29	9.48	5.04

* Per 1 000 population, 1960.

TABLE 7.2

Variation in hospital demand

Demand measure	Mean	Standard deviation	Coefficient of variation	Range
Admissions*	78.05	7.49	9.6	63.56 90.66
Number of admissions plus increased waiting list*	77.87	7.47	9.6	63.55 91.03
Beds used*	4.146	0.528	12.7	3.239 5.330

* Per 1 000 population, 1960.

7.3.1. *The influence of availability*

A simple general measure of the relation between bed demand and the number of beds available per 1 000 population is given by the correlation coefficients presented in table 7.3. The substantial correlations could be interpreted in several ways. First, they could indicate that supply had been adjusted in past years to satisfy an exogenously determined demand. Conversely, regional levels of demand may have adjusted themselves to an exogenously determined supply. Finally, demand and supply may both be endogenous, interacting with each other and being acted upon by other factors, in a way that produced the observed correlations.

TABLE 7.3

Correlation of bed demands and availability

Demand measure	Correlation coefficient (R)	R^2
Number of admissions* (D_1)	0.6508	0.4235
Number of admissions plus increased waiting list* (D_2)	0.6556	0.4298
Beds used* (D_3)	0.8380	0.7021

* Per 1 000 population, 1960.

If the correlations did reflect the adjustment of supply to demand, the magnitude of the correlation would be an indication of the success with which this adjustment had been made. It would also mean that observed demand might be useful as a basis for planning the regional allocation of hospital beds. For either of the other two interpretations, high correlations would be no indication of the desirability of current relative supplies but rather would be a warning against the use of measured demand as a planning guide. If the observed demand actually reflects available supply, it cannot serve as the basis for evaluating what the supply *should be.*

It is always hazardous to infer causality from correlation. The danger is particularly acute when considering a relationship such as supply and demand in which both variables may be endogenous. But the circumstances of the particular problem studied here make it clear that causality flows from supply to demand and not vice-versa. The current pattern of supply is a legacy of history. Nearly half the hospitals are more than seventy years old and a fifth have stood for more than a century: there has been almost no construction during the past twenty-five years. (Cmnd. 1604, p. 1.) Further, the N.H.S. administrative regions were designed to be natural catchment areas; almost all patients treated in a region are also resident there. Supply does not adjust to demand by the temporary migration of patients. Finally, we may safely assume that the number of persons living in each region has not been affected by the availability or demand for beds. In contrast, it is easy to understand how doctors adjust their requests to local supply. Where beds are relatively abundant general practitioners may send more patients to hospital, out-patient departments may recommend more admissions, and consultants may keep patients in hospital for longer stays. If changes in waiting list lengths are taken into account, demand may still be self-regulating: doctors may adjust to longer waiting lists by referring fewer persons for in-patient care and consultants may shorten length of stay. We are therefore justified in treating per capita bed supply as exogenous and examining its effects on the demand for hospital care.

Although per capita bed supply is exogenous, its correlation with demand could still be misleading as an indication of causality. First, an element of arbitrariness is always introduced when geographical areas are the units of study; if the country were divided into eleven different areas, the correlation values would be different. Second, there may be other factors that are statistically correlated but not causally linked with both supply and demand. If, for example, those regions with relatively greater availability happened by chance to have a substantially higher proportion of older people, a spurious correlation between supply and demand would result. Nevertheless, there is no reason to believe that either of these problems has substantially affected our results; this assumption is supported by the results of section 7.5 and chapter 9.

The meaning of the correlations presented in table 7.3 is now more clear. A substantial proportion of the inter-regional variation in observed demand can be explained by availability differences: 42 per cent if demand is measured as the number of cases treated (D_1), 43 per cent if changes in waiting list length are included (D_2), and 70 per cent if beds used (D_3) is the adopted measure. Beds used per 1 000 population is more highly correlated than the others because the average length of stay also increases when there are relatively more beds available. For each measure, the probability of observing such a high correlation by chance is less than 0.05. We must therefore reject observed demand as too dependent on available supply to be a useful planning guide.

7.3.2. *The insatiable demands for bed days and hospital admissions*

Although the demand observed in each region cannot serve as an indicator of the appropriate supply for that area, the relationship across the regions between supply and bed-day demand [8] might be considered an alternative basis for planning.

If the current pattern of response to regional differences in availability indicated some level of supply that would satiate demand for bed days, this would at least provide an upper limit to appropriate provision and might indicate the number of beds that it would be desirable to provide if resources for health care were not limited. Unfortunately there is no evidence that as availability increases bed-day demand tends toward such a limit; on the contrary, the data suggests that, at least within the observed range of supply, bed-day demand increases proportionately with availability.

A proportional linear relationship is shown in equation (7.1), where demand (D_3) is the number of beds used per 1 000 population and supply (S) is the number of beds available per 1 000 population.[9]

$$D_3 = 0.205 + 0.726 \, S \qquad (7.1)$$
$$(0.861) \quad (0.158) \qquad R^2 = 0.702$$

An estimated constant term at least as large as the observed one would occur with probability 0.8 if the true value were actually zero. Equation (7.2) presents a similar result; the proportion of beds used (D_3/S) is not affected by relative availability.

$$\frac{D_3}{S} = 0.800 - 0.649S \qquad (7.2)$$
$$(2.952) \qquad R^2 = 0.005$$

When quadratic equations analogous to (7.1) and (7.2) were estimated, the second order terms were insignificant and of "incorrect" sign. These are presented in equations (7.3) and (7.4).

$$D_3 = 1.653 + 0.209S + 0.005S^2 \qquad (7.3)$$
$$(2.900) \quad (0.026) \quad R^2 = 0.706$$

---

[8] The results are stated in terms of beds used (D_3) rather than bed days; $D_3 = 365$ bed days.

[9] In this chapter, there is generally no need to complicate variables with a subscript to identify the unit of observation in the way that was done in chapters 2 to 6.

$$\frac{D_3}{S} = 0.81 - 0.01S + 0.0004\,S^2 \tag{7.4}$$
$$(0.54) \quad (0.0479) \quad R^2 = 0.005$$

The multiple correlation coefficients also indicate that including a second order term does not increase the equations' explanatory power.

Finally, an attempt was made to describe the data by an S-shaped curve, using a logarithmic-reciprocal transformation,[10] as shown in equation (7.5a).

$$\log D_3 = 2.406 - 5.319S^{-1} \tag{7.5a}$$
$$(1.204) \quad R^2 = 0.684$$

The meaning of this equation is clearer when it is rewritten in exponential form:

$$D_3 = e^{2.406 - 5.319\,S^{-1}} \tag{7.5b}$$

This would suggest that demand has an upper limit of 11.1 beds used per 1 000 population ($e^{2.406} = 11.1$), more than two and a half times the current average. We need, however, give little credence to this value. The range of observations is insufficient to indicate that an S-shaped curve should be chosen in preference to a straight line; the indicated point of inflection ($S = 2.66$) is located far below the level of the lowest observed supply. There seems no reason to accept this equation in preference to the simpler straight line.

It seems reasonable to conclude, therefore, that the demand for bed days increases proportionately with supply. Current experience does not indicate a level of supply capable of satiating bed-day demand. Part of this increasing demand, however, is for longer stays. We therefore consider whether the demand for admissions tends towards some limit as supply increases.

The linear relations between the two measures of admission demand (D_1 and D_2) and per capita supply (S) are shown in equations (7.6) and (7.7). Although the constant terms in both equations

$$D_1 = 34.6 + 8.01S \tag{7.6}$$
$$(17.0) \quad (3.11) \quad R^2 = 0.424$$

$$D_2 = 34.2 + 8.05S \tag{7.7}$$
$$(16.9) \quad (3.09) \quad R^2 = 0.430$$

---

[10] This method of estimating an S-shaped curve is discussed by JOHNSTON (1963, p. 49).

indicate that the demand for admissions increases less than proportionately with the bed supply, the attempts to fit quadratic equations (see
(7.8) and (7.9)) do not indicate that a non-linear function would be
preferable.

$$D_1 = 21.73 + 12.61S - 0.405S^2 \tag{7.8}$$
$$(57.36) \quad (5.047) \quad R^2 = 0.424$$

$$D_2 = 37.35 + 6.93S + 0.099S^2 \tag{7.9}$$
$$(56.92) \quad (5.008) \quad R^2 = 0.430$$

A similar conclusion is reached about the S-shaped curve (equations
(7.10) and (7.11)). The implication of a limiting value of 142 admissions
per 1 000 population per year ($e^{4.95} = 142$) is therefore given little weight.

$$\log D_1 = 4.95 - 3.229S^{-1} \tag{7.10}$$
$$(1.295) \quad R^2 = 0.409$$

$$\log D_2 = 4.95 - 3.225S^{-1} \tag{7.11}$$
$$(1.287) \quad R^2 = 0.411$$

As a final possible use of demand as a planning indicator, we consider
the extent of unmet demand as shown by waiting list length.

7.3.3. *Unmet demands*

The evidence presented above shows that supplying enough beds to "satisfy
demand" is likely to be an impossible task. An alternative demand-oriented
goal would be to eliminate or reduce waiting lists. It has been customary
to assume that this could be done by providing beds in excess of the number
"needed to meet current requests" (BAILEY, 1956). We have already seen
that such an approach is unlikely to succeed. Furthermore, waiting lists
are themselves likely to be self-regulating; longer lists are likely to encourage doctors to treat more cases on an out-patient or domiciliary basis.

The small size of the effect on waiting lists of a more ample bed supply
is shown by equation (7.12), where W is the number of persons on waiting
lists per 1 000 population.

$$W = 18.87 - 1.65S \tag{7.12}$$
$$(0.89) \quad R^2 = 0.276$$

Although the regression coefficient is large in relation to its standard error, it is too small to be of much practical importance. An approximate elasticity of waiting list with respect to bed supply, calculated at the means, is seen to be only 0.9. Finally, we see from equation (7.13) that there is no evidence of nonlinearity.

$$W = 14.32 - 0.027S - 1.143S^2 \qquad (7.13)$$
$$(16.411) \quad (1.444) \quad R^2 = 0.276$$

The obvious but important conclusion that emerges from the results of this section is that in health care, as in other fields of government expenditure, appropriate standards of provision cannot be determined by reference to levels of "need" inherent in or manifest by the community. Planning requires choice.

As discussed in the introduction to this chapter, a proper choice of a hospital bed supply policy requires conditional predictions of the pattern of health care utilization associated with different levels of availability. In section 7.4 we consider how different uses of hospital beds are affected by hospital bed scarcity. A more general model is presented in chapter 9.

7.4 Effects of bed availability differences on type of use

This section examines the effects of regional differences in hospital bed availability on the ways in which these beds are used. The results provide a partial and preliminary analysis of the type required for conditional prediction planning. They are also important as an example of the type of analytic "monitoring information" that could improve the allocation of currently available hospital facilities.

One of the most striking features of the hospital service is the variation in the number of beds available per thousand population in different regions of the country. Table 7.4, column 2, shows that the Sheffield region has the smallest number of hospital beds per thousand population, only 4.6, while the Liverpool region has almost 50 per cent more, some 6.8 beds per thousand population. As indicated in section 7.3, this regional variation reflects history rather than deliberate policy; it is the legacy of a previous distribution of population and a past type of medical care.

We have already seen that, within the current range of bed availability, the intensity of bed utilization is not affected by the relative scarcity of beds. What are the consequences of this regional variation in scarcity and overall

TABLE 7.4

Availability and use of non-mental hospital beds

Region (1)	Beds avail- able* (2)	Beds used* (3)	Percen- tage utili- zation** (4)	Admissions* (5)	Mean stay (6)
Birmingham	5.02	3.73	74.3	71.26	19.2
East Anglia	5.06	3.66	72.3	63.56	21.1
Leeds	5.94	3.98	67.0	79.37	18.3
Liverpool	6.79	5.33	78.5	90.66	21.5
Manchester	4.89	4.03	82.4	78.14	18.9
Newcastle	5.15	3.96	76.9	85.16	17.0
Oxford	5.35	4.46	83.4	83.73	19.5
Sheffield	4.61	3.24	70.3	67.85	17.5
S. Western	5.95	4.37	73.4	77.81	20.5
Wales	5.87	4.56	77.7	81.50	20.5
Wessex	5.04	4.29	85.1	79.46	19.8

* Per 1 000 population, 1960.

** Percentage utilization $= \dfrac{\text{Beds used}}{\text{Beds available}}$.

bed use? How are different uses of hospital beds and various types of patients affected by relative bed scarcity? Does a region in which beds are relatively more scarce have a lower number of cases treated or a shorter average duration of stay? Are older patients more affected by the scarcity of beds than younger ones? Are treatments for tonsils and adenoids more affected than those for heart disease or hernias? The answers to these questions are surprising and indicate the importance of "monitoring information" in a system that has no built-in mechanism to assure the optimum allocation of available resources.

The effects of availability on different types of bed use have been measured by estimating the elasticity of the particular bed use with respect to the regional bed supply. Although other indices of the availability effects might have been used, a constant elasticity measure has several virtues. First, it is independent of both the unit of measure (bed days, cases treated, etc.)

and of the scale (per 1 000 population, per 10 000 population; per month, per year; etc.). Second, it permits division of the "beds used" elasticity for any patient type (a patient *type* may refer to a particular diagnostic category, a patient age-sex group, persons of one sex, or all persons together) into a "mean stay" elasticity and a "cases treated" elasticity such that the "beds used" elasticity is exactly equal to the sum of the other two. Third, the constant elasticities can be estimated by ordinary least squares regression of the logarithm of the bed use variable on the logarithm of supply. This assures the exact equality between the "beds used" elasticity and the sum of its two components despite the stochastic nature of the equations used to estimate the three elasticities; this is obvious from the estimating formulae and the equality: log (beds used) = log (cases treated)+ log (mean stay)+ a constant. Further, if the stochastic term in the equation is assumed to be normally distributed, confidence intervals can be estimated using the *t*-distribution with nine degrees of freedom. Finally, measuring the availability effect by a regression coefficient allows the application of an error in variables approach to measuring bed supply; this is discussed in section 7.4.1.

The term "bed supply" has not yet been specifically defined. Two measures are possible: the number of beds available per thousand population (table 7.4, column 2) or the total number of beds used per thousand population (table 7.4, column 3). Although the number of beds available may seem the natural choice, the total number of beds used may actually be better for two reasons. First, differences in percentage utilization may reflect various factors about the accessibility of available beds and the size of the hospitals in which they are located; beds used, as the product of beds available and percentage utilization, might therefore be a more appropriate index of *effective* supply or *utilizable* capacity than the unadjusted bed availability data. Less important, there are slight differences in the coverage of the beds used and beds available data. Some elasticities have been calculated with respect to both measures of supply, and the remaining ones only with respect to total beds used; as will be seen below, where both measures are used, the results agree very closely. Similar results are also found when the calculations are treated as an errors in variables problem: beds available and total beds used are each considered as observed values of a true bed supply measured subject to error and an instrumental variable approach is adopted.

Employing "total beds used" as the index of supply raises two problems.

First, although the number of beds available can be treated as exogenously determined, the number of beds used *could* reflect demand as well as the exogenous factors of supply, accessibility, and hospital size. We have seen, however, that percentage utilization is unaffected by bed scarcity; the correlation between percentage utilization and beds available is only −0.07. In contrast, total beds used shows a correlation of 0.84 with beds available and an elasticity of 0.957. It therefore seems reasonable to conclude that total numbers of beds used do not reflect differences in demand. Second, even if total beds used can generally be considered as exogenously determined and a good measure of effective supply, the identity linking total beds used to total mean stay and total cases treated could introduce a simultaneous equations bias into the estimation of the elasticity values for "all persons". For this reason, we have used beds available as well as beds used as the measure of supply when estimating these "all persons" equations. As noted above, the results from both methods are very similar. When patients are classified by age and sex, or by diagnostic category, the total number of beds used is taken as the measure of supply.

7.4.1. *Shorter stays or fewer cases*

The most basic allocation of beds is between the number of cases treated and the mean duration of stay per case. Before this study was begun, it was anticipated that bed scarcity would influence duration of stay more than it influenced the number of cases treated. Where beds are scarce, it should not be difficult to reduce the average stay – especially since Britain has rather long stays in comparison to the United States and several continental countries. But the number of cases requiring treatment should be less variable; the same number of hernias is likely to need repair, appendices to need removal, heart attack victims to require care. Put another way, as a potential patient I would be happier if I thought that the relative scarcity of beds in my area affected the length of time that I might stay in hospital rather than the chance of getting a hospital bed when I "needed" one. It is therefore surprising, and somewhat discomforting, to find that the number of cases treated is about 50 per cent *more* responsive than the average stay per case. The greater responsiveness is indicated by the data in columns 4 and 5 of table 7.4. Column 4 shows that in the Sheffield region (where beds are scarcest) there were some 68 admissions per thousand population during the year; the Liverpool region, where beds are least scarce, hospitalized some 91 persons per thousand population. Living near Sheffield decreases the chance of being admitted to hospital by more than 25 per cent in comparison with residing near Liverpool. Column 5 shows that the average stay per case is less influenced by bed scarcity; the range is narrower (from 17.0 to 21.5 days or only 23 per cent of the average in comparison to the 38 per cent spread of the number of admissions) and the average stays are less closely correlated with bed availability.

Elasticities with respect to the number of available beds per 1 000 population are shown in table 7.5. For "all persons", the number of admissions per 1 000 population has an elasticity of 0.580; in contrast, mean stay per case

TABLE 7.5

Elasticity with respect to bed availability

	Beds used*	Admissions*	Mean stay
All persons	0.947	0.580	0.365
	(0.218)	(0.233)	(0.184)
Males	1.044	0.638	0.409
	(0.250)	(0.204)	(0.184)
Females	0.875	0.523	0.351
	(0.262)	(0.260)	(0.247)

* Per 1 000 population, 1960.
Figures in brackets are standard errors of elasticity values.
The sum of admissions and mean stay elasticities does not exactly equal the beds used elasticity because of rounding in the three separate series.

has an elasticity of only 0.365. This is the result referred to in the last paragraph when it was noted that bed scarcity has a 50 per cent greater effect on the number of admissions than on the average duration of stay. Table 7.5 also shows that this relationship between the elasticities of admissions and average stay holds separately for both males and females; the values are 0.638 and 0.409 for males, 0.523 and 0.351 for females. The treatment of male patients is more responsive to bed scarcity than the treatment of female patients; the number of beds used for males shows an elasticity of 1.044 while for females it is only 0.875.

Table 7.6 presents the elasticity values that are found when supply is measured as the total number of beds used per 1 000 population. The

TABLE 7.6

Elasticity with respect to total bed use

	Beds used*	Admissions*	Mean stay
All persons	(**)	0.646	0.349
		(0.149)	(0.151)
Males	1.032	0.657	0.373
	(0.136)	(0.130)	(0.154)
Females	0.968	0.627	0.338
	(0.102)	(0.172)	(0.207)

* per 1 000 population, 1960.
** 1.000 by definition.
Figures in brackets are standard errors of elasticity values.

results are very similar to those shown in table 7.5. The elasticity of admissions is 0.649 while the value for mean stay is only 0.349. The corresponding results for each sex (males 0.657 and 0.373, females 0.627 and 0.338) also agree with the previous findings. Finally, the elasticity values for males again exceed those for females.

The number of beds available per 1 000 population and the number of beds used per 1 000 population are both imperfect measures of the theoretical "bed supply" whose effect on bed use we wish to study. Even if our measures of supply differ from true supply only by a stochastic term with zero mean, ordinary least squares estimates of the elasticity values may be biased and inconsistent. If the error in the measurement of the supply variable is distributed independently of the true supply and of the error in the equation, we would expect ordinary least squares regression to underestimate the elasticities of the various forms of bed use to the true supply of beds (JOHNSTON, 1963, pp. 148–150).

Consistent estimates can be obtained even when the explanatory variable is subject to measurement error by the use of an instrumental variable (SARGAN, 1958; JOHNSTON, 1963, pp. 165–175). We have employed the instrumental variable method to estimate the elasticities of admissions and of mean stay for "all persons". For each of the two observed measures of supply, two different instrumental variables were used. To be appropriate, an instrumental variable should be highly correlated with the observed explanatory variable and should be uncorrelated with the error of observation and the error in the equation. The first type of instrumental variable used was the rank order of the observed explanatory variable. This would obviously be highly correlated with it; also, with only eleven observations the rank order is not so fine a graduation as to preclude its independence from the error of observation. The second type of instrumental variable was the alternative measure of supply; e.g., if the logarithm of beds *available* per 1 000 persons was the explanatory variable in the equation, the logarithm of beds *used* per 1 000 persons was used as the instrumental variable.

The results of these instrumental variable estimates appear in table 7.7; the ordinary least squares results are presented (estimates numbers 1 and 4) for comparison. It is obvious that the various instrumental variable estimates

TABLE 7.7

Instrumental variable estimates of elasticities

Estimate no.	Measure of supply	Instrumental variable	Elasticity values	
			Admissions*	Mean stay
1	Beds available*	None	0.580 (0.233)	0.365 (0.184)
2	Beds available*	Rank of beds available*	0.580 (0.246)	0.335 (0.194)
3	Beds available*	Beds used* (log)	0.580 (0.433)	0.335 (0.341)
4	Beds used*	None	0.646 (0.149)	0.349 (0.151)
5	Beds used*	Rank of beds used*	0.658 (0.157)	0.338 (0.158)
6	Beds used*	Beds available* (log)	0.609 (0.182)	0.380 (0.183)

* per 1 000 population, 1960.
Figures in brackets are standard errors of elasticity values.

support the previous conclusion that the number of admissions is substantially more responsive to differences in bed scarcity than is the mean stay per case. In each pair of instrumental variable estimates, the responsiveness of cases treated is more than sixty per cent greater than the responsiveness of mean stay per case. The ordinary least squares estimates show no tendency to be lower than corresponding instrumental variable estimates.

That is, we have not found the relationship between these two sets of estimates that might have been expected from their asymptotic properties if "beds available per 1 000 population" and "beds used per 1 000 population" were really related to a "true" bed supply variable by an independent error of observation. This may be because the asymptotic bias has not shown itself in our small sample; it may also reflect the lack of independence of the observation errors from each other or from the true values of the explanatory variables. Nevertheless, the results suggest that at the regional level it would be reasonable to employ the observed number of beds used per 1 000 population as a measure of bed supply. In section 7.4.3 we shall do so in order to evaluate the effects of differences in bed scarcity on use by age, sex, and diagnostic category. Before doing this, we consider some explanations of the results already presented.

7.4.2. *Some explanations*

The results presented above are quite surprising. How can one explain the uncomfortable fact that the number of admissions seems to vary more in response to relative bed scarcity than does the average duration of stay? Two types of explanation are possible; the first might be called "behavioural" and the second might be called "environmental" or "statistical". A behavioural explanation would accept the finding as correct and would seek to explain it in terms of theories about the behaviour of doctors, patients and others. An environmental explanation would suggest that the difference between the two responsiveness values was more apparent than real, i.e., that it could be explained by other factors not yet taken into account; such an explanation would not only help us to understand why this result has been found but would also indicate that the seemingly inappropriate behaviour of the hospital system was only a spurious finding.

After considering various possible environmental explanations, it was concluded that the results cannot be justified in this way. There is real difference between the two responsiveness values that must be explained in terms of the behaviour and attitudes of those involved in determining the use of hospital beds. Before discussing these behavioural theories, we summarize six statistical-environmental arguments that were considered.

First, it may be that the difference between the two responsiveness values is simply fortuitous – i.e., that there is no "real" difference in responsiveness but an apparent difference due only to chance. Although standard statistical tests cannot lead to any very firm statement about the observed differences in responsiveness, this is partly due to the paucity of observations – only eleven. However, the same relationship between the two values was found for most types of patients and disease categories investigated;[11] it is very unlikely that this would be due only to chance.

Differences in the *types* of cases treated in the various regions would provide a second type of explanation. If, for some medical or environmental reason, regions with relatively more beds have a disproportionately low number of the types of cases that require lengthy stays, such as older patients or those with heart disease or bronchitis, this would produce a spurious result suggesting that the number of admissions is less responsive than the average duration of stay. But this explanation will not do. As already pointed out, the greater responsiveness of admissions is observed not only for "all persons" taken together but for most types of patients and disease categories when considered alone.

Another type of environmental explanation would be that the results are due to the way that regions are defined or to the particular time period that was selected. The official hospital regions do provide good catchment areas and there is no reason to suspect that this is a source of bias; similar results are obtained when counties are the fundamental unit of observation, as shown in chapter 9. Similarly the annual time period is the most natural since it overcomes any problems of seasonal variation in disease incidence. The specific choice of 1960 is unlikely to have influenced the results.

If the availability of beds were changing in response to demand or other related factors, the estimated elasticities would be subject to a simultaneous equations bias. But, as indicated above, the actual pattern of bed availability is a reflection of history.

Fifth, if the types of patients who are not admitted to hospital in regions where beds are relatively more scarce would tend, *ceteris paribus*, to be shorter-stay cases, the changing composition of cases in response to bed availability would help to explain why mean stay was not more elastic to bed supply. But although a bed shortage might cause a reduction in the proportion of less "severe" cases, these need not be those with shortest stay. Acute conditions requiring surgery are of less than average duration of stay. More chronic conditions not requiring hospitalization may generally

---

[11] See tables 7.9 and 7.10. A large number of additional elasticities are presented in Appendix 7A.

have longer stays. Further, the evidence of section 7.4.3 indicates that the least severe case types may not be those that are most affected by bed availability. As shown by the appendix of this chapter, the elasticity of the number of admissions is higher than the mean stay elasticity for almost all patient types.

Finally, there is the possibility that other factors that influence admission rates and duration of stay are correlated with relative bed supply. There is no *a priori* reason to expect such specification bias; although a number of variables may affect bed use, they will not influence the elasticity estimates unless they are correlated with bed supply. Unfortunately, data for many of the potentially interesting variables is not available for hospital regions; the individual counties for which data is available are often divided between regions while the ten general administrative regions of England and Wales are not coterminous with the hospital regions. We are therefore unable to consider the effects of general practitioner or local authority services, income and social class variables, and other factors that will be included in the more general study (on a county level) of chapter 9. We have been forced to limit our attention to population age structure and density, hospital waiting lists, and the employment of nursing staff.[12]

Our primary interest is to see if the relative sizes of the elasticities of admissions and mean stay are affected when other factors are taken into account. Because there are only 11 observations, only one additional factor was considered at a time. Two types of estimates were made. In the first, the additional factor (X) was assumed to have a multiplicative effect on the relation between the bed use variable (U) and the supply of beds (S); in logarithms, this becomes an additive relation of the form $\log(U) = \alpha + \beta \log S + \gamma \log X$ where β is the revised elasticity estimate. In the second, the additional factor was assumed to have a direct effect on the elasticity, giving rise to an expression of the form: $\log(U) = \alpha + (\beta_0 + \beta_1 X) \log S$. Table 7.8 presents the revised elasticity (β), the two coefficients $(\beta_0$ and $\beta_1)$ of the "changing parameter" estimate, and the value of this parameter at the mean of the additional factor $(\beta_0 + \beta_1 \overline{X})$. Values for both admissions (columns 3–5) and mean stay (columns 6–8) are shown. Both sets of estimates agree very closely with the original values of the elasticities presented in tables 7.5, 7.6 and 7.7.

---

[12] Data for these studies was derived from the Hospital In-Patient Enquiry for 1960 (Ministry of Health and General Register Office, 1963) and from the Ministry of Health (Statistics Branch, 1961).

TABLE 7.8

*Revised elasticities of admissions and mean stays**

Additional factor (1)	Mean (2)	Admissions			Mean stay			Elasticity to additional factor	
		Revised elasticity (3)	Changing parameter (4)	Changing parameter mean elasticity (5)	Revised elasticity (6)	Changing parameter (7)	Changing parameter mean elasticity (8)	Admissions (9)	Mean stay (10)
Density	0.0014	0.527 (0.252)	$0.495 + 7.27x$ (0.291) (13.52)	0.505	0.383 (0.203)	$0.343 + 1.83x$ (0.232) (1.08)	0.346	0.029 (0.042)	0.010 (0.033)
Population aged 65+**	118	0.561 (0.246)	$0.662 - 8.8^{(10^{-4})}x$ (0.282) (15.4)	0.558	0.398 (0.178)	$0.235 + 1.40^{(10^{-3})}x$ (0.206) (1.12)	0.400	−0.173 (0.314)	0.299 (0.227)
Waiting list 1960**	10.01	0.667 (0.279)	$0.608 - 5.54^{(10^{-3})}x$ (0.246) (8.89)	0.553	0.463 (0.211)	$0.395 + 5.94^{(10^{-3})}x$ (0.189) (6.82)	0.455	0.090 (0.143)	0.107 (0.108)
Change in waiting list 1959–60	−0.07	0.600 (0.251)	$0.597 - 1.10^{(10^{-2})}x$ (0.252) (3.38)	0.598	0.305 (0.170)	$0.305 + 3.86^{(10^{-2})}x$ (0.171) (2.29)	0.302	0.002 (0.004)	0.005 (0.003)
Total nurses	0.015	0.551 (0.259)	$0.542 + 1.12x$ (0.263) (2.74)	0.559	0.286 (0.185)	$0.265 + 2.91x$ (0.183) (1.91)	0.309	0.024 (0.068)	0.066 (0.048)
Trained nurses	0.005	0.562 (0.255)	$0.560 + 2.27x$ (0.256) (7.81)	0.571	0.304 (0.182)	$0.290 + 8.44x$ (0.177) (5.39)	0.334	0.018 (0.063)	0.060 (0.045)

* See text for explanation of column headings.
** per 1 000 population, 1960.

As a by-product of the revised elasticity estimates, the first method estimates the partial elasticities of admissions and mean stay with respect to the additional factors. These are presented in columns 9 and 10. Population density has little effect: there is a very slight tendency for greater density to increase admission rates and decrease mean stay. As the proportion of the population over the age of sixty-five increases, the mean stay per case in the region also increases. As a result, with a given number of beds, the admission rate declines. The effect of waiting-list length is small and, for mean stay, of the wrong sign (positive). Because waiting list length is itself influenced by the use of hospital beds, the equation is inadequately identified. The positive admission rate elasticities probably underestimate the "true" effects of waiting list on admission rates since, with a given number of beds, higher admission rates will decrease waiting list length. Although a longer waiting list should tend to decrease mean stay, a shorter mean stay will decrease waiting list length; the latter effect may dominate and be responsible for the observed positive (but low) mean stay elasticities. Changes in waiting list length between 1959 and 1960 had no effect. Finally, the use of additional nursing staff only slightly increased the number of admissions; this supports the conclusions of chapters 4 and 5 that nursing staff has little effect on hospital output. Surprisingly, larger nursing staff was also associated with longer mean stay; there is no apparent explanation for this but the elasticities are quite small (0.060 for 1960 and 0.066 for 1959).

If the environmental explanations of the types discussed are not satisfactory, what behavioural theories might help us to understand the relative elasticity values? We shall first consider a formal model in which "the hospital decision-maker" is assumed to maximize utility (a function of the number of cases treated, the mean stay per case and the quality of care) subject to constraints on the budget and the number of beds available. Four more general inter-related behavioural explanations will then be discussed.

In chapter 5, section 5.4.5, we introduced a model in which the hospital management selects the number of cases to be treated per year (N), the average duration of stay per case (S), and the quality of care (Q) to maximize a cardinal utility function $U = U(N, S, Q)$ that is separable by a logarithmic transformation. Maximizing is done subject to the constraints imposed by the number of available beds (B) and the total expenditure (E) allowed by the budget: $B = NS/365R$ and $E = NSD = NS^{1+\alpha}Q^{\beta}A$ where R is the proportion of beds occupied and D is the cost per patient day. The budget constraint implies the assumption that D is a constant elasticity function of S and Q, i.e., $D = AS^{\alpha}Q^{\beta}$. We also assumed that R is constant. We shall retain these assumptions. In chapter 5 we were interested in investigating the effects on N and S of changes in the budget constraint when the number of beds remained constant. We now consider the effects of changes in both the number of available beds and the budget constraint. The results derived below are consistent with the relationship between the elasticities of mean stay and cases treated observed in tables 7.5 to 7.7, and suggest some interesting principles for policy to change the situation.

It is again convenient to state the problem as maximizing the logarithm of utility subject to the same constraints. Writing lower-case letters for the logarithm of the corresponding upper-case variable, we have (as in equation 5.26) the maximand:

$$u^* = u[n, s, q] + \mu_1[n+s-r-\log 365 - b] + \mu_2[n+(\alpha+1)s+\beta q+a-e]$$

$$(7.14)$$

The first-order maximum conditions are (writing u_n for $\partial u/\partial n$, etc.):

$$\begin{aligned}
u_n + \mu_1 + \mu_2 &= 0 \\
u_s + \mu_1 + (\alpha+1)\mu_2 &= 0 \\
u_q + \beta\mu_2 &= 0 \\
n+s-r-\log 365 - b &= 0 \\
n+(1+\alpha)s+\beta q+a-e &= 0
\end{aligned}$$

$$(7,15)$$

With these assumptions we obtain the following second-order relations:

$$\begin{bmatrix} u_{nn} & 0 & 0 & 1 & 1 \\ 0 & u_{ss} & 0 & 1 & 1+\alpha \\ 0 & 0 & u_{qq} & 0 & \beta \\ 1 & 1 & 0 & 0 & 0 \\ 1 & 1+\alpha & \beta & 0 & 0 \end{bmatrix} \begin{bmatrix} dn \\ ds \\ dq \\ d\mu_1 \\ d\mu_2 \end{bmatrix} = \begin{bmatrix} 0 \\ 0 \\ 0 \\ db \\ de \end{bmatrix} \qquad (7.16)$$

Denoting the bordered Hessian matrix by H, and element i, j of its inverse by H^{ij}, we obtain:

$$dn = H^{14}db + H^{15}de \qquad (7.17)$$

$$ds = H^{24}db + H^{25}de \qquad (7.18)$$

We may therefore express the elasticity of the number of cases treated with respect to the number of available beds as

$$\frac{dn}{db} = H^{14} + H^{15}\left(\frac{de}{db}\right) \tag{7.19}$$

where (de/db) is the elasticity of total budget with respect to the number of available beds. Similarly the mean stay elasticity is given by

$$\frac{ds}{db} = H^{24} + H^{25}\left(\frac{de}{db}\right) \tag{7.20}$$

When the elements of the inverse are calculated and simplified, we obtain:

$$\frac{dn}{db} = \left[\beta^2 u_{ss} + \alpha\left(1 - \frac{de}{db}\right)u_{qq} + \alpha^2 u_{qq}\right]|H|^{-1} \tag{7.21}$$

$$\frac{ds}{db} = \left[\beta^2 u_{nn} - \alpha\left(1 - \frac{de}{db}\right)u_{qq}\right]|H|^{-1} \tag{7.22}$$

Necessary and sufficient conditions for $dn/db > ds/db$ are:

$$2\alpha\left(1 - \frac{de}{db} + 0.5\alpha\right)u_{qq}|H|^{-1} > \beta^2(u_{nn}-u_{ss})|H|^{-1}, \tag{7.23}$$

or, since the stability conditions imply $|H| < 0$,[13]

$$2\alpha\left(1 - \frac{de}{db} + 0.5\alpha\right)u_{qq} < \beta^2(u_{nn}-u_{ss}). \tag{7.24}$$

The elasticity of cost per patient day with respect to duration of stay, α, has been estimated [14] to be -0.192 for large, acute, non-teaching hospitals. For the more general set of hospitals to which the current chapter refers, absolute values slightly lower than that obtained for acute hospitals (although certainly substantially negative) may be more appropriate. In the context of the data that we are currently analyzing, (de/db) is a measure of the extent to which the funds allocated to a region are proportional to the number of beds that it has inherited. Against the general tendency to provide the same budget per available bed in all regions, the Ministry of Health presumably balances its desire for a "fair" distribution of funds in relation to population. As a result, (de/db) might reasonably be expected

---

[13] $|H| < 0$ is actually sufficient but not necessary.
[14] See chapter 5, p. 160. This estimate is based on the constant elasticity equation $d = -0.192s + \mathbf{p}'\hat{\gamma}$.

to be somewhat less than one. This, together with the low absolute value of α, probably implies that $(1 - de/db + 0.5\alpha) > 0$. If $u_{qq} < 0$ and $(u_{nn} - u_{ss}) \geqq 0$, the inequality of equation (7.24) is satisfied. Of course, these are sufficient and not necessary conditions. They were selected because of their plausibility: in particular $u_{qq} < 0$ implies that the elasticity of utility with respect to quality decreases as quality increases, while $(u_{nn} - u_{ss}) \geqq 0$ implies that the elasticity of utility with respect to duration of stay decreases at least as rapidly as the elasticity with respect to the number of cases.

More specifically, the observed result that $(dn/db) = 1.5 \ (ds/db)$ would be implied by the model if (for $\alpha = -0.2$):

$$\frac{de}{db} = 0.92 - 2\beta^2 \left[\frac{u_{ss} - 1.5 \ u_{nn}}{u_{qq}} \right] \tag{7.25}$$

Although little can be said about the term $[(u_{ss} - 1.5 \ u_{nn})/u_{qq}]$, if its absolute value is not large the implied value of (de/db) would agree with our expectations.

Although the model being discussed is extremely simple, it does suggest elasticities that are quantitatively as well as qualitatively in agreement with observed behaviour. The policy implications of the model are clear from equations (7.21) and (7.22): a decrease in (de/db) will increase (ds/db) and decrease (dn/db). A re-distribution of funds from regions where beds are relatively more abundant to regions where they are relatively more scarce will reduce the effect of bed availability on the number of cases treated.

Of course, such a highly simplified model must be interpreted with caution. For example, the results of chapters 4 and 5 suggest that the budget constraint may be less important than the limit on medical staff. The number of doctors, like the overall budget, is likely to increase slightly less than in proportion to the number of available beds per capita. The elasticity of medical cost per day with respect to duration of stay is also negative. The basic results of the model would therefore remain unchanged. The policy implications would, of course, differ. A redistribution of medical staff, rather than general funds, would be necessary to reduce the effects of bed availability on the number of cases treated.

The formal statement and analysis of the model is deceptive. It seems to imply a single decision-maker for each region who makes optimizing choices in the light of a known cost function. This characterization is not necessary. The same behaviour will be approximated in the actual process of hospital operation as doctors in regions of relatively high bed availability find that budgetary limitations and their own (greater) responsibilities prevent further increases in admission rates and reductions in length of stay.

In addition to the relations suggested by the model, there are a number of other behavioural and institutional characteristics that help to explain why the elasticity of admissions is relatively higher than that of mean stay.

First, there is the hospital physician's feeling of greater responsibility for the patient in his own personal care than for the people who are waiting for admission. Medical training, medical ethics, and the law of negligence all emphasize this asymmetry of responsibility. "The best possible care for my patient" forms the basis of the clinician's decision-making. This is, of course, an attitude to be admired in the doctor and one that, as potential patients, we all hope exists. But it does offer an explanation of why doctors allow the number of patients treated to vary more in response to differences in bed scarcity than they do allow the care given to the patients already admitted to hospital.

A second and closely related explanation is that the doctor and ward sister are "playing safe" by not decreasing patients' durations of stay in response to relative bed scarcity. No one wants to take the risk of making a decision that can later be pointed to as having endangered the health of the patient. Although British durations of stay are comparatively long, decisions are safest if they reflect prevailing practice. This cautiousness is reinforced by the decision-making framework. The decision to discharge a patient from a large hospital often rests on the advice of the ward sister or a junior medical person. They are likely to be less willing to incur the risk of making a "wrong" decision than are the more senior doctors who select cases for admission or the general practitioners whose referral decisions will not come under professional scrutiny.

This desire to do what constitutes "prevailing practice" suggests a third explanation. The prevailing practice with regard to average duration of stay may be easier to *learn* than the prevailing practice in admission; similarly, it may be easier to identify departure from duration of stay norms than from standards for hospital admission.

Finally, the patient's duration of stay may in some cases be determined by the patient himself. To the extent that this is true, average duration of stay would be unaffected by relative bed scarcity.

The formal model and each of the four more general reasons is compatible with the assumption that doctors *realize* they allow relative bed scarcity to affect admissions more than durations of stay. Such an assumption is almost certainly unwarranted. Explicitly discarding it does not weaken any of the previous theories but does make it easier to understand why it has been possible for the observed relative responsiveness values to exist: doctors do not recognize the choice they are implicitly making. An individual doctor, working in one place, is aware only of the feeling that in his area beds are not as abundant as he would like; he does not know the local *relative* scarcity of beds nor realize how his standards of admission and discharge compare with those in other places. As a result, he simply may not recognize that, for a variety of unconscious reasons, he is making a choice that he might not find acceptable if it were made explicit.

To conclude this study of the effects of bed scarcity, we consider the elasticities for patients of different ages and diagnostic categories.

7.4.3 *Elasticities by age, sex and diagnostic category*

The most interesting of the problems associated with patient age is the effect of bed scarcity on older patients. The National Health Service has frequently been criticized for allowing the *hospitals* to provide accommodation and care for aged patients who could be more appropriately looked after by the general practitioner and local authority services. The first four columns of table 7.9 show that older people use the hospital relatively much more than the rest of the population.

In calculating elasticities, the total number of beds used per 1 000 population has been taken as the measure of bed supply. While the results are neither clear-cut nor easy to summarize, the following pattern seems to emerge: for mean stay, younger patients (those between 35 and 65) tend to show a rather greater elasticity to bed scarcity than older patients; the same is true for the number of beds used. Although the number of admissions is more elastic among older men than younger ones, among women both groups seem equally sensitive. In short, although one would probably have expected and wanted to see that bed use, number of cases and particularly mean stay were more elastic among older patients than among younger ones, the reverse seems to be true. How can we explain this? Again, the most important factor is probably that doctors are not aware that they have implicitly chosen to make younger patients as affected or more affected

TABLE 7.9

*Use and elasticities by age and sex**

Age and sex	Use			Elasticity		
	Beds used**	Admissions**	Mean stay	Beds used**	Admissions**	Mean stay
(1)	(2)	(3)	(4)	(5)	(6)	(7)
Males						
35 –	2.3	46.9	17.8	0.79(0.59)	0.54(0.35)	0.25(0.38)
45 –	3.5	63.1	20.2	1.06(0.27)	0.66(0.23)	0.40(0.22)
55 –	6.1	97.5	23.0	1.52(0.28)	0.61(0.15)	0.91(0.27)
65 –	9.5	122.8	28.2	0.77(0.56)	0.89(0.16)	–0.12(0.58)
75 –	18.1	162.4	40.7	0.67(0.57)	0.73(0.31)	–0.06(0.45)
85 +	30.1	203.0	54.2	1.82(1.11)	1.38(0.69)	0.44(1.10)
Females						
35 –	3.6	88.2	14.9	1.17(0.52)	0.63(0.20)	0.54(0.52)
45 –	3.4	69.5	17.7	1.46(0.40)	0.65(0.24)	0.80(0.44)
55 –	4.2	68.5	22.4	0.71(0.35)	0.68(0.25)	0.03(0.21)
65 –	8.2	88.5	33.8	1.37(0.30)	0.70(0.24)	0.66(0.28)
75 –	17.9	122.2	53.4	0.58(0.49)	0.62(0.35)	–0.04(0.62)
85 +	35.9	139.3	82.5	–0.42(0.92)	0.55(0.32)	–0.97(0.81)
All persons	4.1	77.3	19.2	–	0.65(0.15)	0.35(0.15)

* Elasticities calculated with respect to total number of beds used per 1 000 population.

** Per 1 000 population, 1960.

Figures in brackets are standard errors of elasticity values.

by bed scarcity than older patients. A recognition of this may not only alter doctors' behaviour but also encourage more adequate provision of community facilities for the infirm aged.

The elasticity values for patients in several diagnostic categories appear in table 7.10.[15] In each calculation bed supply has again been measured as the total number of beds used per 1 000 population. Although separate estimates were made for males and females, the results are usually quite

TABLE 7.10

Elasticities by diagnostic category*

Disease (1)	Beds used** (2)	Admissions** (3)	Mean stay (4)
Acute appendicitis	0.15(0.36)	−0.16(0.33)	0.31(0.17)
Acute upper respiratory infections	2.57(1.00)	1.53(0.52)	1.04(0.74)
Peptic ulcer	0.85(0.52)	0.29(0.40)	0.56(0.51)
Abdominal hernia (female)	1.39(0.44)	0.52(0.22)	0.87(0.44)
Haemorrhoids	1.14(0.62)	0.70(0.48)	0.44(0.24)
Tonsils and adenoids	0.55(0.46)	0.23(0.38)	0.33(0.38)
Arteriosclerotic heart disease	2.22(0.70)	1.14(0.51)	1.08(0.99)
Malignant neoplasms	0.58(0.30)	0.68(0.29)	−0.10(0.20)
Varicose veins (female)	1.40(0.70)	0.78(0.41)	0.62(0.67)
Males	1.03(0.14)	0.66(0.13)	0.37(0.15)
Females	0.97(0.11)	0.63(0.17)	0.34(0.21)
All Persons	—	0.65(0.15)	0.35(0.15)

* Elasticities calculated with respect to total number of beds used per 1 000 population.
** Per 1 000 population, 1960.
Figures in brackets are standard errors of responsiveness index values.

similar; in table 7.10 all results refer to males, except abdominal hernia and varicose veins. As noted above, the elasticity for the numbers of beds used by each type of patient is the sum of the corresponding values for cases treated and for mean stay. By using this property we can see not only how the number of beds used for each particular diagnostic category responds to bed scarcity, but also how much of this elasticity is concentrated in each of the two components of bed use.

---

[15] The elasticities of a large number of other diagnostic categories are presented in Appendix 7A; separate estimates for males and females are given.

The elasticity values for acute appendicitis and acute upper respiratory infections are quite satisfactory. Appendectomies are very inelastic to bed scarcity while the less serious respiratory infections are highly elastic; in addition, the former's elasticity is properly concentrated on the mean stay while the latter's is almost completely in the number of admissions. The values for peptic ulcer also seem appropriate, showing a low overall elasticity which is concentrated on the mean stay.

The results for some other disease groups are not as satisfactory. Cases of abdominal hernia and of haemorrhoids show greater than average overall elasticity. It seems inappropriate that important surgical repair procedures such as these should occupy a smaller proportion of beds in regions of greater relative scarcity and that the number of cases treated should be no less elastic than average.

In contrast, it would seem desirable that admissions for tonsillectomy and adenoidectomy should be highly elastic; in regions where beds are relatively more scarce, tonsillectomy and adenoidectomy cases should occupy a smaller proportion of available beds. The decision to operate for tonsillitis has often been cited as an example of medical fashion that is not founded on medical knowledge. Nevertheless, one in twenty hospitalizations in Britain are for tonsillectomy and adenoidectomy. And, more important for our current discussion, the number of these procedures and the length of stay show very low elasticity to bed scarcity.

Arteriosclerotic heart disease, including coronary, usually presents very serious medical cases; nearly a third of hospital admissions in this category die in hospital. Despite this, the number of cases admitted is extremely elastic to bed scarcity. Patients with malignant neoplasms (cancer) also have a high hospital fatality rate; more than a fifth of all admissions die in hospital. This is about 50 per cent higher than in the United States, reflecting in part the greater tendency in Britain to keep terminal cancer cases in hospital after there is no longer any hope of helping them. As the table shows, this length of stay is unaffected by relative bed scarcity.

Women with varicose veins enter hospital for a surgical operation. The high elasticity of bed use for varicose veins, with the greater proportion of this due to the number of cases, probably reflects a greater reliance on alternative methods of outpatient treatment, as well as a generally lower rate of care, in those regions in which beds are relatively more scarce.

It is difficult to understand why such striking examples of inappropriate elasticities should have been found. It may be possible that some of the results can be explained by differences among the regions in the actual incidence of the diseases. Since the hospital statistics on which this study has been based provide the only sound measure of morbidity for these conditions, the influence of area-specific incidence rates could only be studied for those diseases in which mortality is a good indicator of morbidity. Doing so for heart disease and cancer does not suggest that the geographical pattern of mortality would explain our findings.

We shall not try to offer any behavioural explanations of the individual elasticity values. To do so properly, we should have to develop a complex theory of medical admission and treatment decisions based on the factors that motivate patients to seek care and the way in which doctors diagnose and treat each type of disease. But again it is likely that any explanation should begin by recognizing that the doctors themselves are not aware of the allocation patterns that they have established.

7.5 Conclusion

Current approaches to planning the supply of hospital beds are inappropriately based on trying to meet a demand which is assumed to be exogenous. The historically determined and unchanging pattern of bed supply in Britain provides strong evidence that demand for admissions and for days of hospital care closely reflects available supply. Providing enough hospital beds "to keep pace with demand" appears to be an effectively limitless goal. An alternative approach, to be developed in chapter 9, recognizes the influence of supply on demand and requires the policy-maker to choose his desired supply level by selecting among alternative conditionally forecast utilization patterns.

A preliminary investigation of the effect on hospital use of bed supply and selected additional variables produced results that are interesting in their own right. Among a number of surprising and discomforting elasticities of use with respect to supply, the most important is the finding that admissions are far more sensitive to bed availability than is mean stay per case. If local medical authorities and individual clinicians are made aware of how differences in bed availability influence patterns of care, they may alter their behaviour in ways that improve the operation of the system. An alternative method of reducing the extent to which the probability of hospital admission depends upon local bed availability is suggested by the model of hospital behaviour discussed in section 7.4.2.: if areas with fewer beds in relation to population are allocated more money per available bed, their average durations of stay would be reduced and more patients treated.

In a system without prices to signal preferences and opportunity costs to decentralized decision makers, monitoring information must be relied upon to maintain efficiency. The next chapter focuses on the use of monitoring information at a less aggregate level for the planning of local supply and the allocation of available facilities among individuals.

Effects of bed availability differences on particular patient types

The two tables of this appendix present detailed information on the effects of regional differences in bed availability. Table 7A-1 contains the bed use, admission rate and mean stay elasticities by age-sex group. Table 7A-2 shows separate elasticities for males and females in 32 major diagnostic categories. All results are based on the data and method described in section 7.4, especially 7.4.3.

TABLE 7A-1

Hospital use elasticities by patient age and sex

Patient type	Beds used Elasticity	Beds used Standard error	Admission rate Elasticity	Admission rate Standard error	Mean stay Elasticity	Mean stay Standard error
M						
0—	1.2718	0.6471	0.8439	0.4921	0.4279	0.3980
1—	1.7064	0.5063	0.8849	0.2165	0.8214	0.4641
5—	1.2738	0.3676	0.5845	0.1950	0.6893	0.2976
10—	1.3005	0.3833	0.6100	0.2071	0.6905	0.2871
15—	0.7056	0.3341	0.4994	0.2245	0.2062	0.1640
25—	0.8254	0.5545	0.7447	0.2655	0.0807	0.4349
35—	0.7923	0.5885	0.5382	0.3511	0.2542	0.3833
45—	1.0556	0.2748	0.6605	0.2272	0.3951	0.2225
55—	1.5190	0.2809	0.6128	0.1467	0.9061	0.2673
65—	0.7713	0.5556	0.8912	0.1562	−0.1199	0.5820
75—	0.6693	0.5737	0.7298	0.3055	−0.0605	0.4541
85+	1.8150	1.1088	1.3758	0.6938	0.4392	1.0996
F						
0—	1.3545	0.7706	1.1860	0.5748	0.1686	0.3121
1—	1.4346	0.5533	0.8603	0.1981	0.5744	0.4885
5—	1.1283	0.3619	0.2088	0.3623	0.9195	0.3364
10—	1.0281	0.4743	0.5211	0.2075	0.5070	0.3694
15—	0.7477	0.1840	0.4738	0.1634	0.2739	0.1370
25—	1.1729	0.2857	0.7277	0.2589	0.4452	0.1590
35—	1.1683	0.5223	0.6262	0.2038	0.5421	0.5233
45—	1.4550	0.3968	0.6515	0.2351	0.8035	0.4359
55—	0.7121	0.3457	0.6807	0.2497	0.0313	0.2135
65—	1.3652	0.2974	0.7009	0.2362	0.6643	0.2847
75—	0.5754	0.4920	0.6176	0.3531	−0.0422	0.6154
85+	−0.4180	0.9213	0.5488	0.3243	−0.9668	0.8101

TABLE 7A-2

Hospital use elasticities by diagnostic category and sex

Patient type		Beds used		Admission rate		Mean stay	
		Elasticity	Standard error	Elasticity	Standard error	Elasticity	Standard error
Tuberculosis	M	1.1166	0.7333	0.8560	0.6604	0.2605	0.3428
	F	1.7803	0.9862	0.9358	0.4948	0.8445	0.6384
Infectious and parasitic	M	1.4260	0.6960	1.3318	0.5449	0.0939	0.3694
	F	2.2110	0.9343	1.4974	0.5696	0.7137	0.5542
Malignant neoplasms	M	0.5801	0.3010	0.6820	0.2827	−0.1019	0.2034
	F	0.8569	0.3067	0.4648	0.2852	0.3921	0.2108
Benign and unspecified neoplasms	M	0.3749	0.3704	0.5703	0.2785	−0.1953	0.4638
	F	0.8615	0.4237	0.3784	0.2390	0.4830	0.3590
Allergic, endocrinal metabolic and nutritional	M	0.4731	0.3421	0.4247	0.2170	0.0483	0.2344
	F	2.9849	1.5580	2.5502	1.6898	0.4347	0.2478
Eye	M	0.1194	0.4706	0.4181	0.3678	−0.2987	0.3698
	F	0.1664	0.2217	−0.0249	0.2284	0.1912	0.2531
Ear and mastoid	M	1.8714	0.8738	1.6342	0.6634	0.2372	0.5913
	F	1.3053	0.8256	1.4235	0.5524	−0.1182	0.6244
Circulatory	M	1.0962	0.7373	0.6386	0.2247	0.4576	0.7950
	F	0.2404	0.6468	0.7174	0.2239	−0.4771	0.7544
Respiratory	M	1.3490	0.4036	0.6578	0.2338	0.6912	0.3405
	F	1.1630	0.5338	0.6682	0.2384	0.4948	0.5404
Digestive	M	0.9592	0.2693	0.5622	0.1102	0.3970	0.2771
	F	1.0631	0.3318	0.7307	0.2147	0.3323	0.2679

TABLE 7A-2 (continued)

Patient type		Beds used		Admission rate		Mean stay	
		Elasticity	Standard error	Elasticity	Standard error	Elasticity	Standard error
Urinary	M	1.5002	0.4474	1.3293	0.2121	0.1709	0.3503
	F	0.8320	0.8410	1.2812	0.2465	−0.4409	0.7482
Male genital	M	1.1527	0.3930	0.8197	0.2378	0.3330	0.3161
Breast, female	F	0.5759	0.4726	0.2992	0.4270	0.2766	0.3193
Skin and cellular	M	1.2487	0.4257	1.1387	0.3756	0.1100	0.2972
	F	2.0095	0.5346	1.5096	0.3102	0.4999	0.5538
Bones and organs	M	0.8264	0.4243	0.7676	0.2091	0.0588	0.5402
of movement	F	1.3524	0.5238	0.8115	0.3366	0.5409	0.6505
Diabetes	M	0.2139	0.5621	0.3256	0.3367	−0.1117	0.4359
	F	0.7720	0.3686	0.5254	0.3159	0.2466	0.5241
Other allergic, endocrinal,	M	0.7261	0.9724	−0.2159	0.6509	0.9420	0.9190
metabolic and nutritional	F	1.7439	0.9742	0.8903	0.6738	0.8536	0.5455
Haemorrhoids	M	1.1374	0.6228	0.7014	0.4838	0.4361	0.2372
	F	1.1509	0.6167	0.7913	0.4347	0.3597	0.2497
Acute upper	M	2.5786	0.9954	1.5306	0.5153	1.0480	0.7422
respiratory infections	F	2.7132	1.2052	2.0710	0.6851	0.6422	0.7640
Pneumonia	M	0.9153	.6000	0.6369	0.5867	0.2783	0.3320
	F	0.9740	1.1612	0.7845	0.5962	0.1895	1.0169
Bronchitis	M	1.3310	1.0825	1.1056	0.7421	0.2254	0.7605
	F	0.8291	1.0265	1.5110	0.6541	−0.6819	0.8975
Cerebral paralysis	M	2.0088	1.1842	1.1005	0.5592	0.9084	1.0415
	F	3.5665	1.5976	1.1578	0.6073	2.4086	1.1955

TABLE 7A-2 (continued)

Patient type		Beds used		Admission rate		Mean stay	
		Elasticity	Standard error	Elasticity	Standard error	Elasticity	Standard error
Arteriosclerotic heart including coronary	M	2.2198	0.7035	1.1400	0.5063	1.0799	0.9876
	F	0.5369	1.3853	0.9017	0.6591	−0.3648	1.4071
Other heart	M	1.2378	1.3989	0.2435	0.2937	0.9942	1.4374
	F	0.1916	1.2506	0.8048	0.3586	−0.6132	1.1193
Varicose veins	M	1.1279	0.7255	0.6701	0.2790	0.4578	0.9035
	F	1.4002	0.7000	0.7814	0.4137	0.6188	0.6748
Tonsils and adenoids	M	0.5541	0.4562	0.2261	0.3783	0.3280	0.3815
	F	0.5299	0.5029	0.1687	0.3080	0.3611	0.4360
Other upper respiratory tract	M	0.5424	0.3195	0.2757	0.4520	0.2667	0.4166
	F	1.6436	0.4357	0.6429	0.4961	1.0007	0.3932
Peptic ulcer	M	0.8488	0.5193	0.2924	0.4006	0.5564	0.5103
	F	1.1674	0.6414	1.0251	0.6116	0.1422	0.2212
Acute appendicitis	M	0.1516	0.3610	−0.1559	0.3314	0.3076	0.1771
	F	0.2967	0.4158	−0.0041	0.4473	0.3008	0.1576
Other and unspecified appendicitis	M	1.0348	0.6872	1.1685	0.7595	−0.1338	0.2411
	F	1.3952	0.6213	1.0320	0.6057	0.3632	0.1625
Hernia of abdominal cavity	M	0.6419	0.2593	0.1106	0.3070	0.5313	0.2412
	F	1.3938	0.4376	0.5245	0.2208	0.8693	0.4412
Other digestive	M	1.4710	0.5046	1.1944	0.2467	0.2766	0.4934
	F	1.2143	0.4436	1.0681	0.3133	0.1461	0.3907
Uterovaginal prolapse	F	0.2782	0.5653	−0.1404	0.4984	0.4186	0.1996

SYMBOLS IN CHAPTER 7

A list of symbols used only in section 7.4.2 is given below main list.

D_1 demand for hospital care: number of cases treated (per capita)
D_2 demand for hospital care: number of cases treated plus net change in waiting list (per capita)
D_3 demand for hospital care: number of beds used (per capita)
S supply of beds (per capita)
W number of persons on waiting list (per capita)

Section 7.4.2. Notation:

Lower case letters correspond to the logarithm of the corresponding upper case variable.

B number of available beds in hospital
D average cost per patient day
E total available budget
N number of cases treated per year
Q quality of care
R proportional rate of occupancy of available beds
S average duration of stay per case
U utility of hospital "decision-maker"
α elasticity of average cost per patient day with respect to duration of stay
β elasticity of average cost per patient day with respect to quality of care

CHAPTER 8

HOSPITAL MATERNITY CARE: ANALYSIS AND PLANNING

8.1 Introduction

Chapters 7 and 9 study the use of health care resources at an aggregate level. They are concerned with the way that various factors affect the general allocation of hospital facilities among alternative uses. The current chapter employs a microanalytic approach to investigate the distribution of health care among individuals.

A primary reason for establishing the National Health Service was to remove the allocation of patient care from the market, to "ensure that in the future every man, woman, and child can rely on getting all the advice and treatment and care which they may need in matters of personal health . . [and] that their getting these shall not depend on whether they can pay for them . . ." (A National Health Service, Cmd. 6502, 1944, p. 5.) However, when medical care is not rationed by the price mechanism, an individual's use will still depend not only on his medical condition but also on the local availability of facilities, his desire and ability to make requests of the health service, and the treatment habits of the doctor who cares for him. An important purpose of microanalytic studies is to provide monitoring information on the extent to which factors other than the patient's medical condition influence his use of medical services. Such information should be directly useful in modifying the operation of the health service. In addition, it may indicate possible improvements in the specification of aggregate planning models.

Conditional prediction models, applied at the micro level, may help to assess the impact of care on patient health. For this purpose, we require models for calculating the expected values of some measure(s) of a patient's health, conditional on different methods of care. If such models can be developed, the process of supply planning can go beyond the selection of an expected utilization pattern (as discussed in chapters 7 and 9) to a comparison of the costs and health benefits of additional facilities and services. In addition, an ability to assess the extent to which each patient is expected to benefit from alternative types of treatment will enable doctors to improve the allocation of patients to different channels of care. Prediction models that are not explicitly conditional can still help medical decision-making by measuring the risk[1] associated with each patient.

This chapter focuses on the use of hospital maternity services. Maternity care was selected because of its policy importance and the ease with which it can be studied. Although the incidence and prevalence rates of almost all medical conditions are unknown, there is no difficulty in measuring the exact number of potential users of maternity care in each year. In addition, it is possibly to study a large number of medically homogeneous cases by limiting attention to those deliveries that are classified as medically "normal".

The provision of maternity care is one of the major tasks in the management of the National Health Service. This year approximately 800 000 babies will be born in England and Wales. One third of these deliveries will be at home. Of the two-thirds that take place in hospital, half will be in cottage hospitals. Therefore only one-third of all confinements occur in fully equipped hospitals.

Hospital confinement is more than a social convenience. Despite important progress during recent decades, perinatal mortality is still a problem of major national importance (BUTLER and BONHAM, 1963). Today nearly three per cent of all babies (more than 24 000 per year) are born dead or die within the first month (Ministry of Health, 1965b). To reduce this loss requires a better use of the nation's maternity services.

Current government policy is based on the recommendation of the Cranbrook Committee (Ministry of Health, 1959) that 70 per cent of births should occur in hospitals or maternity homes. Although some writers have advocated an increase in this overall proportion and a shift from maternity homes to general hospitals (PAIGE, 1962; BUTLER and BONHAM, 1963; Maternity Services Emergency Informal Committee, 1963), the Cranbrook Committee recommendation appears firmly established in the hospital construction programme (Cmnd. 1604) and in current medical practice.

---

[1] The meaning of "risk" in this context will be clarified in section 8.4.

With only one delivery in three occurring in a fully equipped hospital, it is important to monitor the efficiency with which this scarce resource is allocated. The Cranbrook Committee recommended 100 per cent hospitalization for all mothers of 35 years of age or more, all women aged 30 or more having their first child, women who have had four or more children or who have had a stillbirth. Section 8.3.2 shows that current practice does not fully follow these recommendations. A more general analysis of the factors determining hospital obstetric admission is presented.

The second important aspect of hospital maternity care is the duration of stay per case. It affects both the cost of the maternity service and the number of beds required to hospitalize a given proportion of births. Section 8.3.3 studies the factors influencing duration of stay, particularly the important differences between doctors.

Finally, section 8.4 discusses the use of statistical models for evaluating the risks of individual cases, for assessing the expected gains from alternative types of maternity care, and for improving the assignment of women to different care groups.

8.2 An aggregate study: Effects of bed availability on maternity care

Before beginning our micro studies of the factors affecting hospital maternity care, we shall use the aggregate approach of chapter 7 to assess the effects of differences in regional bed availability on the admission rates and average durations of stay for maternity care.

Table 8.1 compares the elasticity values for maternity care with those for "all persons" and for "females" for the year 1960.[2] For this purpose, hospital maternity care has been defined to include not only deliveries but also the disorders of pregnancy, childbirth and puerperium.[3] Maternity care admission rates and beds used are based on the female population aged 15–44. The bed supply is measured by the total number of beds available per 1 000 population.

The number of beds used for maternity care has a lower elasticity with respect to bed availability than the number of beds used for patients in other categories. The elasticity for maternity bed use is 0.710 in

---

[2] See chapter 7 for a discussion of the calculation of elasticity values and a description of the Hospital In-Patient Enquiry data.

[3] The "puerperium" is the period of confinement after childbirth.

comparison to the overall elasticity of 0.957. Nevertheless it is clear that the total number of available beds in an area influences very much the number of beds that are used for maternity care.

TABLE 8.1

Effects of bed supply on hospital care, 1960

	Beds used*	Admissions*	Mean stay
Deliveries and disorders of pregnancy, childbirth and puerperium	0.710 (0.239)	0.555 (0.269)	0.155 (0.141)
All females	0.875 (0.262)	0.523 (0.260)	0.351 (0.247)
All persons	0.947 (0.218)	0.580 (0.233)	0.365 (0.184)

* Per 1 000 population, 1960. For "Deliveries and Disorders of Pregnancy, Childbirth, and Puerperium", rates are per 1 000 female population, aged 15–44.

More important, this elasticity is concentrated almost entirely on the number of cases treated. The elasticity of maternity admissions is 0.555 in comparison to a mean stay elasticity of 0.155. This result seems rather surprising. In spite of the strong and growing demands for hospital confinements, regions where beds are scarce reduce the number of women admitted rather than shorten the average duration of stay. This is especially difficult to understand in view of the relatively long average stays in Britain; the 9.8 day national average for 1960 is more than twice the stay that an American mother would expect.

More detailed elasticity values are shown in table 8.2. These are based on special maternity care tabulations provided by the 1959 Hospital In-Patient Enquiry (Ministry of Health and General Registry Office, 1963a) and not available for other years. The first row shows the 1959 elasticity of admissions for maternity care. The value of 0.469 is of the same order of magnitude as the corresponding 1960 value of 0.555. The difference indicates that between 1959 and 1960 the admission rates grew most rapidly in the regions where beds were most available; the correlation between the 1959 to 1960 increase in maternity admissions and the number of beds available was 0.33.

TABLE 8.2

Effects of bed supply on hospital maternity care, 1959

	Elasticity	Standard error
Admissions for deliveries and disorders of pregnancy, childbirth and puerperium per 1 000 female population aged 15–44 years	0.469	(0.279)
Hospital deliveries per 1 000 female population aged 15–44 years	0.416	(0.254)
Hospital deliveries per 1 000 births	0.421	(0.210)
Non-delivery admissions per 1 000 female population aged 15–44 years	0.636	(0.418)
Mean duration of antenatal stay	0.127	(0.123)
Mean duration of postnatal stay	0.083	(0.177)

The elasticity of deliveries per thousand population at risk (0.416) and per thousand births (0.421) are slightly less than the elasticity of all maternity admissions. However, since deliveries are such a large part of total maternity admissions, approximately 78 per cent in 1959, the difference indicates that non-delivery maternity admissions are substantially more elastic than delivery admissions. Table 8.2 shows non-delivery maternity admissions have an elasticity of 0.636. One reason for this may be that non-delivery admissions, especially those during pregnancy, do not compete directly with either "booked" delivery admissions or emergency deliveries. Rather they are treated more like general medical and surgical admissions and have an elasticity value of a corresponding level.

The final figures of table 8.2 show the elasticity values for mean duration of antenatal stay (0.127) and postnatal stay (0.083). These support the 1960 results that duration of stay is hardly affected by bed availability and that the reduction of maternity beds used is achieved primarily by decreasing the number of admissions.

Why should the mean stay elasticity be so much lower than that for admissions? With a national average stay of nearly ten days and strong pressure of demand for hospital confinement, why do not regions in which beds are relatively scarce reduce stays and thus be able to admit more women? The answer is by no means clear.

In addition to the "statistical" explanations considered in chapter 7 (and rejected as insufficient to explain the difference between the two elasticities), there are two sources of bias in the maternity mean stay elasticity. Both are likely to be small, however, and to work in opposite directions. In areas where beds are more abundant and admissions rates higher, a greater proportion of cases will be straightforward, "completely normal" deliveries. These will remain in hospital for shorter stays than deliveries in which complications arise. This shortens the mean stay in regions where beds are of more than average abundance and increases the mean stay in regions of relative scarcity, thus reducing the calculated elasticity of duration of stay. The size of the bias which this introduces is unlikely to be very great. The percentages of completely normal births only ranged from 56.5 per cent to 63.7 per cent. Balancing the effect of an increasing percentage of "normal" cases in regions of greater abundance is the effect of an increased proportion of booked cases. Since booked cases receive slightly longer stays than unbooked cases, this would tend to increase the mean stay difference between regions of high and low availability and thus bias the elasticity upwards. Again, the quantitative effect is likely to be of little importance. In 1959, more than 85 per cent of all cases were booked and this percentage showed an elasticity of only 0.207 to bed availability. Similarly, the differences in average mean stay between booked and unbooked cases was small, only 0.2 antenatal days and 0.4 postnatal days.

The simplest explanation would be that the ten day stay represents "appropriate medical practice", i.e., that shorter stays would be harmful and that this would not be outweighed by the benefits received by those for whom beds are freed. But the notion of an "appropriate" rigid dose of ten days does not accord with observed behaviour. The study reported in section 8.3 shows substantial variation in duration of stay among individuals. A related and somewhat more sophisticated explanation might claim that although different individuals "require" different lengths of stay, the distribution of "medically necessary" stays is the same everywhere – thus resulting in rigid mean stays. The study referred to above, particularly the material to be presented in section 8.3.4, calls this explanation into question by showing that the distributions of stay differ substantially among doctors, reflecting their individual adjustments to the conflict between longer stays and more cases.

The general behavioural explanations of chapter 7 are applicable in this special area. If funds and staff for maternity care do not increase in proportion to the number of available beds, the mean stay elasticity is likely to be less than that of cases treated. Of course, any acceptable explanation of the inelasticity of mean stay should recognize that the observed elasticities do not generally reflect a conscious choice by the individual doctors. Although each doctor must determine the length of stay of his own cases, he can have little influence on the total number of cases that are hospitalized in his region. This is particularly true of the general practitioner who has only a few beds in a cottage hospital[4]. In a situation such as this it is not surprising that the doctor should limit his feeling of responsibility to the mothers already occupying his hospital beds and focus on providing them with the best possible care. This is no doubt reinforced by a natural aversion to risk; the mother and baby who have enjoyed a ten-day hospital confinement are less of a risk to discharge and, should any complications subsequently arise, less of a burden on the doctor's conscience, than the mother and baby discharged after five days. The asymmetry of the doctor's responsibility and the aversion to perceived risk no doubt contribute to the low elasticity values for mean stay.

The results of this section have been presented to show, at an aggregate level, how bed availability differences affect hospital maternity care. The next section studies this further at the micro level and investigates the way that other factors affect the admission and duration of stay of individual patients. The aggregate elasticities raise several questions. When maternity admission rates are reduced, what types of cases are not hospitalized? What can be done to reduce the average duration of stay and to make mean stay more responsive to bed scarcity? How can we evaluate the effects of hospitalization on the risks of childbirth? Although the first of these questions must remain outside the scope of this study, the other two will be dealt with in the sections that follow.

8.3. A micro study: Hospital admission and duration of stay

A fundamental aspect of National Health Service efficiency is the functioning of the non-market system that allocates hospital care among individuals. The current section investigates one facet of this system: the factors that influence hospital admission and duration of stay for maternity care.

---

[4] In the results presented in section 8.3.4, the doctors whose duration of stay policies have the greatest impact on the number of possible admissions in the area do have the shortest mean stays. This supports the theory that stays would be shorter if doctors recognized the opportunity costs of longer stays.

It assesses the extent to which actual practice corresponds to the standards recommended for medical or social reasons and evaluates the influence of other factors that may indicate a suboptimal functioning of the allocation process.

A number of general investigations of the consumption of medical care by families or individuals have previously been conducted in the United States (ANDERSON and FELDMAN, 1956; ANDERSON, COLETTE and FELDMAN, 1963; United States National Center for Health Statistics, 1965a; WEEKS, 1961; WEISBROD and FIESLER, 1961; WIRICK, 1964). The purpose of these studies has generally been to measure and explain household or individual variation in total expenditure for medical or hospital care. Although their results are valuable for studying the incidence of medical costs in the American community, they tell little about the efficiency with which medical services are distributed among individuals. First, expenditure for health care reflects not only the quantity consumed but also the price paid. Because doctors and (to a lesser extent) health institutions are price discriminators, it is difficult to make inferences about factors affecting the quantity of medical care by using expenditure data. Second, the heterogeneity of health services included in previous studies have precluded evaluating the influence of medical factors on the pattern of consumption. Third, because patients' geographical locations have not been identified, the effects of availability and proximity of care have not been studied. Finally, previous investigations have not attempted to assess the extent to which the doctors, rather than their patients, are responsible for the observed variation in the consumption of medical care.

The current study differs from earlier work in a number of ways. Attention focuses on the allocation of hospital care for a single medical condition, "normal delivery"[1]. It is therefore possible to evaluate the extent to which the distribution of care reflects the medical characteristics of the population. The consumption of medical services is limited to hospital in-patient care as measured by admission and duration of stay; care in fully-equipped teaching hospitals is analyzed separately. The importance of locally available hospital facilities is assessed. The general practitioner is shown to have an important effect on his patients' hospital admissions;

---

[5] A "normal delivery" as defined by the four-digit International Standard Classification 660.0 is one in which there is no complication of pregnancy, delivery or puerperium. About one-half of the deliveries in the area covered by the current study were classified as normal.

the existence of substantial differences between the mean durations of stay of hospital obstetricians is also analyzed.

The analysis of this section is based on detailed records of all births occurring in 1962 in an area surrounding the City of Oxford. More specifically, the data was provided by the Oxford Record Linkage Study (ACHESON, 1964), a project that collects information concerning every delivery (whether at home or in hospital), discharge from hospital, and death in the population of Oxford County Borough, Oxfordshire (except Henley) and part of Berkshire. Of the 5 999 births in this area, 3 491 were classified as normal deliveries. This includes private patients delivered in National Health Service hospitals and is complete for the population at risk with the exception of a small number of cases in which delivery occurred to residents of the area at a distance (e.g., in London) or in non-N.H.S. obstetric beds.

A method of multivariate analysis has been used to evaluate simultaneously the net effects of several different factors. The method is described in section 8.3.1. It is then used to analyze hospital admissions (section 8.3.2) and duration of stay (section 8.3.3).

8.3.1. *The estimation method*

The estimation procedure is based on multiple regression equations in which each of the explanatory variables is binary (SUITS, 1957; JOHNSTON, 1963, p. 221; FELDSTEIN, 1966). In the equations used to analyze hospital admission, the dependent variable is also binary. Binary variable regression analysis permits the use of classificatory explanatory variables and allows cardinally measurable variables to be used without any arbitrary assumptions about the form of the relationships. As discussed below, parameters derived by a transformation of the regression coefficients can be interpreted as the percentage increase or decrease in the expected value of the dependent variable [6] specifically associated with membership in a particular sub-class of a given factor.

The adopted specification of each regression equation implies the absence of interaction between different factors, i.e., that the specific effect of being in a particular sub-class of one factor is independent of the sub-classes of other factors to which the observation belongs. Although such complete

---

[6] For the hospital admission equations, the expected value of the dependent variable is the probability of admission.

absence of interaction is not a necessary assumption for binary variable regression analysis, it has been assumed because of the substantial reduction in calculation and increase in the number of factors that it allows. Including all first-order interaction terms would only be possible if the number of factors (or sub-classes) was considerably reduced, thus substituting one source of specification bias for another. An alternative approach, developed by MORGAN and SONQUIST (1963a; 1963b) uses a branching search process of two-way analysis of variance calculations to discover the set of interactions which, subject to certain rules of the search procedure, minimizes the unexplained variance. Although such a formulation is very economical of degrees of freedom, it precludes examining the effects of specific factors: it discovers relations otherwise hidden in the data but does not allow the analyst to ask specific questions with the aid of the data. This objection is important whenever the explanatory variables are not orthogonal, for then any stepwise analysis procedure may fail to identify important variables because they are highly correlated with others already selected in previous steps. Nevertheless, such a method can be useful by indicating specific interactions that could be incorporated into a general binary variable multiple regression analysis. The complete absence of interaction terms should be borne in mind in interpreting the results presented below.

Two specific problems arise in the analysis of hospital admissions because the dependent variable assumes only the values of zero and one. First, because the relation between the dependent variable and the explanatory variables is linear[7], the predicted value of the dependent variable can fall outside the zero-one range. This difficulty could have been avoided by a suitable transformation of the variable; see, for example, TOBIN (1958) or the excellent survey of alternative procedures by ZELLNER and LEE (1965). Because of the greater ease of calculation and interpretation, the linear approximation has been accepted. There appear to be very few situations in which the predictions are unacceptable[8]. The second problem raised by the binary dependent variable is that the errors cannot be homoscedastic (GOLDBERGER, 1964). Although ordinary least squares estimates

---

[7] Note that the linear relation between the dependent variable and the individual binary explanatory variable does *not* imply a linear relation between hospital admission and the actual value of a factor such as age.

[8] One such situation is that very young, unmarried women having their first child have a calculated probability greater than one of admission to hospital. Fortunately, this is not a significantly large group.

are inefficient when there is heteroscedasticity, they are unbiased. The efficiency of the estimates can be improved by using a two stage procedure: ordinary least squares estimates of the regression coefficients are used to estimate the error variance for each observation and the regression coefficients are then re-estimated by generalized least squares using the weights implied by the estimated error variances (GOLDBERGER, 1964). But with a sample of nearly 3 500 observations, the gain in efficiency probably does not justify the additional calculations[9]. However, in interpreting the results of the hospital admission analysis it should be remembered that the estimated standard errors will be biased.

Although it would be possible to use a binary variable equation to explain the overall variation in the number of hospital days per case, this has been eschewed in favour of separate equations for admission and for duration of stay of hospitalized cases. The two equations more clearly indicate the ways in which each factor influences the total use of hospital beds. In addition, the error term of the single equation would tend to be bimodal – a negative error for cases not hospitalized and a positive error for the others.

Interpretation of the regression results is facilitated by calculating the difference between each regression coefficient and the weighted average of the regression coefficients of all the subclasses of that factor, weighting by the population proportion in the corresponding subclass. The "adjusted deviation" of a particular subclass of a given factor as calculated in this way is the difference in the expected value of the dependent variable associated with an observation being in that subclass, rather than being "average" in terms of the dependent variable with respect to the given factor, after adjustment has been made for the effects of other factors. If a_i is the regression coefficient for subclass i, n_i is the number of persons in subclass i, and N the total sample size, the adjusted deviation (d_i) is defined as:

$$d_i = a_i - N^{-1} \sum_j a_j n_j \qquad (8.1)$$

[9] In the ordinary least squares calculation, the normal matrix $(X'X)$ has as its i, jth element the number of persons in the sample who are in sub-class i and subclass j. If the number of explanatory factors is Q, the matrix can be written from the information contained in $Q(Q-1)/2$ two-way classification tables. The vector of cross-products between the dependent and explanatory variables is simply the number of persons hospitalized in each subgroup. All of these simplifications are lost if the two-stage procedure is used. The weighted normal matrix must then be re-calculated for each regression. See FELDSTEIN (1966).

where the summation extends over all the subclasses of the factor including subclass *i*. For earlier applications of this method see MORGAN *et al.* (1962) and WIRICK and BARLOW (1964). In the results presented below, the adjusted deviation is expressed as a percentage of the mean value of the dependent variable.

A special problem in calculating the adjusted deviations may arise from the accidental singularity of the sample's normal matrix. Although in usual regression problems exact singularity is highly unlikely, the use of a large number of binary variables makes it a serious possibility. If a redundant column and row of the normal matrix is omitted and non-singularity achieved[10], the remaining regression coefficients can be obtained. Adjusted deviations can then be calculated for all factors except the one from which the column was omitted. To obtain adjusted deviations for this factor, the previously omitted column and row are replaced, a redundant column and row elsewhere are removed, and a new regression is calculated which now contains the requisite number of coefficients for the required factor. Unfortunately, the variable to be omitted and the resulting estimates are not necessarily unique.

Although earlier studies using adjusted deviations did not present standard errors, this poses no difficulty if the dependent variable is continuous. Because the adjusted deviation is a linear combination of a subset of the regression coefficients, its variance can be written as a linear combination of their variances and covariances. To see this clearly it is convenient to rewrite the expression for d_i in equation (8.1) as:

$$d_i = a_i(1 - n_i N^{-1}) - \sum_{j \neq i} a_i(n_j N^{-1}) = w_i' a \qquad (8.2)$$

where, if the factor has $r + 1$ subclasses,

$$w_i' = (-n_1 N^{-1} - n_2 N^{-1} \dots (1 - n_i N^{-1}) \dots - n_r N^{-1}).$$

If V is the covariance matrix of the regression coefficients, and V_1 is the relevant r by r submatrix, we calculate

$$\text{var } (d_i) = w_i' V_1 w_i. \qquad (8.3)$$

To obtain a simple estimate of the standard error of the adjusted *percentage*

---

[10] It may be necessary to omit more than one column. The number of columns that must be omitted can be found efficiently by calculating the number of zero latent roots of the normal matrix.

deviation, the mean of the dependent variable is treated as a known constant. With a sample of 3 491 cases, the mean proportion hospitalized (0.612) has a standard error of only 0.008; the mean duration of stay of 2 125 hospitalized cases [11] (8.305) has a standard error of only 0.065.

8.3.2. *Factors affecting hospital admission*

For maternity care, as in other diagnostic categories, the probability of hospital admission is influenced by four types of variables: the patient's medical condition, her social characteristics, the extent to which services are available to her, and her attitudes about hospital use. This study is concerned with the first three of these.

The most basic medical factors influencing hospitalization are the woman's age, parity (number of previous children) and past obstetric history (complications of previous pregnancies and deliveries). As noted above, the Cranbrook Committee recommended 100 per cent hospitalization for all mothers of 35 years of age or more, all women aged 30 or more having their first child, women who have had four or more children or who have had a stillbirth. Social class may influence hospitalization in two ways. Lower social class generally implies that home conditions are inadequate for domiciliary delivery and should increase the probability of hospitalization. For this reason, unmarried mothers are almost always hospitalized. But social classes may also differ in attitudes and in ability to obtain what they want from health services. This may increase the amount of care going to those in the upper social classes. Finally, hospital admission will be affected not only by the availability of local maternity beds (and the general practitioner's attitude about hospital and domiciliary obstetrics) but also by the availability of domiciliary midwifery services.

Each of these factors will now be examined. Separate analyses are made of the admission to hospital and the admission to the maternity departments of the teaching hospitals. The analysis relates to the 3 474 normal deliveries in the Oxford Record Linkage Study area in 1962; although the fact that a delivery will be normal can only be known with certainty after the event, this method of selecting cases seemed the best way of reducing the importance of variation in the medical conditions of different women.

---

[11] Seventeen cases are omitted from this analysis because they were not in any of the hospitals covered by this study.

TABLE 8.3

Medical factors affecting hospital admission

Factor (1)	Subclass (2)	Cases (3)	All hospitals		Teaching hospitals	
			Unadjusted (4)	Adjusted** (5)	Unadjusted (6)	Adjusted** (7)
				Percentage deviation in admission probability*		
Age	<20	277	31.31	12.95	28.72	6.53
			(3.91)	(5.36)	(9.90)	(10.58)
	20 —	1159	4.25	−0.55	0.79	−2.80
			(2.31)	(2.87)	(4.56)	(5.67)
	25 —	1051	−7.62	−4.37	−6.62	− 0.27
			(2.50)	(2.34)	(4.68)	(4.61)
	30 —	925	−5.68	1.09	−6.39	−0.75
			(2.66)	(1.12)	(4.99)	(2.21)
	≧40	62	11.04	10.28	64.32	38.90
			(9.69)	(14.53)	(21.55)	(28.67)
Parity***	0	960	28.91	26.00	29.11	26.52
			(2.16)	(2.88)	(5.32)	(5.68)
	1	1146	−9.41	−7.82	−10.81	−8.50
			(2.40)	(2.70)	(4.42)	(5.34)
	2	729	−12.99	−11.20	−24.07	−21.06
			(3.02)	(2.33)	(5.24)	(4.61)
	3	336	−22.15	−19.41	−15.10	−13.42
			(4.45)	(3.72)	(8.02)	(7.35)
	4	140	−11.25	−10.95	18.86	23.29
			(6.88)	(5.76)	(13.69)	(11.37)
	≧5	163	9.32	1.37	27.09	5.40
			(6.03)	(8.84)	(12.87)	(17.43)
Past obstetric history	Normal	2977	−0.44	−1.30	−1.90	−2.69
			(1.46)	(0.54)	(2.85)	(1.06)
	Miscarriage	346	−7.86	−3.09	−9.70	−3.90
			(4.36)	(3.80)	(8.07)	(7.51)
	2 or more miscarriages	96	19.21	24.88	52.11	51.21
			(7.42)	(7.64)	(17.24)	(15.08)
	Stillbirth	55	39.70	46.19	72.88	80.87
			(7.77)	(10.03)	(22.89)	(19.78)

 * Percentage deviations from average admission probabilities of 0.612 for all hospitals and 0.294 for teaching hospitals.

 ** Factors included in adjustment are: age, parity, past obstetric history, social class, marital status, hospital proximity, urban-rural location, general practitioner variable (see text).

*** Number of previous children.

Table 8.3 shows the effects of the medical factors affecting hospital admission. Column 4 presents the percentage deviation from the mean probability of hospital admission (0.612) associated with each subclass of age, parity and past obstetric history. The corresponding adjusted percentage deviations given in column 5 are based on a binary variable equation including age, parity, past obstetric history, social class, marital status, hospital proximity, urban-rural location, and general practitioner variables. Columns 6 and 7 present unadjusted and adjusted percentage deviations from the mean probability of admission to a teaching hospital (0.294).

Women in the lowest age group have the highest probability of hospital admission: 31.31 per cent above average. This is primarily due to factors other than age, as shown by the much lower *adjusted* percentage deviation (only 12.95 per cent). The high admission rates in this youngest age group reflect the large proportion of women having their first child (a high-risk group) and the significant number of unmarried mothers (almost all of whom are hospitalized). The same results are observed for teaching hospital admissions. It is rather surprising that women in the 30 to 40 year age group have average admission probabilities; this is a high risk group with 100 per cent hospitalization recommended for all women over 35. Even in the highest age group ($\geq$ 40 years) the admission probability is only 11 per cent above average; more than 30 per cent of the women in this group, for which complete hospitalization is recommended, are cared for at home. It is interesting, however, that a much higher proportion of those hospitalized in this age group are cared for in the teaching hospital, although some of this is due to other factors (primarily complications in previous pregnancies).

Women having their first child (parity 0) are hospitalized more frequently than average, but the proportion is far from the recommended 100 per cent. A more serious problem is that women with four previous children (parity 4), although also recommended for 100 per cent hospitalization, actually have a lower than average probability of hospital admission. Those in the extreme group with five or more previous children are little different from average in their use of hospital care. Again, however, a larger proportion of hospital admissions in these groups are to the teaching hospitals.

Complications of previous pregnancies (except single miscarriages) greatly increase the probabilities of admission and of teaching hospital care. This is particularly true of the group with a previous stillbirth.

In brief, standard medical criteria generally have an important influence on hospital admission, although a number of high risk groups are not receiving the recommended care.

Table 8.4 presents an analysis of social class and marital status. Although hospital care should probably be used to compensate for the less adequate home facilities of women in the lower social classes, the probability of admission to hospital is higher in the upper classes (I and II) than in the lower (IV and V). When adjustment is made for other factors this conclusion remains unchanged. Also significant is the high proportion of social class

TABLE 8.4

Social factors affecting hospital admission

			Percentage deviation in admission probability*			
			All hospitals		Teaching hospitals	
Factor	Subclass	Cases	Unadjusted	Adjusted**	Unadjusted	Adjusted**
Social class***	I	242	−2.05	−0.79	22.08	27.25
			(5.15)	(4.78)	(10.48)	(9.44)
	II	319	15.31	16.20	1.13	11.94
			(4.17)	(4.11)	(8.79)	(8.11)
	III	1453	−1.55	−1.28	0.73	−0.08
			(2.10)	(1.53)	(4.07)	(3.01)
	IV	597	−7.44	−8.51	18.88	14.75
			(3.32)	(2.78)	(6.63)	(5.49)
	V	376	−8.26	−6.28	−5.17	−4.86
			(4.18)	(3.68)	(8.10)	(7.26)
	A.F.	250	23.59	22.29	−34.80	−25.30
			(4.44)	(4.60)	(8.46)	(9.08)
	Misc.	237	−2.05	−5.23	−31.22	−46.19
			(5.20)	(4.79)	(8.87)	(9.45)
Marital status	Married	3348	−1.85	−1.50	−5.37	−5.29
			(1.38)	(0.25)	(2.63)	(0.50)
	Single	126	49.21	39.94	142.56	140.61
			(6.92)	(6.73)	(13.67)	(13.28)

  * Percentage deviations from average admission probabilities of 0.612 for all hospitals and 0.294 for teaching hospitals.
  ** Factors included in adjustment are: age, parity, past obstetric history, social class, marital status, hospital proximity, urban-rural location, and general practitioner variable.
  *** Based on Registrar General Classification; I is highest; A. F. stands for Armed Forces.

ı hospital cases that are cared for in the teaching hospital; when adjustment is made for other factors, social class ıı cases are also found to be hospitalized more frequently than average. These findings suggest that the patient's attitude and ability to use the system, as reflected by social class, are more important determinants of hospitalization than her home conditions. If this pattern is widespread, it may indicate a serious inefficiency in the allocation of health service resources.

An important exception to the general social class findings is the treatment of unmarried women. Almost all such cases are delivered in hospital, with a very high proportion occurring in the teaching hospitals.

Availability of care has many dimensions. We have already seen that hospital admission may be more readily available to a woman in a higher

TABLE 8.5

Availability factors affecting hospital admission

			Percentage deviation in admission probability*			
			All hospitals		Teaching hospitals	
Factor	Subclass	Cases	Unadjusted	Adjusted**	Unadjusted	Adjusted**
Hospital proximity	Hospital in area	2078	2.29 (1.74)	19.00 (1.96)	14.44 (3.52)	7.14 (3.87)
	No hospital in area	1396	−3.50 (2.15)	−28.28 (2.92)	−21.40 (3.83)	−10.62 (5.76)
Urban-rural	Urban	2350	−3.93 (1.66)	−16.78 (1.66)	10.10 (3.28)	3.89 (3.27)
	Rural	1124	8.21 (2.31)	35.08 (3.47)	−21.40 (4.27)	−8.12 (6.84)
General practitioner obstetrics	Obstetrical practice	3011	1.31 (1.45)	1.25 (0.50)	−6.73 (2.76)	−6.29 (0.99)
	No obstetrical practice	219	3.76 (5.32)	0.57 (4.92)	75.22 (11.47)	72.83 (9.71)
	Unknown***	244	−19.60 (5.23)	−15.92 (4.66)	15.52 (9.40)	12.27 (9.19)

* Percentage deviations from average admission probabilities of 0.612 for all hospitals and 0.294 for teaching hospitals.

** Factors included in adjustment are: age, parity, past obstetric history, social class, marital status, hospital proximity, urban-rural location, and general practitioner variables.

*** Primarily doctors from other administrative areas (see text).

social class. Table 8.5 presents an analysis of other factors. Although the Oxford Record Linkage Study area is not large (some 200 square miles), differences in hospital proximity within the area have substantial effects. To study this, the overall area was divided into smaller natural units and patients were classified according to whether their residence area contained a hospital providing maternity care; approximately 60 per cent (2 078) lived in areas in which a hospital was located. Although this factor has little effect on the unadjusted probabilities of hospital admission, the adjustment procedure reveals a very substantial impact: a 28 per cent decrease in the probability of admission if there is no hospital in the area.

A substantial difference between urban and rural admission probabilities is also revealed by the adjusted deviations. The adjusted probability of admission is about 50 per cent higher in rural than in urban areas. This partly reflects the better domiciliary midwifery services available in the urban areas. A second important reason is that difficult cases from rural areas and areas without hospitals come to the urban areas, thus reducing the remaining supply.

Finally, women were divided according to whether their doctor was certified to do obstetrical practice[12]. Although almost all general practitioners do give obstetrical care, 219 of the studied women were on the lists of doctors who did not[13]. Although these women did not differ from average in the probability of hospital admission, they had a remarkably higher probability of admission to the teaching hospitals. Presumably, doctors who do not do domiciliary obstetrics believe that women who are delivered in hospital should use the fully-equipped teaching hospitals. Obviously, the type of care that a woman receives depends very much on her doctor's own opinion[14].

The general picture of hospital admission for normal delivery that emerges from this section indicates that social class and availability factors,

---

[12] Under the National Health Service, general practitioners may qualify to give obstetrical care to women who are booked for home delivery. They receive a fee for each case treated.

[13] An additional group of 244 women were on lists of doctors practicing outside the Oxford Executive Council area. No information about the obstetrical qualifications of these doctors was obtained.

[14] An extensive study of the general practitioner's role in hospital admission in all diagnostic categories is currently in progress. Unfortunately, it is still not possible to present any of the results related to maternity care.

as well as medical condition, determine selection for hospital care and admission to the teaching hospitals. The analysis uncovers a number of weaknesses in the current allocation process: certain high risk groups are not being hospitalized more frequently than average; women in higher social classes obtain admission to hospitals (and especially teaching hospitals) more often; women in urban areas or areas without hospitals have a substantially lower chance of receiving hospital care. This does not reflect the conscious choice of a single individual or policy group, but rather the thousands of individual decisions by the women and their doctors. But monitoring information of the type presented in this section could make these doctors more aware of the current allocation pattern and thus influence their future behaviour.

8.3.3. *Factors affecting duration of stay*

This section examines the substantial variation in duration of stay among normal hospital deliveries. Associated with the mean duration of stay of 8.31 days was a standard deviation of 3.31. More than ten per cent of the cases stayed for less than five days; an additional nine per cent remained longer than eleven days. Much of this variation in use of the scarce hospital resource cannot be justified by the mother's medical or social condition.

The most important single factor influencing any woman's expected stay is the standard practice of the obstetrician in charge of her case. Examining the ways that doctors differ in duration of stay supports the hypothesis that the low elasticity of mean stay with respect to bed availability (see section 8.2) reflects a traditional approach to maternity care and an aversion to risk. The effects of age, parity, social class, and other patient characteristics, although relatively small, are often contrary to the generally accepted standards of good maternity care; these are examined below.

Table 8.6 analyzes the mean duration of stay for each doctor-hospital combination (column 4). The distribution of cases by hospital and doctor is shown in columns 1–3. It is useful to note the characteristics of the six hospitals: numbers 1 and 2 are maternity departments of the teaching hospitals: numbers 4 and 6 are cottage hospitals served only by general practitioners; number 5 is a maternity cottage hospital run by several general practitioners who have a special relation with a consultant obstetrician who supervises antenatal and postnatal care; number 3 is the maternity department of a district hospital and is served by both con-

TABLE 8.6

Duration of stay by doctor-hospital combination

Doctor	Hospital	Cases	Mean stay	Percentage deviation in mean stay*		Modal stay
				Unadjusted	Adjusted**	
(1)	(2)	(3)	(4)	(5)	(6)	(7)
A	1	126	6.99	−15.8 (3.2)	−16.5 (3.2)	8
B	1	177	7.02	−15.6 (2.7)	−16.3 (2.7)	7
C	1	145	6.27	−24.5 (3.0)	−25.4 (3.0)	8
C	2	276	7.61	−8.4 (2.1)	−7.8 (2.1)	
D	1	79	7.65	−7.9 (4.1)	−8.9 (4.1)	8
D	2	220	7.79	−6.2 (2.4)	−6.4 (2.4)	
E	3	176	8.91	7.3 (2.7)	7.6 (2.7)	8
F	3	23	9.43	13.6 (2.6)	13.7 (7.7)	—
G	3	20	8.85	6.6 (8.3)	6.5 (8.2)	—
X	5	312	7.69	−7.4 (1.9)	−1.3 (1.9)	8
Y	3	156	9.82	18.2 (2.9)	18.8 (2.9)	10
Y	4	208	10.74	29.3 (2.4)	30.1 (2.5)	
Y	6	207	9.18	10.5 (2.5)	11.4 (2.5)	

* Percentage deviation from overall mean stay of 8.31 days.
** Adjusted for age, parity and social class.

sultants and general practitioners. Doctors A–F are consultant obstetricians; G denotes a group of several doctors in the district hospital; X is the group of general practitioners who have a special relation with the consultant obstetrician, and Y represents all other general practitioners. The mean stay for each doctor-hospital combination is also expressed as a percentage deviation from the overall mean and an approximate standard error (based on assumed homoscedasticity) is given (column 5). Column 6 shows the corresponding percentage deviation, adjusted for age, parity and social class. Finally, the modal duration of stay for all but the two smallest groups appears in column 7.

Doctors differ substantially in mean duration of stay – from 25 per cent below average (Dr. C in hospital 1) to 30 per cent above average (general practice group Y in hospital 4). The percentage deviations are very large in comparison with their standard errors. Adjustment for age, parity and social class (as well as other adjustments not presented) have little effect on these deviations. In short, there is clear evidence of wide variation in the use of hospital maternity beds that cannot be related to the patient's medical or social condition.

Although hospitals may also be characterized as short stay or long stay, there is marked variation among the doctors within individual hospitals. Nevertheless, the hospital does influence the doctors practicing within it. The mean stays of doctors C and D in each hospital depart from their mean stays in the other hospital in the direction of the other doctors in the original hospital.

The similarity of model stays suggests the way in which some doctors achieve shorter mean stays – not by shifting the distribution but by increasing its variation. A more detailed examination of the individual distributions indicates that the shorter mean stays are achieved by increasing the proportion of cases discharged during the first week. These flatter and more varied distributions indicate that shorter stays occur when doctors depart from a rigid duration of stay rule and determine an appropriate stay for each case. The rigidity that causes longer stays is no doubt also partly responsible for the low mean stay elasticities.

It is not surprising that the greater rigidity characterizes the general practitioner groups. The ten-day stay represents a low-risk "norm" of good practice that is easily applied to nearly all cases. Because each doctor cares for only a few patients, his duration of stay policy does not reflect a concern to make the best use of the available beds. The opposite conclusions apply to the consultant obstetricians. As a result, the G.P. group in close relation to a consultant (Drs. X) has substantially shorter stays than the other G.P. groups.

These observations suggest that a reorganized service in which all cases are at least indirectly under a consultant's supervision would reduce mean stays. In addition, by focusing the sense of responsibility for all maternity cases on a few individuals, the elasticity of mean stay would be likely to increase. Although the evidence of this chapter is limited to maternity care, these conclusions may have more general relevance to other diagnostic categories.

Table 8.7 shows the duration of stay effects of several medical and social patient characteristics. In general, they are of little importance. The differences in mean stays between patient subclasses are smaller than the differences between doctor-hospital groups.

A few of the percentage deviations are worth noting. Women in the highest social class have the longest mean duration of stay. When adjustment is made for the doctor and hospital giving the care, and for the woman's age and parity, duration of stay is found to decrease monotonically from the highest to the lowest social class. Longer stays are not being used to compensate for inferior home conditions: instead they appear to reflect a demand for more hospital care by women of higher social class and an ability to make the system satisfy those demands. The duration of stay evidence supports the interpretation of social class differences in admission probabilities (section 8.3.2).

A second problem uncovered by the analysis is that women with a substantial number of previous children (parities 3, 4 and 5+) have shorter than average stays. The observed relation contrasts with the medical opinion that high parity women should be given longer stay because rest at home would be more difficult.

Changes in the social class and parity duration of stay patterns could improve the use of maternity beds. But more substantial gains would be made if the variation among doctors were reduced, especially if general practitioners became more flexible in determining the duration of stay for each case.

Information of the type presented in this section should help doctors recognize current weaknesses of the maternity care system and motivate them to improve the allocation process. Such improvements can be achieved without any increased knowledge of the optimum admission and duration of stay policies. Of course, quantitative estimates of the way that a woman's medical-social characteristics and the care she receives affect the risks of her case could contribute more directly to the planning of maternity services. The use of statistical models for this purpose is discussed in the next section.

TABLE 8.7

Factors affecting duration of stay

Factor	Subclass	Cases	Percentage deviation in mean stay*		
			Unadjusted	Adjusted for doctor-hospital combination	Adjusted for doctor-hospital, age, parity and social class
Social class	I	145	8.53 (3.19)	14.62 (0.51)	13.12 (3.02)
	II	225	2.58 (2.51)	0.34 (0.33)	0.41 (2.37)
	III	875	−0.57 (1.03)	−0.73 (0.97)	−1.08 (0.96)
	IV	338	−4.57 (1.99)	−2.31 (1.88)	−2.26 (1.86)
	V	211	−0.82 (2.60)	−2.12 (2.44)	−0.79 (2.43)
	AF**	189	1.67 (2.77)	−1.74 (2.64)	−0.36 (1.92)
	Others	142	0.56 (3.23)	−0.01 (3.23)	
Age	15 −	222	3.86 (2.53)	2.92 (2.38)	−2.15 (2.66)
	20 −	737	0.93 (1.19)	0.80 (1.12)	−1.67 (1.32)
	25 −	592	−2.78 (1.39)	−2.59 (1.30)	−2.06 (1.27)
	30 −	532	−0.49 (1.50)	0.33 (1.39)	3.80 (1.23)
	40 −	42	8.65 (6.09)	15.47 (5.70)	21.64 (5.81)
Parity***	0	757	8.29 (1.15)	7.29 (1.10)	8.64 (1.35)
	1	635	−4.25 (1.31)	−4.39 (1.22)	−3.91 (1.20)
	2	388	−1.01 (1.81)	−1.66 (1.70)	−2.65 (1.62)
	3	160	−9.77 (3.00)	−7.18 (2.81)	−9.38 (2.73)
	4	76	−10.81 (4.44)	−6.93 (4.16)	−9.28 (4.09)
	5+	109	−7.32 (3.68)	−3.74 (3.46)	−7.54 (3.69)

TABLE 8.7 (continued)

Past	Normal	1813	−0.09	−0.55
obstetric			(0.36)	(0.34)
history	Stillbirth	47	8.11	11.17
			(5.75)	(5.37)
	Miscarriages	195	2.19	3.80
			(2.72)	(2.53)
	2+Miscarriages	70	−9.18	−3.88
			(4.69)	(4.39)
Marital	Married	2010	−0.11	−0.56
status			(0.21)	(0.26)
	Single	115	1.87	9.71
			(3.12)	(3.41)
Urban	Urban	1381	−2.16	0.08
			(0.63)	(0.62)
	Rural	744	4.01	−0.16
			(1.18)	(1.15)
Distance	Near	905	2.76	1.69
to			(1.00)	(0.98)
hospital	Medium	614	−1.97	−0.05
			(1.37)	(1.34)
	Far	606	−2.13	−2.48
			(1.36)	(1.33)

* Percentage deviation from mean duration of stay of 8.31 days. Standard errors shown in parentheses.

** Armed Forces. Combined with "others" in final column because of singularity of normal matrix.

*** Number of previous children.

8.4. Improving the planning of hospital maternity care

The basic short-run problem in the management of the maternity service is assigning patients to a place of delivery (home, cottage hospital, or other hospital) and a form of antenatal care (general practitioner, local authority clinic, hospital out-patient department).[15] Although the supply

---

[15] The problem is more complicated than this. Until delivery has actually occurred, women originally booked for delivery in one place may be reassigned to another. Antenatal care groups may also be changed. Original assignments must leave slack to allow for this. The possibility of premature and postmature births also requires slack. For simplicity, these problems will be ignored. See NEWELL (1964c).

of hospital beds and certain antenatal services is limited in the short run, additional capacity in each care group can be purchased in time subject to an overall budget constraint. The long-run planning problem is fixing the level of activity of each care group.

The primary purpose of improved maternity services is the reduction of perinatal mortality. More than 25 000 stillbirths or deaths within the first month of life were recorded in Britain in 1964, some 3.5 per cent of all births. The risk of perinatal mortality is the resultant of a large number of biological and social influences: age, parity, social class, height, past obstetric history, physical condition during pregnancy, etc. The Cranbrook Committee (Ministry of Health, 1959) oversimplified the problem by focusing on the four situations for which they recommended 100 per cent hospitalization: women of 35 years of age or more, women aged 30 having their first child, women who have had at least four children or who have had a stillbirth. Although each of these conditions is an indication of high risk, a woman may be in an above average risk group for one condition (say, parity) but be below average in risk for other influences (say, social class and age). The Cranbrook report provides no guidance for comparing the risks of a 38-year-old woman in social class I having her fourth child and a 23-year-old woman in social class V having her third child; although hospitalization is prescribed for the first and not for the second, we will see below that they have approximately equal risks.

The perinatal mortality rate could no doubt be reduced if all deliveries were in fully-equipped hospitals and all women received intensive antenatal care under the supervision of a hospital consultant. In the short run such care is not available; to make it available in the future might be excessively expensive.

Determining an appropriate assignment of patients and an optimum provision of facilities requires comparing the benefits and costs of alternative arrangements. A set of optimum conditions is easily stated and provides a basis for determining operational rules: (1) assign women to care groups in the way that minimizes the expected number of perinatal deaths; (2) change the supply of each service so that (subject to the prevailing budget constraint) the risk reduction per pound of marginal expenditure on each service is equal; and (3) set the overall level of expenditure by comparing the marginal cost of a reduction in risk with the opportunity cost of these funds.

To be useful, decision rules would have to be capable of application in a decentralized system on a case by case basis[16]. Any optimizing assignment system would require that the decision maker be able to state the probabilities of perinatal death for each case conditional upon assignment to different care groups. The differences between perinatal mortality risks (i.e., between conditional probabilities of perinatal death) measure the net benefits of different types of care. A set of shadow prices would be required to indicate the opportunity cost of each constrained service. The shadow price of any service would be the reduction in perinatal risk if one more unit were available (assuming optimal assignment of patients both before and after the increase in service). In general, this reduced perinatal mortality risk consists of a direct component (enjoyed by the woman who uses the new unit of service) and an indirect component (enjoyed by the other women who are reassigned to better care groups).

This definition of shadow price and the rules to be developed follow from the simple welfare goal of minimizing the perinatal mortality rate. They tacitly assume that the same weight should be given to a decrease of 0.01 in the probability of a perinatal death regardless of whether the reduction refers to a single case or to the sum of reductions in a number of cases. Similarly, no distinction is made between different types of women. Much more complicated rules would be implied by a welfare function with increasing marginal disutility of individual perinatal mortality risk or by a welfare function that distinguished between individuals (e.g., giving greater weight to women having their first child).

If conditional risk and shadow price information were available, the following rules would yield an assignment of patients that minimized total perinatal mortality risk. Tentatively assign each case to the care group that minimizes the risk of that case. For each possible reassignment of the case, consider whether the loss in benefits (i.e., the increase in risk) exceeds the reduced opportunity cost (in some cases the change in opportunity cost may even be positive). If so, the case remains in the tentatively assigned care group; if not, the case is reassigned to the next care group and the process repeated. Because there are only a few care groups, this process is quite short.

Estimated shadow prices also provide the basis for longer term planning. When physical constraints on individual types of care are relaxed and

---

[16] In developing a set of rules, the optimum average duration of stay will be assumed known and all benefits other than reduced perinatal mortality will be ignored.

replaced by an overall budget constraint, the provision of each type of care should be adjusted until the last pound spent on each yields the same risk reduction (i.e, has the same shadow value). This is then the measure of the marginal improvement in perinatal mortality risk that can be purchased by an increased budget; authorities may determine an optimum budget by weighing costs against this reduction in perinatal mortality risk.

How are the shadow prices to be calculated? It is easiest to discuss this if we consider the assignment process as a single centralized decision. In practice, a first set of approximate shadow prices would have to be centrally calculated on a basis of the characteristics of the cases that required care in the previous period. As more information becomes available during the pregnancy of any "vintage" of cases, the shadow prices could be re-calculated and patients reassigned. If care group assignments were made in a centralized decision, alternative shadow prices could be tried and adjusted until they produced an allocation in which the shadow prices were actually equal to the opportunity costs. With a small number of care groups, an informal iterative procedure would be adequate. Alternatively, the optimum allocation and corresponding shadow prices could be calculated as the solution of a linear programming problem. Divide the cases into K categories such that the members of each category have the same "risk set" (i.e., set of conditional probabilities); in practice, the categories would be defined in terms of the patient's medical-social characteristics. Define the following notation: N_i, the number of patients in category i; N_{ij}, the number of patients in category i and in care group j ($j = 1, \ldots, Q$); R_{ij}, the risk of a patient in N_{ij}; and S_j, the maximum number of cases that can be treated in care group j. If care group Q refers to domiciliary delivery, it is assumed that $S_Q = \infty$. The assignment problem may be stated as: select N_{ij}'s to minimize $\Sigma_i \Sigma_j N_{ij} R_{ij}$ subject to $\Sigma_j N_{ij} = N_i$ ($i = 1, \ldots, K$) and $\Sigma_i N_{ij} \leqq S_j$ ($j = 1, \ldots, Q$) where the N_{ij}'s are non-negative integers. This yields not only the optimum allocation (the N_{ij}'s) but also a set of "dual" shadow prices (HADLEY, 1963)[17]. The differences between these dual shadow prices are the appropriate incremental opportunity cost prices required for the decision rules. Because the information about the patients is continually changing, the shadow prices available to the doctors are always approximate.

---

[17] If each type of case is assigned to only one care group, there will be only K non-zero N_{ij}'s. If the K equality constraints and $Q-1$ resource constraints are binding, some of the constraints will be linearly dependent. If each resource constraint divides a case type into two care groups, there will be $K+Q-1$ non-zero N_{ij}'s.

Their decentralized reassignment decisions would be made before the central authority gathers sufficient information to recalculate shadow prices.

8.4.1. *Risk prediction models*

The assignment and planning processes described above are crucially dependent on our being able to obtain conditional probabilities of perinatal death. Ethical considerations preclude estimation from controlled experiments in which patients are assigned to care groups randomly. But the imperfections of the current assignment process provide a natural experiment. With a sufficient number of observations, a binary variable multiple regression model estimated separately for persons in each care group could yield the required conditional probabilities of perinatal death[18]. With these estimation equations, shadow prices could subsequently be calculated from a description of the medical and social characteristics of any population at risk[19]. In assigning an individual case, a doctor could either rely solely on the conditional probabilities derived from the regression equation or could use these to modify a set of prior distributions based on his clinical judgement.

A project currently in progress will develop such risk prediction models. Unfortunately, because of technical difficulties during the past eighteen months in the analysis of the large quantity of data, no explicit conditional prediction equations are yet available. More success has been achieved with a simpler approach that permits estimating the approximate risk of each case in an unconditional way. Although such estimates do not indicate a particular care group for each case, they could usefully supplement the doctor's personal judgement. Because the risks of different types of perinatal dealths are important in determining the appropriate care group (e.g., hospitalization reduces the risk of asphyxia during delivery but not of certain fatal congenital malformations), statistical estimates of each type of risk would be more helpful than a single risk estimate.

Information of this type is currently being prepared. Binary variable multiple regression models are being developed to estimate probabilities

---

[18] Because higher risk cases are generally assigned to more intensive care, it would be important to include in the specification of the estimation equation any factor that influences both risk and care group assignment.

[19] For example, the data collected by the Oxford Record Linkage Study; see section 8.3.2.

of perinatal death from different causes as a function of several medical and social characteristics. These are being estimated using data collected by the Perinatal Mortality Survey (BUTLER and BONHAM, 1963): 16 994 single births during one week in March 1958 (some 98 per cent of all births during that week) and 7 117 perinatal deaths during a three month period beginning with that week (an estimated 94 per cent of all deaths at risk).

The simple model shown in table 8.8 indicates the basic features of this statistical evaluation process. A model such as this would be used to assess

TABLE 8.8

Factor values for assessing perinatal mortality risk with age and parity information*

Age	*A*-Value	Parity**	*P*-Value
<20	43.33	0	68.37
20—	30.92	1	33.12
25—	33.21	2 and 3	53.19
30—	51.70	4+	87.28
35—	75.96		
40+	138.29		

* Risk = *A*+*P*. Average risk of 100 corresponds to perinatal mortality rate of 33.58 per 1 000 births.
** Number of previous children.

a woman's perinatal mortality risk if age and parity were the only available information. The relative risk of a particular age-parity combination is the sum of the age effect (*A*-value) and the parity effect (*P*-value); the scale of these factor values has been chosen so that a risk of 100 corresponds to the average perinatal mortality rate of 33.58 perinatal deaths per 1 000 births.

A slightly more complex model is shown in table 8.9. It is interesting to contrast the results of tables 8.8 and 8.9 with each other and with the Cranbrook recommendations. Consider again the following two cases (referred to above, page 253): a 38-year-old woman in social class I who is having her fourth child would have a risk of 107.65, while another who is 23 years old, in social class V, and having her third child would have a risk of 107.51. Thus both women are slightly above average in risk and not very different from each other. The contrast between these results and those obtained when age and parity are considered without social class (129.15

TABLE 8.9

Factor values for assessing perinatal mortality risk with age, parity, and social class information*

Age	A-Value	Parity**	P-Value	Social class	S-Value
<20	−66.86	0	−25.98	I and II	172.19
20−	−71.53	1	−61.80	III	191.90
25−	−64.71	2 and 3	−44.97	IV	202.80
30−	−44.58	4+	−16.37	V	224.01
35−	−19.57			No husband	236.72
40+	41.15				

* Risk $= A+P+S$. Average risk of 100 corresponds to perinatal mortality rate of 33.58 per 1 000 births.

** Number of previous children.

and 84.11) indicates the increased accuracy obtained by using models that incorporate a larger number of factors. The results of table 8.9 also indicate the weakness of the Cranbrook recommendation which would hospitalize the first woman (risk 107.65) but not necessarily the second (risk 107.51). In some cases, a woman in the 35 to 39 year age group may actually be below average in risk: a woman in social class I having her second child would have a risk of 90.82.

These models are of course highly simplified. They restrict attention to three factors and assume no interaction. The relation between the explanatory factors and the probability of perinatal death is specified to be linear in the binary variables. Heteroscedasticity is ignored in applying ordinary least squares. None of these simplifications is necessary. The most obvious extension is to include many more factors and perhaps selected interactions. Including variables to describe the antenatal care and delivery would reduce the downward bias in the estimated coefficients of high risk subclasses that are generally given more intensive care. Although a non-linear transformation of the dependent variable would be statistically desirable, it would make the results less readily understood by the medical authorities for whom they are intended. A generalized least squares estimation procedure would greatly increase the computational task. The final form of these models would have to reflect a balancing of these considerations.

An obvious problem in applying any multi-factor model to an individual case is that information for that woman must be available about all factors in the model. Separate prediction models are therefore being prepared to utilize the different sets of information that a doctor may have. In particular, certain models will be suitable for use at the time the pregnancy is diagnosed while other models will be capable of incorporating information that becomes available during the following months.

These statistical models would supplement rather than replace the doctor's clinical impression. They would focus his attention on the different risks of perinatal mortality and the relevant medical-social factors. In addition, they would indicate the directions in which his prior estimates should be modified. Although conditional prediction models capable of assessing the efficacy of care as well as the risks of individual cases would be substantially more useful, the simpler approximate risk evaluation models could have an important effect on the planning of maternity care.

8.5. Conclusion

Removing financial barriers and incentives does not assure an optimal allocation of care to patients. In a highly decentralized system without a price mechanism, decision-makers may ignore or incorrectly assess opportunity costs. Actual allocations may therefore not be those that medical authorities would choose if fully informed.

The evidence of this chapter shows that this problem prevails in the important field of maternity care. Regional differences in bed availability affect maternity admissions but have little influence on patient durations of stay. Detailed examination of admissions shows that social class, hospital proximity, and general practitioner attitudes, as well as medical condition, have important influence. Duration of stay variation among patients reflects substantial differences in practice habits of the responsible physicians.

The provision of information can improve the maternity care allocation process. First, monitoring information of the type presented above can show the directions in which change is desirable. Second, individual decisions would be improved if the responsible doctors were more aware of the high opportunity costs of longer durations of stay and the low marginal financial costs of substituting more cases for longer stays. Third, the method of conditional risk assessment described in the previous section would not only improve the assignment of women to care groups but would indicate the directions in which availability of services should be changed.

Although the field of maternity care provides an easy as well as important area in which to study these problems, similar microanalysis for other medical conditions would probably show a comparable range of problems and possibilities.

CHAPTER 9

AN AGGREGATE PLANNING MODEL FOR THE HEALTH SECTOR

9.1. Introduction

Chapter 7 discussed the potential use of an aggregate econometric model of the health sector for conditional prediction planning and for monitoring the operation of the health care system. The current chapter develops such a model and investigates its properties.

A simple nine equation structure allows us to study the interrelationships between hospital, local authority and general practitioner services, as well as the effects on these health sector activities of the demographic and social characteristics of the population. The structural equations were estimated with cross-section data for 1960 with 60 observation units corresponding approximately to geographic counties. Because the analysis is based on cross-section data, the estimates may not be directly appropriate to inter-temporal prediction. We return to this problem in section 9.5.

Although the model presented in this chapter must be regarded as simplified and preliminary, it is the result of experiments with a large number of alternative specifications. Recursive versions of the model were rejected in favour of the current fully interdependent system. Further aggregations and disaggregations of individual variables were also examined. Lagged dependent variables were used to introduce an important dynamic element into the cross-sectional model. Although ordinary linear models were considered, a model that is linear in the logarithms of the original variables was finally selected. This implies behavioural relations of constant elasticity, a property already found convenient in the analysis of hospital use in chapter 7.

Section 9.2 describes the specification of the model, explains the construction of the observation units, and defines the way in which each variable has been measured. Section 9.3 discusses the estimation procedure and examines the estimated structural equations. Section 9.4 presents a number of alternative sets of reduced form equations corresponding to different assumptions about central government policy with respect to local authority health care and the availability of general practitioner services. A final section considers some of the ways in which the model could be improved.

9.2. Specification of the model

A brief overview of the general structure of the model is useful before we examine the specification of each individual equation (section 9.2.1). The exact definitions of the variables and the data used are considered in 9.2.2.

The model is a set of relations determining the per capita levels of local authority expenditure for midwifery, health visiting, home nursing and domiciliary care; the availability of general practitioner services; and the rate of admission to hospital and mean stay per case. Although information about hospital use in individual diagnostic categories is available from the Hospital In-Patient Enquiry, it was not incorporated into the current model. Similarly the local authority expenditures are taken as proxies for the corresponding activities. Information about the use of general practitioner services remains a serious gap in health service data. Finally, no attempt was made to link health care expenditures and activities to improvements in mortality and morbidity rates. Our estimation of a model that excludes variables for general practitioner use and health improvements reflects the implicit assumption that a full health sector model might reasonably be described as partly recursive (i.e., block recursive) with the current set of variables constituting an interdependent block that is structurally prior to the omitted variables.

The demographic and social characteristics of the population that are assumed to influence the health sector activities are age and sex structure, population density, social class, and income. Other exogenous and predetermined variables used in the model are: the ratable value of property in the local authority area; the previous level of local authority health expenditure; past availability of general practitioners; and the supply of hospital beds.

In addition to providing monitoring information and a basis for policy prediction, the model helps to elucidate the extent to which local authority expenditures, general practitioners and hospital facilities are complements and substitutes for each other. In contrast to the common assumption that different types of health services are all potential substitutes for each other, the estimated model indicates important complementarities between general practitioner and local authority care.

9.2.1. *The individual equations*

We now consider the specifications of the individual structural equations. Because each equation is assumed to be linear in the logarithms of the variables we need only discuss which variables are included in each equation.

Midwifery (MIDW)[1]

Local authority expenditure on midwifery services represents the antenatal supervision of women who will subsequently be delivered in hospital as well as the care of those women who will be delivered at home. The birthrate is therefore an important determinant of midwifery expenditure. Because the forecasting of local birthrates would introduce additional problems in the application of the model to prediction planning, the birthrate is not included specifically. Instead the more slowly changing (and therefore more predictable) population characteristics that are associated with the birthrate are used: the proportion of females in the population (FEM), the proportion of the population in the lower social class groups (SOC), and the proportion of children under fifteen years of age (CHI). The effect of the female proportion on midwifery expenditure is uncertain. If the number of births per 1 000 females is independent of the proportion of females in the population, or (probably equivalently) if the age and marital status composition of the female population is independent of its proportion of the total population, midwifery expenditure should rise with the female proportion. But because there are more females than males in almost all areas, a higher proportion of females in a particular area indicates a more uneven sex ratio and therefore may imply a lower probability of being married. Moreover a higher female proportion also suggests more older persons beyond childbearing

---

[1] In this chapter variables will be represented by a combination of two to four letters that can act as an obvious mnemonic device. To reduce the amount of notation, this symbol will signify both the name of the variable and the logarithm of its value

age. The net effect remains to be determined from the estimated equation. The higher birthrate in the lower social class groups makes SOC a relevant variable. Finally, a high proportion of children in the population indicates a population of childbearing age and high birthrate.

Because the local authority provides substantially more care for women booked for delivery at home than for those scheduled for hospital delivery, factors which influence the division of deliveries between home and hospital will affect midwifery expenditure. Chapter 8, section 8.2, showed that on a regional level the supply of beds had an important impact on the probability of hospital admission for maternity care. The measurement of bed supply for an individual county raises a number of problems which will be considered in more detail in section 9.2.2. The solution adopted for the local authority expenditure equations is to employ the number of beds used per capita (BU) as a measure of supply. BU is itself an endogenous variable defined in equation (9.8). The microanalysis of section 8.3.2 suggested that hospitalization for maternity care may be negatively influenced by population density (DEN) and the proportion of lower social class groups (SOC).

Although hospital maternity care and local authority midwifery are basically substitutes, the services of the general practitioner are complementary to the provision of domiciliary midwifery services. Every case booked for home delivery is supervised by a general practitioner who receives a special fee for this service. In areas in which general practitioners are relatively abundant, doctors will have more time for obstetric work and, because fewer patients per doctor imply lower average capitation incomes, more desire to undertake the fee-paying antenatal supervision. General practitioner availability (GPA), to be defined in section 9.2.2, is therefore included in the midwifery equation. GPA is an endogenous variable; see structural equation (9.5).

The ratable value of property in the area (RAV) may influence midwifery expenditure in both directions. A larger rate base increases the authority's ability to afford more expenditure on midwifery. But areas of low property value are likely to contain home conditions that warrant more intensive care. Low value property may also be associated with a social class distribution that implies higher birth rates and a higher proportion of home deliveries.

Finally, the local authority's expenditure on midwifery in any particular year may reflect past levels of spending on midwifery or on health care in general. To incorporate this relation without allowing it to dominate the determination of current midwifery expenditure, the effect of the past is represented by the local authority's per capita expenditure on all health services six years before (LAE_{-6})[2].

The midwifery expenditure equation may be summarized as:

$$\text{MIDW} = \phi \ (\text{FEM, SOC, CHI, DEN, RAV, BU, GPA, LAE}_{-6}) \qquad (9.1)$$

Home nursing (HONU)

The equations for home nursing and the remaining categories of local authority health expenditure are more difficult to specify than the midwifery equation. Work in these areas is less homogeneous than midwifery. Moreover, we do not have a detailed study comparable to chapter 8 for these other subjects. The specifications are therefore more speculative and uncertain than equation (9.1).

Home nursing activity is likely to rise with the proportion of aged persons in the population (AGE). Home nursing is a substitute for hospital admissions and longer durations of stay; it should therefore decrease in areas of higher bed use (BU). Although home nursing should be a partial substitute for general practitioner services, it may actually happen that home nursing services are provided in response to demands from general practitioners and may therefore be positively associated with general practitioner availability (GPA).

A high proportion of the population in lower social class groups (SOC) would indicate the desirability of more intensive home nursing activity. But a population of generally lower social class should also have additional local authority expenditure for midwifery, health visiting, etc. If the *total* local authority health budget cannot respond adequately, some expenditure categories may actually show a decline. The net effect for home nursing is therefore uncertain.

Also included in the home nursing equation are population density (DEN), ratable value of property (RAV) and past local authority health expenditure (LAE_{-6}).

$$\text{HONU} = \phi \ (\text{AGE, SOC, DEN, RAV, BU, GPA, LAE}_{-6}) \qquad (9.2)$$

---

[2] The six year lag has no special significance. It was chosen because it was the longest lag for which information about past general practitioner availability (a variable to be used in equation (9.5)) was available and it was thought desirable that both lags should be of the same length.

Domiciliary care (DOMC)

Domiciliary care consists of a range of non-professional services (home helps; meals-on-wheels; etc.) designed to permit persons to live in their own homes who might otherwise require institutional care. It is therefore a direct substitute for hospital care (BU) and requires supporting general practitioner services (GPA). Unlike home nursing, there is no possibility of domiciliary care acting as a substitute for general practitioner services.

If the service is operating properly, DOMC should show positive elasticities with respect to age (AGE) and lower social class (SOC). The effects of DEN and RAV are less certain. Finally, we again include LAE_{-6}).

$$DOMC = \phi \ (AGE, SOC, DEN, RAV, BU, GPA, LAE_{-6}). \qquad (9.3)$$

Health visiting (HEVI)

The health visitor is a nurse whose chief functions are health education and social advice, with particular reference to mothers and children of school and preschool age. The proportion of females, children and those of low social class should all increase health visiting expenditure. Health visiting activities, unlike other forms of local authority expenditure, are not a substitute for hospital care. If the number of beds used has any effect, it is likely to be indirect and positive: more beds used by persons in the area reduce the demand for other local authority services and permit greater spending for health visiting.

The general practitioner is not a complementary input for the production of health visiting services in the same way that he is for other local authority activities. By an argument analogous to that just stated for the effect of BU, the elasticity with respect to GPA may even be negative. Against this must be balanced the official policy to encourage the attachment of health visitors to general practices and to meet doctors' requests for health visitors' services whenever possible. The other variables in this relation, shown in equation (9.4), will be discussed when we consider the structural estimates in section 9.3.

$$HEVI = \phi \ (FEM, CHI, SOC, DEN, RAV, GPA, BU, LAE_{-6}) \qquad (9.4)$$

General practitioner availability (GPA)

A general practitioner selects the location in which he wishes to work. The

Ministry of Health has determined that a few areas have relatively too many doctors and has designated these closed to additional practitioners. In a few other areas deemed to have a severe relative shortage of doctors, the Ministry provides a special inducement payment to doctors who will establish a practice. With these exceptions, the national distribution of general practitioners reflects the relative desirability of practicing in different areas and the pressure toward a uniform distribution which the system of capitation payment generates.

Population age distribution (AGE and CHI), social class composition (SOC) and density (DEN) are included in the general practitioner availability equation. These are factors that doctors may consider in assessing the desirability of an area. In addition, the coefficients of these variables will provide useful monitoring information about whether general practitioners are directing themselves to areas where their services are in greatest demand. Children and older persons are both relatively high users of general practitioner services. The same is probably true of people in lower social class groups. Because of the doctor's greater travel time in areas of low population density, providing the same volume of services requires a larger number of general practitioners.

The availability of hospital beds may be an important factor in a doctor's choice of area. The bed availability within the county (BAC) may be less important than the bed availability in a somewhat larger surrounding area (BAA). Both variables are therefore included.

The level of local authority health spending may be a positive inducement to general practitioners. An alternative hypothesis, consistent with the discussion of the four previous equations, is that local authorities generally provide services at the request of general practitioners or, for health visiting, because of the absence of general practitioners. If this is true, there is no substantial causal effect of local authority health spending on general practitioner availability. If there is an effect, it should be in terms of the overall level of local authority spending rather than individual expenditures. We therefore use the local authority's average expenditure in the four groups (LAHE). To preserve the model's property of being linear in the logarithms of all the variables, the geometric mean is used instead of the arithmetic mean. (See equation (9.9).) The geometric mean will be lower than the arithmetic mean with the relative difference increasing with the variation among the four expenditure levels. Because domiciliary care is generally substantially greater than expenditure in the other categories, using the geometric mean gives greater weight to expenditure on the more professional services. The specific importance of this will be considered again when we look at the structural estimates of the general practitioner availability and hospital utilization equations.

When a general practitioner has become established in an area, the probability that he will change to a different location within a year is very low. The existing distribution of doctors therefore depends substantially upon the previous distribution. We incorporate this into the model by specifying a stock adjustment mechanism in the general practitioner availability equation. As with the local authority equations, we use a six year lag to prevent this term from completely dominating the relation.

General practitioner availability is therefore specified as:

$$\text{GPA} = \phi \left(\text{AGE, CHI, SOC, DEN, BAC, BAA, LAHE, GPA}_{-6} \right) \qquad (9.5)$$

Hospital admissions (ADM)

The hospital admission rate is an important policy target in our health sector model. It is also important as a component of beds used (see equation (9.8)) which influences local authority activities. The use of county observations permits us to study a number of variables that could not be explored in the regional analysis of chapter 7. The substantial increase in the number of observations also allows the simultaneous inclusion of several variables.

The relevant supply of beds is represented in the hospital admission equation by the beds available in the county (BAC) and in the wider area (BAA). Population age and sex composition (AGE and FEM) and density (DEN) are also included.

Greater availability of general practitioners may permit more home care of patients and thus decrease the demand for hospital admissions. Against this must be balanced the possibility that doctors with shorter lists may see patients more frequently, give more thorough examinations, and therefore refer more patients to hospital. This positive association between general practitioner availability and admissions would be reinforced if doctors with shorter lists were more apt to work in cottage hospitals where they admitted patients who would otherwise be cared for at home.

Higher levels of local authority health expenditure should reduce the demand for hospital admissions. This reduction will not be uniform for all types of patients. If the patients cared for by the local authority are primarily those who would require longer than average hospital stays, local authority expenditure may actually increase the total number of possible admissions. Finally, if local authority services are ample, hospitals may adopt a policy of discharging and subsequently readmitting chronic patients. This would increase the number of admissions and decrease the mean stay per admission.

Any variable that influences the mean stay per admission (MS) has an indirect influence on the number of admissions. With a given bed supply, longer mean stays imply fewer admissions. If we omit the mean stay variable from the admission rate equation, the result would be a partially reduced form equation. Mean stay is therefore explicitly included.

$$\text{ADM} = \phi \ (\text{BAC, BAA, AGE, FEM, DEN, GPA, LAHE, MS}) \qquad (9.6)$$

Mean stay (MS)

The mean stay per admission is also important both as a target variable and (through the bed use variable) as an influence on local authority activities. The primary exogenous determinant is the bed supply (BAC and BAA). In addition to AGE, FEM and DEN, we allow for the effect of mean per capita income (INC). Because individuals do not pay for hospital care, the only relevant prices associated with longer duration of stay are the opportunity cost of the individual's time and the small subsidy of free hospital food. Areas of high mean income should therefore have shorter mean duration of stay. This is reinforced by the better home conditions for post-hospital recovery in these areas.

The availability of home nursing, health visitors and domiciliary care should permit earlier hospital discharge. Although the availability of general practitioner services should operate in the same way, a number of preliminary estimates suggest that GPA has either no effect or a very small effect of the wrong sign '(positive). Only the LAHE variable is therefore included.

Finally we explicitly introduce the effect of admission rate on mean stay.

$$\text{MS} = \phi \ (\text{BAC, BAA, AGE, FEM, DEN, INC, LAHE, ADM}) \qquad (9.7)$$

Beds used (BU)

The number of beds used is defined as the number of admissions multiplied by the mean stay and divided by the number of days in the year. Because our model is specified in the logarithms of the variables, we obtain:

$$\text{BU} \equiv \text{ADM} + \text{MS} - \log 365 \qquad (9.8)$$

Local authority health expenditure (LAHE)

As already indicated in the discussion of the GPA equation, the geometric mean of expenditure in the four groups is used instead of the arithmetic mean in order to preserve the linearity of the system. Thus:

$$\text{LAHE} \equiv 0.25 \, [\text{MIDW} + \text{HONU} + \text{DOMC} + \text{HEVI}] \qquad (9.9)$$

This completes our simplified model relating nine endogenous variables (MIDW, HONU, DOMC, HEVI, GPA, ADM, MS, BU, LAHE) and eleven predetermined variables (AGE, CHI, FEM, SOC, DEN, INC, RAV, BAC, BAA, LAE_{-6}, GPA_{-6}) by seven structural equations and two identities.

9.2.2. *The variables and data*

Although information about local authority expenditure and certain population characteristics is published separately for administrative counties and the independent county boroughts within their boundaries, hospital use data is only available on a geographical county basis. The sixty observation units used to estimate the model of this chapter are therefore generally equivalent to the geographic counties of England and Wales.

Although the Executive Council areas for which general practitioner availability is measured generally correspond to geographic counties, in a few instances the Executive Council is responsible for larger areas. Grouped together in this way are: Rutland and Leicestershire; Flintshire and Denbighshire. Hospital use and other information is available for parts of the largest counties: separate observations are included for the three areas of Lincolnshire (Holland, Kesteven, and Lindsey); East and West Suffolk; East and West Sussex; and the three Ridings of Yorkshire. Finally, income was not available separately for the divisions of the larger geographic counties and an assumption of uniform income was therefore made.

We now consider the definitions and sources of the endogenous variables. Unless otherwise stated, variables are measured on a per capita and per year basis. The population refers to 30th June, 1960 but the dates for the other variables differ as noted below. Local authority health expenditures, defined to exclude general administration costs, are obtained from Institute of Municipal Treasurers and Accountants and Society of County Treasurers (1962), and refer to the year ending 31st March, 1961. Because a person may be cared for by a doctor who lives in a different county, general practitioner availability is defined in terms of the proportion of the population who are on doctors' lists with less than 2 500 persons. The information for calendar year 1960 is provided in the Annual Report of the Ministry of Health (Cmnd. 1418).[3] Finally hospital admissions and mean stays for the calendar year 1960 are provided by the Hospital In-Patient Enquiry (Ministry of Health and General Register Office, 1963). These relate to persons living in the county regardless of where hospitalization occurs.

The age and sex composition of the population was obtained from the county tables of the 1961 Census (General Register Office, 1964c). AGE was defined as the proportion of the population over the age of 75 while CHI was defined as the proportion under 15. The social class variable corresponds to the proportion of the population in the lowest social class groups (group d). Approximately one third of the population is in this group which is defined in terms of the occupation of the head of the household. Density, measured as persons per acre, was calculated from information provided by the Institute of Municipal Treasurers and Accountants and Society of County Treasurers (1962). The ratable value of the area, defined as the receipts from a penny rate divided by the population, was obtained from the same source. Per capita income for the year ending 31st March, 1961 is based on Inland Revenue information (Cmnd. 1598).

The measurement of bed availability posed a difficult problem. The county is not a unit of hospital service administration; information on bed supply is therefore not available for counties. The Hospital-Inpatient Enquiry analyzes bed *use* by the county of residence of the patient rather than by the location of the hospital. Because the county is an inadequate catchment area, relative availability cannot be inferred from data about use. Although the precise number of beds located in each county could have been obtained by a detailed analysis of the available list of all hospitals, the potential information did not seem to warrant the effort involved. The bed supply of the population of a county would have to take into account beds located outside the county boundaries. Measurement of correct catchment areas seemed an impossible task with the available information. The following solution was adopted. The number of beds available in each county was measured by the number of non-mental hospital inmates shown in the census (General Register Office, 1964b). Bed supply for a county was then defined as two separate variables: the number of beds available

---

[3] The alternative available measure of GPA is the proportion of persons on lists of less than 3 500. The two measures are very highly correlated.

per capita in the county (BAC) and the average number of beds available in the county and all contiguous counties (BAA).

The lagged value of total local authority expenditure on health services (defined to include not only midwifery, home nursing, domiciliary care and health visiting but also local authority clinics, ambulance services and administration), was obtained for 1954 from Institute of Municipal Treasurers and Accountants and the Society of County Treasurer's (1955). GPA$_{-6}$ was published in the Annual Report of the Ministry of Health for 1954 (Cmd. 9566).

Table 9.1 presents the mean and standard deviation of each variable.

9.3 The estimated structural equations

The parameters of the structural equations were estimated by two-stage least squares applied to the logarithms of the original variables.

This procedure provides consistent estimates, a desirable property with a sample of 60 observations. Simulation experiments with small samples indicate that two-stage least squares estimates of both structural and reduced form parameters are also generally better than those obtained by ordinary least squares and not worse than limited information maximum likelihood estimates[4]. Full information maximum likelihood and three-stage least squares methods would be inappropriate for a model such as this in which the exact specification of all equations is still very uncertain.

The application of two-stage least squares presented no particular difficulties. The number of predetermined variables in the model is small relative to the number of observations so that it was unnecessary to select among alternative instruments for the first stage of the estimation procedure. Because the sample is a cross section, the usual time-series estimation problem of autocorrelated errors did not arise. But the advantage of the cross-section sample was not without its cost. The multiple correlation coefficients of the first stage equations were lower than is usual in time-series models, implying that the estimated values of the endogenous explanatory variables of the second stage could differ substantially from their

---

[4] Appendix 9A presents ordinary least squares estimates of the structural equations and reduced form parameters.

[5] The circumflex over an explanatory variable indicates that the variable is endogenous and has been replaced by a first stage estimate.

TABLE 9.1

Means and standard deviations of health sector model variables

Variable		Mean	Standard deviation
MIDW	$(\pounds)$	132.46	34.71
HONU	$(\pounds)$	190.59	71.38
DOMC	$(\pounds)$	286.76	60.94
HEVI	$(\pounds)$	93.93	34.19
LAHE*	$(\pounds)$	175.93	34.74
GPA	(%)	56.30	18.37
ADM	(**)	76.31	9.35
MS	(days)	18.93	2.93
BU	(**)	3.97	0.84
BAC	(**)	4.87	1.10
BAA	(**)	5.06	0.45
DEN	(***)	1.93	5.68
CHI	(%)	23.04	1.50
AGE	(%)	4.65	0.95
FEM	(%)	51.24	1.26
SOC	(%)	33.05	52.51
INC	$(\pounds)$	292.15	264.32
RAV	(****)	5.43	1.61
LAE_{-6}	$(\pounds)$	921.89	187.91
GPA_{-6}	(%)	59.45	19.27

* The arithmetic mean of expenditure on the four local authority activities.
** Per 1 000 Population.
*** Persons per acre.
**** Product of the ld. rate $(\pounds)$ per 100 Population.

observed values. This is particularly a problem for the mean stay variable.

We now review the estimated structural equations. In general, parameters are compatible with the qualitative properties anticipated in the discussion of section 9.2.1. The effects of bed availability on admission rate and mean stay confirm the findings of chapter 7. Some elasticities are contrary to expectations, usually suggesting that the system is not behaving in an optimal way. Unfortunately several parameter estimates have very large standard errors, precluding any confident inference about their true values.

Midwifery: [5]

$$\text{MIDW} = 4.7605 \, \text{FEM} + 0.7330 \, \text{SOC} + 1.7999 \, \text{CHI}$$
$$(2.1204) \qquad (0.2557) \qquad (0.7833)$$
$$+ 0.0665 \, \text{DEN} - 0.7069 \, \text{RAV} - 0.4803 \, \widehat{\text{BU}}$$
$$(0.0820) \qquad (0.2422) \qquad (0.3262)$$
$$+ 0.0706 \, \widehat{\text{GPA}} + 0.2379 \, \text{LAE}_{-6} + 3.2154 \qquad\qquad (9.10)$$
$$(0.2770) \qquad (0.1891)$$

The positive elasticities with respect to the three population characteristics (FEM, SOC and CHI) are in accord with our previous discussion.
The quite high values for FEM and CHI require some explanation. One possibility is that small increases in FEM and CHI are associated with larger
proportional increases in the birthrate. In addition, if the proportion of
deliveries occurring in hospital decreases as the birthrate increases (as suggested by the evidence of chapter 8 that first births are most likely to be
hospitalized), the number of home deliveries and therefore the amount
of midwifery expenditure rises more than proportionately with the birthrate.

The positive elasticity with respect to population density, although
smaller than its standard error, is supported by the evidence of chapter 8
that hospital deliveries are probably less common in urban areas. Midwifery expenditure decreases as the ratable value of property in the county
increases, suggesting that social conditions and the higher birthrate have a
greater effect than the ease with which the authority can afford to provide
the services.

A negative elasticity with respect to beds used shows that local authority
midwifery provides additional services in areas of low bed supply.[6] The
value of the elasticity is less than one. This probably reflects a lower than
average response of maternity bed use to bed supply (see chapter 8, section
8.2) and a tendency of local authorities to decrease cost per case as the
number of cases increases. The anticipated positive effect of general practitioner availability appears to be small and is substantially less than its
standard error. This may in part indicate that the chosen measure of general

---

[5] The circumflex over an explanatory variable indicates that the variable is endogenous
and has been replaced by a first stage estimate.

[6] For computational convenience the number of beds used is measured as the number
of bed-days used per year. Thus BU = MS+ADM, without the subtraction of log 365.
This will affect the constant terms of the structural and reduced form equations but not
the elasticities.

practitioner availability (the proportion of persons on lists of less than 2 500 persons) is not the most relevant one for this purpose. The results provide only weak support for the hypotheses that general practitioner services are complementary to the provision of domiciliary care and that general practitioners are more eager to do obstetric work when they have fewer patients. An additional explanation is that doctors with smaller lists may do more cottage hospital obstetrics, thus lowering the number of home deliveries.

Finally the previous level of local authority spending for health care has only a weak effect on current midwifery expenditure.

Home nursing:

$$\text{HONU} = 0.2567\,\text{AGE} - 0.2550\,\text{SOC} - 0.0098\,\text{DEN}$$
$$(0.2180) \quad (0.1812) \quad (0.0648)$$
$$-0.0809\,\text{RAV} - 0.3897\,\widehat{\text{BU}} + 0.4943\,\widehat{\text{GPA}}$$
$$(0.2098) \quad (0.2466) \quad (0.1797)$$
$$+0.6057\,\text{LAE}_{-6} - 0.2126 \quad\quad\quad (9.11)$$
$$(0.1494)$$

Home nursing is clearly a substitute for hospital care and a complement to general practitioner services. A higher proportion of older persons in the population also increases home nursing expenditure. Population density and ratable value appear to have no effect.

There is no apparent reason for the negative elasticity with respect to the proportion of the population in lower social class groups. It would be justified if it reflected a policy to hospitalize persons with inferior home conditions rather than to provide home care. But the SOC variable was found to have no effect on the hospital admission rate. The negative elasticity probably indicates an inappropriate functioning of the local authority health care system. One explanation may be that persons of higher social class are better able to obtain the services that they want, a characteristic already noted in chapter 8 with respect to maternity hospitalization and length of stay. A second and more optimistic explanation is that the increases in expenditure for midwifery services and health visiting associated with a higher SOC value reduces the funds available for home nursing.

A moderate elasticity with respect to past local authority health spending shows that home nursing expenditure changes less rapidly in response to other factors than does expenditure for midwifery.

Domiciliary care:

$$\text{DOMC} = -0.2102\,\text{AGE} - 0.2612\,\text{SOC} - 0.0052\,\text{DEN}$$
$$(0.1875)(0.1553)(0.0555)$$
$$+0.0433\,\text{RAV} - 0.0139\,\widehat{\text{BU}} + 0.2903\,\widehat{\text{GPA}}$$
$$(0.1798)(0.2113)(0.1540)$$
$$+0.5336\,\text{LAE}_{-6} + 1.2096 \qquad\qquad (9.12)$$
$$(0.1280)$$

Equation (9.12) indicates that non-professional domiciliary care is not functioning properly as a supplement to hospital facilities and a service to older persons and those of lower social class. There is no apparent response to BU and the elasticities with respect to AGE and SOC are negative. The provision of these domiciliary services appears to respond to the demands of general practitioners and persons in the upper and middle social class groups. Population density and local ratable value are without effect. Past local health spending has a moderate influence. This equation is an important piece of monitoring information. Because domiciliary care accounts for the highest proportion of local authority health budgets, a more detailed study of these activities and expenditure decisions would be desirable.

Health visiting:

$$\text{HEVI} = 2.2756\,\text{FEM} + 0.6789\,\text{CHI} + 0.2304\,\text{SOC}$$
$$(2.7667)(1.0221)(0.3337)$$
$$-0.0936\,\text{DEN} - 0.0098\,\text{RAV} + 0.1310\,\widehat{\text{GPA}}$$
$$(0.1070)(0.3160)(0.3614)$$
$$+0.2272\,\widehat{\text{BU}} + 0.6378\,\text{LAE}_{-6} + 1.7210 \qquad (9.13)$$
$$(0.4257)(0.2467)$$

As anticipated, health visiting expenditure increases with FEM, CHI and SOC. Density and ratable value have no appreciable effect. The low positive elasticity with respect to BU reflects the fact that health visiting, unlike other local authority care, cannot be a substitute for inpatient care. Because the general practitioner is not a cooperating input in the production of health visiting services the corresponding elasticity is small and much less than its standard error. Previous local authority spending is again of substantial importance.

General practitioner availability:

$$\text{GPA} = -0.0648 \text{ AGE} - 0.9692 \text{ CHI} + 0.2053 \text{ SOC}$$
$$(0.1728) \quad (0.4721) \quad (0.1414)$$
$$-0.0348 \text{ DEN} - 0.0564 \text{ BAC} + 0.4808 \text{ BAA}$$
$$(0.0331) \quad (0.0884) \quad (0.2769)$$
$$+0.2187 \widehat{\text{LAHE}} + 0.6678 \text{ GPA}_{-6} - 2.8594 \qquad (9.14)$$
$$(0.2109) \quad (0.1079)$$

The GPA variable is not a direct measure of the number of general practitioners in the county but of the proportion of the county's population that are on general practitioner lists of less than 2 500 persons. While the two variables are likely to be highly correlated, in individual counties GPA may be low because doctors are serving a large number of persons living outside the county or because few persons within the county are cared for by doctors living elsewhere. The variable is therefore better for measuring the care available to the population than for studying the behaviour of the general practitioners. We are nevertheless forced by lack of a better alternative to use GPA for both purposes.

Equation (9.14) expresses the supply of general practitioners as a stock adjustment function. The coefficient of GPA_{-6} indicates a rather slow rate of response to changes in the equilibrium level of GPA. Because the equation is stated in logarithmic form, the coefficient cannot be interpreted directly as a measure of proportional response to a gap between the equilibrium and lagged values; rather it implies that the ratio of actual to lagged general practitioner availability responds to changes in the ratio of equilibrium to lagged values with an elasticity of 0.332 for a six year period. This is approximately equivalent to closing the gap between actual and equilibrium values by only five per cent per year.

The availability of hospital beds is an important determinant of general practitioner location. Although the equation indicates that the supply of beds within the county (BAC) is of little importance, a greater supply of beds in the wider surrounding area (BAA) does increase GPA. A higher level of local authority health expenditure also appears to attract more general practitioners.[7] These conclusions, if correct, are quite important for an un-

---

[7] LAHE refers to the geometric mean of expenditure on MIDW, HONU, DOMC and HEVI. It seems reasonable to assume that doctors are likely to be attracted least by additional expenditure for non-professional services, i.e., for DOMC. Since DOMC is almost always

derstanding of the operation of the health sector. They indicate that general practitioners are not going into areas in which their services can substitute for less amply available hospital and local authority care. Even when allowance is made for the negative elasticity of LAHE to BU, the result is a tendency for areas to be either well provided with both home and hospital care or badly provided with both.

The response of GPA to SOC and DEN are appropriate; the first is positive and the second is negative. But the negative elasticities with respect to AGE and CHI indicate that general practitioners are not locating in areas where their services are in greatest demand.

A simplified aggregate equation like (9.14) must be interpreted with care. But it does suggest that stronger inducement to direct general practitioners to areas where their services will be most productive may be desirable.

Hospital admissions:

$$
\begin{aligned}
\text{ADM} = \ &0.2053 \ \text{BAC} + 0.2594 \ \text{BAA} - 0.2005 \ \text{AGE} \\
&(0.0641) \quad\ (0.1894) \quad\ (0.1484) \\
&+ 0.8559 \ \text{FEM} + 0.0390 \ \text{DEN} + 0.1435 \ \widehat{\text{GPA}} \\
&(1.0092) \quad\ (0.0257) \quad\ (0.0950) \\
&+ 0.2016 \ \widehat{\text{LAHE}} - 0.0851 \ \widehat{\text{MS}} - 6.9943 \\
&(0.1597) \quad\ (0.1624)
\end{aligned}
\tag{9.15}
$$

Hospital admission rates are substantially influenced by local bed supply. If a one per cent increase in "supply" is represented by one per cent increases in both BAC and BAA, the elasticity of ADM with respect to supply is 0.4647. The elasticity with respect to BAA is slightly higher than that to BAC, indicating that the former is a more relevant measure of bed supply than the latter and narrower definition.

The positive elasticity with respect to FEM reflects the fact that women have a much higher hospitalization rate than men. The negative elasticity with respect to AGE is more difficult to interpret. Older persons are hospitalized very much more frequently than the rest of the population. But the mean stay increases even more rapidly with age. Older persons therefore

---

the largest of the four expenditures, LAHE will increase relative to the arithmetic mean when DOMC obtains a smaller share than usual. The elasticity of GPA with respect to LAHE may therefore be somewhat larger than an elasticity of GPA with respect to the corresponding arithmetic mean.

occupy so many more bed days that the overall admission rate for the population must decrease. Although this effect should be allowed for by the inclusion of the mean stay variable in the ADM equation, for reasons noted below the MS variable may inadequately represent the way in which longer stays would *ceteris paribus* decrease admissions.

The clear positive elasticities with respect to GPA and LAHE are rather surprising. Both of these variables might have been expected to act as substitutes for hospital care and thus reduce the demand for admission. The discussion of the admission equation in section 9.2.1 suggested some reasons why GPA and LAHE might also tend to increase ADM: doctors with more time to discover illness and to treat patients in cottage hospitals; local authorities providing care which permit shorter hospital stays or the discharge and subsequent readmission of chronic patients. Additional local authority expenditure on health visiting and home nursing may also lead to more case finding and recommendation for hospital care.[8] But confident interpretation of these results cannot be made until more detailed studies of the hospital admission process are available.[9]

The negative elasticity with respect to MS indicates that, with a given bed supply, a longer mean stay decreases the possible number of admissions. On the basis of this interpretation, the MS elasticity should be much closer to -1. The absolute size of the MS effect is probably underestimated because BAC and BAA are inadequate measures of the available bed supply. We have omitted from equation (9.15) a variable that might be called "other bed supply". The elasticity of admissions with respect to this variable would be positive; similarly the partial correlation of the omitted variable and MS would be positive. The result is that the estimated elasticity of MS in equation (9.15) is of greater algebraic value than the true elasticity. Another reason for lack of confidence in the specific estimated value of the elasticity is that the first stage equation defining MS is not well determined ($\bar{R}^2 = 0.278$).

---

[8] Because non-professional domiciliary care contributes less than other local authority services, the elasticity with respect to LAHE is somewhat higher than it would be with respect to the arithmetic mean of the four expenditures.

[9] A study of the role of the general practitioner in determining hospital admissions is currently in progress. The research refers to all admissions during one year of patients on the lists of more than 100 doctors in the Oxford area. Unfortunately no analysis of the material is yet available.

Mean stay:

$$\text{MS} = 0.1378 \text{ BAC} + 0.1519 \text{ BAA} + 0.3850 \text{ AGE}$$
$$\quad (0.1257) \qquad (0.3125) \qquad (0.2083)$$
$$\quad - 1.9630 \text{ FEM} - 0.0156 \text{ DEN} - 0.1000 \text{ INC}$$
$$\quad (1.5938) \qquad (0.0404) \qquad (0.0546)$$
$$\quad - 0.0298 \widehat{\text{LAHE}} + 0.2621 \widehat{\text{ADM}} + 2.9526 \qquad\qquad (9.16)$$
$$\quad (0.2600) \qquad\quad (0.4669)$$

The implied mean stay elasticity with respect to bed supply is 0.2897, approximately two-thirds of the admission rate elasticity (0.4647). This is the same as the ratio reported in chapter 7 for regional observations. The earlier conclusion that the hospital system inappropriately responds to lower bed supply by decreasing admissions proportionately more than mean stay is therefore confirmed.[10] Although the reduced form equations presented in section 9.4 indicate more nearly equal elasticities, 0.4168 and 0.4797, both sets of estimates do show the admission rate elasticity to be greater than the mean stay elasticity.

The positive elasticity with respect to AGE and the negative elasticity with respect to FEM reflect the longer mean stays of older persons and the shorter stays of women. The negative elasticity with respect to income, which is nearly twice its standard error, supports the analysis presented in 9.2.1.

Although the effect of LAHE is of the expected sign, the elasticity is extremely low and very much smaller than its standard error. The large standard error makes any precise inference impossible so that a final conclusion about the effect of local authority care on mean stay must be held in abeyance.

The positive elasticity with respect to ADM probably reflects a specification bias analogous to that affecting the elasticity of ADM with respect to mean stay.

In section 9.5 we consider a number of ways in which the structural model of the health sector can be improved. Before doing so we examine reduced form equations corresponding to alternative policy assumptions with regard to GPA and the local authority health expenditures.

---

[10] The sum of the mean stay and admission rate elasticities, 0.8965, indicates that our measure of bed supply is reasonably good.

9.4. Reduced form equations

The structural equations help us to understand the interrelations among endogenous variables as well as the effects of predetermined variables. A coefficient in a structural equation is a partial elasticity, measuring the impact that one variable would have on another if all of the other endogenous variables remained unchanged. In contrast, a coefficient of a reduced form equation shows the total effect of one predetermined variable on an endogenous variable, allowing for adjustments in all of the other endogenous variables.

Each reduced form equation therefore states an endogenous variable as a linear combination of all of the predetermined variables of the system, with the possibility that some of the coefficients in the linear combination are zero. The structure of the present model is such that all of these reduced form coefficients are in fact non-zero.[11]

The reduced form equations are important not only because they show the total effects of each exogenous variable but also because they are of direct use in conditional prediction planning.[12] Given forecast values of the predetermined variables outside the control of the policy maker (e.g., DEN), the reduced form equations predict values for each endogenous variable as a function of those exogenous variables that are policy instruments. As the model is currently specified, the bed supply is the only policy instrument that may be controlled directly by the central government. The reduced form equations may therefore be used to predict the effects of changes in bed supply on each of the endogenous variables. Because the model is linear in the logarithms, these predicted effects take the form of proportional changes in each endogenous variable in response to a proportional change in the bed supply, the proportionality factors being independent of the values taken by the other predetermined variables.

We may also use the estimated structural model to investigate what would happen if the central government took direct control over a variable that

---

[11] The matrix of reduced form coefficients is calculated by inverting the matrix of the structural coefficients of the endogenous variables, postmultiplying this inverse by the matrix of structural coefficients of the predetermined variables and multiplying the product by -1. Using the familiar notation that y and x are the vectors of endogenous and predetermined variables, the structural form of the model may be stated as $\Gamma y + Bx = 0$. This implies $y = -\Gamma^{-1}Bx$. The reduced form matrix is therefore $-\Gamma^{-1}B$.

[12] This again ignores the problem of using estimates based on cross-section analysis for predicting changes through time. We return to this in the next section.

had previously been endogenous (e.g., if the Ministry of Health determined the national distribution of general practitioners). To do this we delete the corresponding equation from the model, reclassify the variable as "exogenous", and calculate the new reduced form equation. Because we use the structural parameters estimated for a period in which the newly adopted policy instrument was actually an endogenous variable, we implicitly assume that the partial elasticities with respect to this variable remain unchanged when it becomes a policy instrument. The implications of this in a particular instance are discussed below.

Table 9.2 presents the reduced from coefficients appropriate to the conditions assumed to prevail at present, i.e., that the only policy instruments

TABLE 9.2

Reduced form coefficients

	MIDW	HONU	DOMC
BAC	−0.1719	−0.1713	−0.0259
BAA	−0.2294	0.0269	0.1339
DEN	0.0403	−0.0490	−0.0179
CHI	1.7686	−0.4095	−0.2542
AGE	−0.0436	0.1913	−0.2313
FEM	4.8884	0.2849	0.1232
SOC	0.7126	−0.1667	−0.1927
INC	0.0413	0.0350	0.0021
RAV	−0.6859	−0.0821	0.0319
LAE_{-6}	0.1819	0.6089	0.5641
GPA_{-6}	−0.0259	0.2849	0.2010
Const	5.9302	0.9184	0.5812

	HEVI	GPA	ADM	MS
BAC	0.0694	−0.0728	0.1642	0.1831
BAA	0.1886	0.4874	0.3155	0.2337
DEN	−0.0879	−0.0410	0.0254	0.0231
CHI	0.5493	−0.8788	−0.0408	−0.0230
AGE	0.0093	−0.0688	−0.2415	0.3222
FEM	2.2832	0.4144	1.4373	−1.6428
SOC	0.2795	0.2399	0.0653	0.0124
INC	−0.0190	0.0032	0.0117	−0.0973
RAV	−0.0266	−0.0417	−0.0439	−0.0058
LAE_{-6}	0.6826	0.1114	0.1174	0.0156
GPA_{-6}	0.1273	0.6999	0.1276	0.0291
Const	0.0341	−2.4513	−7.0591	1.0469

of the central government are BAC and BAA. We shall not discuss the reduced form elasticities with respect to the other variables. These are generally very similar to the corresponding partial elasticities of the structural equations, including those that are defined to be zero. The only notable exceptions are elasticities with respect to CHI and FEM. The effect of a higher level of bed supply is to decrease local authority spending for midwifery and home nursing while increasing expenditure for domiciliary care and health visiting. This corresponds to the inferences made from the partial elasticities with respect to BU, except that now the elasticity for DOMC is large and positive. General practitioner availability rises substantially with increased bed supply in the general area. The admission rate increases proportionately more than the mean stay in response to equal proportional increases in BAC and BAA. The elasticities with respect to the broader measure (BAA) indicate that ADM is substantially more responsive than MS.

We now consider the implications of making GPA an instrument directly controlled by the central government. Because GPA is substantially influenced by bed supply and local authority health expenditure and in turn has important effects on hospital use and the provision of local authority services, making GPA an exogenously controlled variable is likely to have important effects on the other reduced form elasticities. This is confirmed by comparing these elasticities, presented in table 9.3, with those given in the previous table. Although elasticities with respect to other variables are also affected (e.g., CHI, FEM, SOC), we limit our attention to the policy instruments. Additional bed supply now causes a more substantial decrease in home nursing and a slight decline in domiciliary care. This occurs because increased bed supply no longer attracts additional general practitioners who then cause an increase in local authority spending. For the same reason, health visiting rises less than when GPA was endogenous. The elasticity of ADM with respect to BAA also falls, making the admission and mean stay elasticities almost exactly equal. The elasticities with respect to GPA are quite similar to those obtained in the structural equations: substantial positive elasticities for HONU, DOMC, HEVI and ADM with very small elasticities for the remaining two endogenous variables.

Table 9.4 presents the reduced form coefficients that would be appropriate if GPA were endogenous but LAHE were exogenous. The calculations implicitly assume that the response of doctors to additional local authority health expenditure is the same whether that expenditure represents local decisions or central government policy. The total elasticities with respect

TABLE 9.3

Reduced form coefficients with general practitioner availability exogenous

	MIDW	HONU	DOMC
BAC	−0.1746	−0.1417	−0.0050
BAA	−0.2114	−0.1715	−0.0061
GPA	−0.0370	0.4071	0.2872
DEN	0.0388	−0.0323	−0.0061
CHI	1.7361	−0.0518	−0.0018
AGE	−0.0461	0.2193	−0.2115
FEM	4.9038	0.1162	0.0041
SOC	0.7214	−0.2643	−0.2616
INC	0.0415	0.0336	0.0012
RAV	−0.6874	−0.0651	0.0438
LAE_{-6}	0.1860	0.5636	0.5321
Const	5.8396	1.9164	1.2853

	HEVI	ADM	MS
BAC	0.0826	0.1774	0.1861
BAA	0.1000	0.2267	0.2135
GPA	0.1818	0.1823	0.0415
DEN	−0.0805	0.0328	0.0248
CHI	0.7091	0.1194	0.0135
AGE	0.0218	−0.2290	0.3251
FEM	2.2078	1.3617	−1.6600
SOC	0.2359	0.0215	0.0024
INC	−0.0196	0.0112	−0.0975
RAV	−0.0190	−0.0363	−0.0041
LAE_{-6}	0.6623	0.0970	0.0109
Const	0.4799	−6.6122	1.1487

to bed supply are very similar to those obtained in the general reduced form (table 9.2); the admission elasticity is larger than that for mean stay and the GPA elasticity is substantial and positive. The elasticities with respect to LAHE are not different from those obtained in the structural equations.

Finally we consider (table 9.5) the situation in which the central government controls GPA and LAHE as well as bed supply. The values of the remaining endogenous variables (ADM and MS) are independent of CHI, SOC, RAV and LAE_{-6}. The reduced form elasticities indicate that MS rises with bed supply but not with GPA and LAHE. The latter two instruments do have substantial positive effects on ADM. This implies that if more general practitioners were encouraged to practice in areas of low bed supply and if LAHE were

TABLE 9.4

Reduced form coefficients with local authority expenditures exogenous

	GPA	ADM	MS
LAHE	0.2187	0.2304	0.0306
BAC	−0.0564	0.1814	0.1854
BAA	0.4808	0.3086	0.2328
DEN	−0.0348	0.0320	0.0240
CHI	−0.9692	−0.1361	−0.0357
AGE	−0.0648	−0.2373	0.3228
FEM	0	1.0007	−1.7007
SOC	0.2053	0.0288	0.0076
INC	0	0.0083	−0.0978
GPA$_{-6}$	0.6678	0.0938	0.0246
Const	−2.8594	−7.4890	0.9899

TABLE 9.5

Reduced form coefficients with general practitioner availability and local authority expenditures exogenous

	ADM	MS
BAC	0.1893	0.1874
BAA	0.2411	0.2149
GPA	0.1403	0.0367
LAHE	0.1996	0.0226
DEN	0.0394	−0.0052
AGE	−0.2280	0.3252
FEM	1.0005	−1.7006
INC	0.0083	−0.0978
Const	−7.0868	1.0948

increased in those areas, the number of admissions would fall very much less. It is an interesting conclusion that general practitioner and local authority services should be increased in low bed supply areas not as a substitute for hospital care but to encourage a more appropriate use of hospital facilities.

9.5. Improving the model

The simple model developed in this chapter has elucidated some of the interrelations among health sector variables, has provided monitoring information that suggests several ways in which health service operations could be improved, and has indicated alternative sets of reduced form equations appropriate to different policy frameworks. But the simplicity of the model emphasizes the need for caution in interpreting these results. Before analysis of this type can actually be used in conditional prediction planning, the model must be improved in a number of ways. We conclude this chapter with a brief review of the directions in which improvements should be sought.

The model should incorporate a more direct and disaggregated specification of the targets of health sector policy. The use of local authority expenditures as proxies for the corresponding activities prevents the examination of a number of questions. For example, midwifery expenditure is the product of the number of cases cared for and the average cost per case. It would be useful to study these two aspects separately. A detailed analysis of hospital use by diagnosis and patient type would provide valuable monitoring information about the allocation of hospital resources and a more relevant basis for prediction planning than the aggregate admission and mean stay variables. Incorporating the use of general practitioner services into the model would permit a better understanding of the way in which general practitioner availability affects the demands for hospital and local authority care. Finally, it may be possible to relate selected measures of population health to the care being received.

Improvements should be made in the way in which a number of variables are measured. Alternative measures of the age and social class structure of the population should be investigated. More important, the measures of general practitioner availability and local bed supply should be strengthened. For studying the location decisions of general practitioners, the number of doctors living in an area may be more appropriate than the proportion of patients on lists in a certain size range. More complex measures of the size distribution of general practitioner lists might also be appropriate for particular studies of the effects of general practitioner availability. The importance of obtaining more accurate measures of bed supply is underlined by the suspected bias in our estimates of the admission and mean stay equations. A detailed analysis of the Hospital In-Patient Enquiry data would more clearly identify the catchment areas appropriate to persons living in each county.

Giving equal weight to each observation implicitly assumes homoscedastic errors. Although this is reasonable for equations describing the collective actions of county authorities, it is less plausible for equations that relate to individuals' actions (such as hospital admission and mean stay). When the dependent variable is a mean value or rate obtained by averaging individual behaviour, the error variance is likely to decrease with the number of persons in the county. If a linear rather than logarithmic specification of the model had been used, the error variance could be assumed inversely proportional to population size[13]. Because a multiplicative equation specified in terms of arithmetic means cannot be treated as an aggregation of microrelations, no precise theory of the error properties can be developed in our current model. If we do assume that the error in such an equation does have a variance which is inversely proportional to the population and is small relative to its mean of 1, then it is appropriate to weight the logarithmic transformation of each observation in proportion to the square root of the population[14]. An alternative method of estimating the error variance for each observation would be to relate the estimated error in a set of unweighted equations to the predetermined variables of the model (including population); this method is discussed in Appendix 3A.

In its current form the model is inadequately dynamic for use in prediction. There are three separate problems. First, time itself must be brought explicitly into the model. Changing medical technology and tastes cause the demand for hospital, local authority, and general practitioner services to alter with time. Second, because the level of general practitioner availability in an area depends upon the total number of doctors in the country, the national general practitioner supply must also enter as a variable. This can only be done if observations at several different points in time are used. Third, an elasticity estimated from cross-section data describes the effect of differences in a variable rather than the response to changes in that variable. The cross-section elasticities are therefore not necessarily relevant to prediction. The best solution to these problems would be to use several sets of cross-section observations. This would allow the specific inclusion of time and the national supply of doctors. When the explanatory variables show sufficient intracounty variance through time, the combined data could be used to estimate reactions to change rather than to intercounty differences. This would not always be possible; the bed supply, for example,

---

[13] This is true even when the individual observations that enter into each county average are not independent if the average intracounty correlation tends to zero as population size increases.

[14] The logarithm of the error (u) has the same variance as the error itself (U) if that variance can be assumed small because $\mathscr{E}(u) = 1$.

changes too little. For such variables, "extraneous" cross-section estimates would have to be used.[15] Although the mixing of cross-section and time-series information in the estimation of a complete system poses a number of difficult problems, it does offer a flexibility and a range of information that is not possible with either a single cross-section or an aggregate time-series.

If the specification and estimation of the model can be improved in these ways, it should become a more valuable tool for health service research and policy formation.

---

[15] Some preliminary studies of the United States health sector indicate that the elasticities of hospital use with respect to interstate bed supply differences are very similar to those obtained when decade changes in bed use are related to changes in supply over the same period. This provides some reassuring evidence of the possibility of using cross-section estimates for prediction in this field.

Ordinary least squares estimates of structural and reduced form coefficients

Ordinary least squares estimates of structural equation parameters are biased and inconsistent because the error in the equation is not uncorrelated with each of the explanatory variables. Although the asymptotic properties of the two-stage least squares estimates presented in the text of this chapter are superior to those of ordinary least squares estimates, the relative merits of the two methods in small samples is less certain. But the size of the current sample and the accumulated small sample simulation evidence indicate that the two-stage least squares estimates would be preferable. However, for comparison we present the ordinary least squares estimates. It is clear that a number of coefficients, particularly those relating to endogenous variables, differ substantially from the corresponding consistent estimates.

$$
\begin{aligned}
\text{MIDW} = {} & 3.7233 \, \text{FEM} + 0.6870 \, \text{SOC} + 1.5952 \, \text{CHI} \\
& (2.0670) \qquad (0.2592) \qquad (0.7230) \\
& -0.0055 \, \text{DEN} - 0.5263 \, \text{RAV} - 0.0206 \, \text{BU} \\
& (0.0578) \qquad (0.2220) \qquad (0.1757) \\
& -0.1108 \, \text{GPA} + 0.2047 \, \text{LAE}_{-6} + 4.7372 \\
& (0.1753) \qquad (0.1892)
\end{aligned}
$$

(9A-1)

$$
\begin{aligned}
\text{HONU} = {} & 0.2161 \, \text{AGE} - 0.2657 \, \text{SOC} - 0.0528 \, \text{DEN} \\
& (0.1966) \qquad (0.1754) \qquad (0.0478) \\
& +0.0208 \, \text{RAV} - 0.1707 \, \text{BU} + 0.3979 \, \text{GPA} \\
& (0.1809) \qquad (0.1305) \qquad (0.1194) \\
& +0.6018 \, \text{LAE}_{-6} + 0.8235 \\
& (0.1394)
\end{aligned}
$$

(9A-2)

$$\text{DOMC} = -0.1557\,\text{AGE} - 0.2708\,\text{SOC} - 0.0316\,\text{DEN}$$
$$\phantom{\text{DOMC} =} (0.1757) \qquad (0.1567) \qquad (0.0427)$$

$$+0.0744\,\text{RAV} + 0.0761\,\text{BU}$$
$$(0.1617) \qquad (0.1166)$$

$$+0.1650\,\text{GPA} + 0.5709\,\text{LAE}_{-6} + 1.9153 \qquad \text{(9A-3)}$$
$$(0.1067) \qquad (0.1246)$$

$$\text{HEVI} = 2.7846\,\text{FEM} + 0.2326\,\text{CHI} + 0.2646\,\text{SOC}$$
$$\phantom{\text{HEVI} =} (2.6089) \qquad (0.9125) \qquad (0.3272)$$

$$-0.1501\,\text{DEN} + 0.0208\,\text{RAV} - 0.1338\,\text{GPA}$$
$$(0.0729) \qquad (0.2803) \qquad (0.2212)$$

$$+0.3263\,\text{BU} + 0.6916\,\text{LAHE} + 2.2400 \qquad \text{(9A-4)}$$
$$(0.2218) \qquad (0.2388)$$

$$\text{GPA} = -0.1062\,\text{AGE} - 1.0522\,\text{CHI} + 0.2189\,\text{SOC}$$
$$\phantom{\text{GPA} =} (0.1669) \qquad (0.4649) \qquad (0.1414)$$

$$-0.0460\,\text{DEN} - 0.0691\,\text{BAC} + 0.5515\,\text{BAA}$$
$$(0.0305) \qquad (0.0877) \qquad (0.2658)$$

$$+0.0221\,\text{LAHE} + 0.6857\,\text{GPA}_{-6} - 2.6707 \qquad \text{(9A-5)}$$
$$(0.0362) \qquad (0.1065)$$

$$\text{ADM} = 0.1784\,\text{BAC} + 0.4208\,\text{BAA} - 0.2042\,\text{AGE}$$
$$\phantom{\text{ADM} =} (0.0621) \qquad (0.1870) \qquad (0.1361)$$

$$+0.0078\,\text{DEN} + 0.0232\,\text{GPA}$$
$$(0.0236) \qquad (0.0677)$$

$$+0.0336\,\text{LAHE} + 0.0138\,\text{MS} - 6.3399 \qquad \text{(9A-6)}$$
$$(0.0261) \qquad (0.0940)$$

$$\text{MS} = 0.1762\,\text{BAC} + 0.1078\,\text{BAA}$$
$$\phantom{\text{MS} =} (0.0938) \qquad (0.2710)$$

$$+0.4199\,\text{AGE} - 2.2508\,\text{FEM} + 0.0396\,\text{DEN}$$
$$(0.1909) \qquad (1.4660) \qquad (0.0315)$$

$$-0.0939\,\text{INC} + 0.0405\,\text{LAHE}$$
$$(0.0498) \qquad (0.0372)$$

$$+0.1232\,\text{ADM} + 1.2919 \qquad \text{(9A-7)}$$
$$(0.2077)$$

Instead of estimating the structural parameters of the model and then calculating the reduced form by the method discussed in the footnote on page 281, reduced form coefficients could be estimated directly by the application of ordinary least squares to the reduced form equations. Such a method is deficient in two ways. The resulting estimates (presented in table 9A-1) do not fully incorporate our prior information about the basic structure of the model. As a result, it is impossible to estimate alternative reduced form equations corresponding to different structural relations.

TABLE 9A-1

Direct least squares estimates of reduced form coefficients

	MIDW	HEVI	HONU
RAV	−0.4915	0.0511	0.1192
	(0.2200)	(0.3025)	(0.1752)
DEN	−0.0191	−0.1630	−0.1723
	(0.0712)	(0.0979)	(0.0567)
CHI	0.9825	0.0551	−1.4256
	(0.8094)	(1.1127)	(0.6445)
AGE	−0.0702	−0.5349	−0.5072
	(0.4064)	(0.5587)	(0.3236)
SOC	0.6049	0.4157	0.0802
	(0.2609)	(0.3587)	(0.2077)
INC	−0.2208	−0.0204	0.0914
	(0.0828)	(0.1138)	(0.0659)
FEM	3.6967	4.7482	4.6814
	(2.4558)	(3.3763)	(1.9555)
BAA	−0.3933	0.6353	0.1076
	(0.4263)	(0.5860)	(0.3394)
BAC	−0.1172	0.1013	−0.1689
	(0.1433)	(0.1970)	(0.1141)
LAE_{-6}	0.3023	0.5681	0.4936
	(0.1941)	(0.2668)	(0.1545)
GPA_{-6}	−0.1522	0.0702	0.1312
	(0.1778)	(0.2445)	(0.1416)
Const	2.5302	−0.7660	1.6423

	DOMC	GPA
RAV	0.0588	−0.0880
	(0.1491)	(0.1341)
DEN	−0.0476	−0.0621
	(0.0483)	(0.0434)

TABLE 9A-1 (continued)

	DOMC	GPA
CHI	−0.1052	−1.2330
	(0.5485)	(0.4933)
AGE	−0.3033	−0.3653
	(0.2754)	(0.2477)
SOC	−0.0833	0.3205
	(0.1768)	(0.1590)
INC	0.0291	−0.0245
	(0.0561)	(0.0504)
FEM	1.3102	2.6411
	(1.6644)	(1.4967)
BAA	0.8105	0.5508
	(0.2889)	(0.2598)
BAC	−0.1496	−0.1030
	(0.0971)	(0.0873)
LAE_{-6}	0.5009	−0.0084
	(0.1315)	(0.1183)
GPA_{-6}	0.0996	0.7021
	(0.1205)	(0.1084)
Const	1.2208	−2.2955

	ADM	MS
RAV	−0.0018	−0.4801
	(0.0822)	(0.1236)
DEN	0.0337	0.1425
	(0.0266)	(0.0400)
CHI	0.6950	0.3933
	(0.3024)	(0.4546)
AGE	−0.2084	0.5992
	(0.1518)	(0.2282)
SOC	0.0490	0.0031
	(0.0975)	(0.1465)
INC	0.0601	−0.0587
	(0.0309)	(0.0465)
FEM	1.9874	−1.5781
	(0.9176)	(1.3793)
BAA	0.2857	0.1462
	(0.1593)	(0.2394)
BAC	0.1915	0.1609
	(0.0535)	(0.0805)

Table 9A-1 (continued)

	ADM	MS
LAE_{-6}	0.1430	−0.0254
	(0.0725)	(0.1090)
GPA_{-6}	0.2130	0.1443
	(0.0664)	(0.0999)
Const	−5.4374	1.5369

SYMBOLS IN CHAPTER 9

ADM   hospital admission rate

AGE   proportion of population aged 75+

BAA   beds available in the area

BAC   beds available in the county

BU   beds used

CHI   proportion of population aged less than 15

DEN   density of population

DOMC   local authority domiciliary care expenditure

FEM   proportion of population female

GPA   general practitioner availability

HEVI   local authority health visiting expenditure

HONU   local authority home nursing expenditure

INC   average per capita income

LAE   local authority expenditure on all health activities

LAHE   local authority expenditure on DOMC, MIDW, HEVI and HONU

MIDW   local authority midwifery expenditure

MS   mean stay per hospital admission

RAV   ratable value of property in local authority area

SOC   proportion of population in lowest social class group

CHAPTER 10

SUMMARY

This chapter presents a survey of the empirical results and policy suggestions contained in the preceding chapters. The treatment is completely non-technical. There is no discussion of the links with economic theory or the problems of econometric method.

The study was divided into two parts. Part One, consisting of chapters 2 through 6, considered the problems of the acute hospital as a producing unit. The second part, chapters 7 through 9, dealt with planning the supply and use of health care resources at a generally more aggregate level.

Chapter 2 discussed the measurement of cost and productivity in acute hospitals. Hospital unit costs vary substantially; there has been no reduction in this variation during the years since the hospital costing scheme was introduced. A large proportion of this variation reflects differences among hospitals in the speciality composition of cases. Useful measures of cost and productivity must therefore take casemix into account.

A theoretical framework for "costliness" comparison was presented and a statistical estimation procedure described. The costliness measure is an index number expressing the actual cost per case in a hospital as a percentage of the cost per case that would be expected for that hospital if its cost per case in each speciality were equal to the national average for that type of case. A productivity index was also proposed: this is the ratio of the actual output of the hospital (a weighted sum of the number of cases treated) to the output of that hospital that would be expected on the basis of the quantities of inputs (beds, doctors, nurses, etc.) that it used. A hospital's costliness reflects not only its productivity but also the appropriateness of the way in which it divides its budget among doctors, nursing staff, etc.; this is represented by the measure of "input efficiency".

These three measures of hospital performance were estimated for the 177 large (i.e., with expenditure exceeding £ 50 000 per year), acute, non-teaching hospitals for the fiscal year 1960–61. The results indicate the importance of allowing for casemix differences when considering hospital costs. There is substantial divergence between the costliness values and corresponding unadjusted measures of relative cost. Hospitals with low relative cost per case tend to have costliness values that exceed their relative cost and vice versa. Costliness variation is due primarily to differences in "productivity", i.e., to differences in the efficiency with which hospitals use the inputs that they have rather than in the efficiency with which they divide their budgets among alternative inputs.

The costliness value should be useful as a summary measure of a hospital's performance, although it should not be interpreted uncritically as a measure of the efficiency of the hospital's management. The productivity and input efficiency values should help to identify the reasons for high or low costliness in individual hospitals. The finding that about thirty per cent of interhospital variation in cost per case can be explained by casemix differences indicates both the importance of taking casemix into account and the substantial room for improving hospital performance.

Chapter 3 investigated the ways in which hospital size affects unit costs. Large hospitals provide opportunities for economies of scale, particularly in the operation of centralized housekeeping activities. But larger size may also increase costs because of the greater difficulties of management and of maintaining staff efficiency.

The empirical studies reported in chapter 3 relate to the 177 large, acute, non-teaching hospitals, ranging in size from 72 beds to 1 064 beds with an average of 303. The evidence shows that *on balance* size has little effect on cost per case. There is some indication that the minimum cost occurs at about the current average size, but an increase to 1 000 beds raises costs by less than ten per cent. The analysis presented underlines the importance of taking casemix into account when studying the effect of size; because larger hospitals treat more expensive cases, a failure to allow for casemix would produce spurious estimates indicating that cost per case rises by nearly thirty per cent between 100 and 1 000 bed hospitals.

The relation between average cost per case and hospital size reflects a balance of the effects of scale on duration of stay per case and on cost per patient day. Larger hospitals have lower "case-flow rates", i.e., treat fewer cases per bed-year. If it were not for this lower intensity of hospital plant use, larger hospitals would have lower costs per case; the minimum average cost hospital would have some 900 beds and case costs twelve per cent below those of the average size hospital. Studies for individual input categories showed that the pure labour component – ward staff costs – have the greatest diseconomies of scale while direct costs and other indirect costs generally enjoy increasing returns to scale when adjustment is made for capacity utilization.

These results indicate that the medium size hospital (300 to 500 beds) is currently at least as efficient at providing general inpatient care as are larger hospitals. But if the case-flow rates of larger hospitals could be raised to that of the average size hospital, some substantial savings would result. In addition to lowering operating costs, this would free beds to treat more cases and thus reduce capital costs.

Chapter 4 developed a number of models of the hospital as a producing unit and investigated their implications. Too little is known about the behavioural characteristics of hospitals for us to be certain that any particular model is best; fortunately, all of the approaches supported the same general conclusions.

First, the estimated production models indicated slight but nonsignificant decreasing returns to scale. This also agrees with the results of chapter 3, which approached the problem in terms of the relation between size and unit cost. Second, the productivity index values discussed in chapter 2 were found to be influenced little by the particular production model selected.

The more important implications of the estimates obtained in this chapter relate to the optimum allocation of hospital budgets between nursing staff, medical staff, etc. and to the optimum redistribution of doctors among the hospitals. Expenditure on nursing staff and medical staff per bed year varies substantially among the hospitals. But within the observed range, differences in the availability of nursing staff have no effect on hospital output, i.e., on the number of cases treated with allowance for differences in casemix. In contrast, increased expenditure on medical staff raises output substantially. More generally, to increase the number of cases treated, hospitals should spend more on doctors, drugs and dressings and less on nursing staff, catering, and other housekeeping activities. Instead of building new hospitals in order to treat more patients, it would be more efficient to increase the number of doctors, even if this requires paying higher salaries. Moreover, until the number of doctors in hospital is substantially increased, the value of the doctors' time should be recognized to be much more than is implied by their hourly rates of pay.

The larger the hospital, the more substantial is the increase in output caused by an increase in medical staff. The reason for this is not clear; it may be due to the currently lower doctor-bed ratios in larger hospitals. A reallocation of medical staff to larger hospitals, and perhaps to those smaller hospitals with below average doctor-bed ratios, should increase the total output of the hospital system.

Chapter 5 examined the implications and causes of the substantial interhospital variation in capacity utilization. A principal finding was that more intensive utilization (i.e., a higher case-flow rate and shorter average duration of stay) increases cost per patient week but decreases cost per case. Starting from the average case-flow rate (23 cases per bed per year), a ten per cent increase in the case-flow rate would yield an eight per cent decrease in the average cost per case. Although savings in cost per case would occur in all input categories, the relative cost decreases are greater for some inputs (especially nursing and domestic staff) than for others (doctors, drugs and dressings).

Estimates of the cost of treating an additional case (i.e., the marginal cost or avoidable cost) also indicate that it is probably desirable to increase the intensity with which hospital beds are used. The marginal cost of treating an additional case with a fixed supply of beds is substantially less than the average cost per case. If the percentage occupancy remains constant and average stay is further reduced, the marginal cost is cut in half. Marginal costs for different case types and input categories, presented in chapter 5, are all substantially below the corresponding average costs. Marginal nursing staff costs are extremely low in relation to the corresponding average while marginal medical staff costs are relatively high; this confirms the results of chapter 4 that medical staff directly produces more cases while nursing staff is a form of general overhead.

An examination of several factors that affect use intensity concluded the chapter. First, larger hospitals and larger departments use capacity less intensively. Second, greater waiting-list pressure increases intensity of use, particularly on a departmental basis. Although waiting-list lengths are poor measures of the numbers of untreated cases in the community (as discussed in chapter 7), doctors appear to respond to longer waiting lists by decreasing average stay per case. This suggests that more intense utilization of available beds could be achieved without any change in inputs by increasing the medical staffs' awareness that current durations of stay are preventing other cases from obtaining admission. Third, greater availability of medical staff was found to increase case-flow rates substantially. Finally, the analysis of a simple behavioural model indicated that hospitals may react to tight budgets by increasing durations of stay and thus decreasing the number of cases treated. These last two findings indicate that an increase in available funds and in the size of the medical staff would increase the intensity with which hospital capacity is used.

Chapter 6 presented an experimental application of linear programming to the selection of an optimal mix of cases for treatment. The problem studied in this way could be summarized as: how many cases in each of nine specialty groups should a hospital treat if (1) each case type has required inputs of medical staff, nursing staff, bed days and other expenditure; (2) the hospital has fixed limited numbers of doctors (or medical staff budget), nurses and beds, and a fixed limited overall budget; (3) certain minimum numbers of cases have to be treated in each speciality; (4) there is a maximum number of cases that can be treated in each speciality; and (5) between these minimum and maximum limits the relative value of each case type is constant. The method of linear programming presents a unique best answer to this question. Several difficulties which arise in trying to apply linear programming in this context were treated in detail and sample calculations were presented. A number of further recommendations for improving this use of linear programming were also made.

Chapter 7 began the second part of this book with a discussion of the supply and use of hospital inpatient care. After a critical review of currently used and proposed methods of supply planning, the chapter showed the inadequacy of any planning method that seeks to provide facilities to meet observed or forecast "demand". All such "manifest demand" methods ignore the effect of available bed supply on the demand for hospital admission and on the average duration of stay per case. This emerged from an analysis of the substantial interregional variation in hospital bed availability and use. The demand for bed days rises proportionately with the exogenous supply; there is no indication of a level of supply at which demand would be satiated. Although the demand for admissions rises less than proportionately, the data again suggests no ceiling on demand.

Instead of trying to match the supply of hospital beds to some estimate of demand, hospital building policy should be part of a general programme for the provision of all types of health care facilities and personnel. Although central government authorities have direct influence on only some health activities, it is important that policy-makers recognize that their decisions have indirect effects on local availabilities of other health services. Chapter 7 suggested a decision framework in which the government determines the levels of provision of directly controlled facilities in order to maximize a "social welfare function" (defined in terms of measures of community health and the costs incurred by the government and by others) subject to the constraints imposed by the relations between government provision, total availabilities, costs, utilization, and health. A less ambitious but more feasible approach was then described: policy formation assisted by an econometric model that provides conditional predictions of the effects of different government policies on availability and utilization patterns.

As a preliminary to the development of such a model (in chapter 9), chapter 7 examined the partial effects of regional differences in the availability of hospital beds on the way in which they are used. The most basic allocation of beds is between the number of cases treated and the mean duration of stay per case. It was surprising, and somewhat discomforting, to find that the number of cases treated is about fifty per cent more responsive to bed scarcity than is the mean stay. Moreover, although one would probably have expected and wanted to see that bed use, number of cases and in particular mean stay were more responsive among older patients than younger ones, the reverse seems to be true. The responsiveness values of admission rates and mean stays were also calculated for a large number of individual diagnostic categories; although many of these agreed with expectations, a substantial number seemed unsatisfactorily high or low. A number of reasons for the undesirably high responsiveness of the number of cases treated were considered. One recommendation which emerged was to allocate relatively larger budgets and more medical staff to hospitals in regions where beds are relatively more scarce, thus permitting them to increase the intensity of capacity utilization by decreasing mean duration of stay. The results of the chapter as a whole emphasize the importance of "monitoring information" in a system that has no built-in mechanism to assure the optimum allocation of available resources.

Chapter 8 examined the way in which the health care system allocates maternity care resources among individual patients and suggested an improved method. A preliminary aggregate study similar to that of chapter 7 showed that obstetrics admissions are highly responsive to bed supply while the mean stay of these cases is almost unaffected. Microanalytic monitoring information about factors affecting hospital admission and duration of stay was then developed. A study of more than 3 000 cases in the Oxford area showed that social class and availability factors, as well as medical conditions, are important determinants of hospital admission. The analysis indicated that high risk cases are generally more likely to be hospitalized but also uncovered a number of inappropriate characteristics of maternity service admissions. A similar analysis of factors affecting duration of stay indicated that the most important single factor influencing any woman's expected stay is the standard practice of the obstetrician in charge of her case. Examining the ways that doctors differ in duration of stay supports the hypothesis that the low responsiveness of mean stay to bed availability reflects a traditional approach to maternity care and a strong aversion to risk. The effects of age, number of previous children, social class, and other patient characteristics, although relatively small, are often contrary to the generally accepted standards of good maternity care.

An awareness of this type of information could in itself lead doctors to decisions which would improve the allocation of maternity care resources. A more direct approach was suggested in the final section of chapter 8. Statistically estimated conditional risk prediction models could provide the information required to assign each woman to one of several possible care groups in the way which minimized the expected perinatal mortality rate of all the women at risk. If this assignment problem is formulated as a linear programming calculation, the "dual shadow prices" would aid in the longer-term planning of the supply of different types of maternity services. The chapter discussed the linear programming specification and the method of calculating conditional risk prediction models. Although empirical results for this method are not yet available, examples were given of a cruder approach that permits estimating the approximate risk of each case in an unconditional way. These estimates are based on the analysis of a national sample of nearly 17 000 births and more than 7 000 perinatal deaths.

Chapter 9 presented a simple nine equation aggregate model of the interrelationships between hospital, local authority and general practitioner services. The effects on these health sector activities of the demographic and social characteristics of the population were also explored. The estimation used data for the sixty geographic counties of England and Wales. The purpose of the model is to provide both a better understanding of the operation of the health care sector and a framework for conditional prediction planning of government policy. It would require too much space to summarize the factors found to influence each variable; this review will therefore be limited to those findings of broader policy relevance.

In contrast to the common assumption that different types of health service activities are all potential substitutes for each other, the estimated model indicates important complementarities. Although home nursing is clearly a substitute for hospital care, greater local availability of general practitioner services increases the use of home nursing services. Expenditure on non-professional domiciliary care is also higher in areas where there are more general practitioners. It was also found that domiciliary services were not functioning properly as a supplement to hospital facilities and an aid to older persons and those of lower social class. Health visiting, unlike other local authority services, is not a substitute for hospital inpatient care; moreover, it does not require general practitioners' services as a cooperating input.

Two of the important determinants of local general practitioner availability are the supply of hospital beds in the vicinity and the level of local authority expenditure. These findings indicate that general practitioners are not going into areas in which their services could substitute for less amply available hospital and local authority care. Even if the negative effect of bed availability on local authority provision is taken into account, the net result is a tendency for areas to be either well provided with both home and hospital care or badly provided with both.

The findings about hospital admission and mean stay supported the results of chapter 7. Hospital admissions were again more responsive to bed supply than was mean stay. Admissions per bed also increased in areas with more general practitioners and higher local authority spending.

The individual behavioural relations of the model were used to solve for conditional prediction planning equations (the model's "reduced form") under alternative assumptions about changes in the extent of government policy. For example, if the government also controlled the geographic distribution of general practitioners, an increase in bed availability in one area would no longer have the indirect effect of increasing the provision of local authority services there (in response to the demands of general practitioners attracted to the area by the more ample bed supply).

The chapter ended with suggestions for improving the model as a tool for health sector policy formation.

Throughout this study, attention has focussed on identifying and estimating economic information that could improve the efficiency of the British National Health Service. A recurrent theme has been that the health service, like many other public sector activities, combines decentralized decision-making with the absence of a price mechanism. As a result, the system lacks automatic regulators to assure technical efficiency, the appropriate input combinations, and the optimal mix and allocation of outputs. The individual chapters developed the application of economic analysis and econometric methods to the problems of achieving these goals. I hope that the work as a whole indicates an important role for such analysis in the health sector and, more generally, in policy formation for decentralized public sector activities.

BIBLIOGRAPHY

This bibliography is primarily a list of works cited in the text. A few additional items dealing with either the National Health Service or econometric methods are also included. Specifically excluded are all periodical government publications (unless explicitly cited). Health service policy is frequently discussed in medical profession periodicals and the national press; no such material is listed below.

All items except government Command papers are listed together in alphabetical order by first author. Several works by the same author are listed chronologically; jointly authored works follow after the full list of an author's own work. Command papers are listed at the end by date of original publication.

Abel-Smith, B. (1964). *The Hospitals: 1800–1948*, London: Heinemann.
Abel-Smith, B. and Titmus, R. M. (1956). *The Cost of the National Health Service in England and Wales*, Cambridge: Cambridge University Press.
Acheson, E. D., (1964). "The Oxford Record Linkage Study", *British Journal of Preventive and Social Medicine*, p. 8.
Acheson, E. D. and Feldstein, M. S. (1964). "Duration of Stay in Hospital for Normal Maternity Care", *British Medical Journal*, p. 95.
Acton Society Trust (1953). *Size and Morale*, London: The Acton Society Trust.
Acton Society Trust (1955). *Background and Blueprint*, vol. 1 of *Hospitals and the State*, London: The Acton Society Trust.
Acton Society Trust (1956). *The Impact of Change*, vol. 2 of *Hospitals and the State*, London: The Acton Society Trust.
Acton Society Trust (1957a). *Groups, Regions and Committees*, I, vol. 3 of *Hospitals and the State*, London: The Acton Society Trust.
Acton Society Trust (1957b). *Groups, Regions and Committees*, II, vol. 4 of *Hospitals and the State*, London: The Acton Society Trust.
Acton Society Trust (1958). *The Central Control of the Service*, vol. 5 of *Hospitals and the State*, London: The Acton Society Trust.
Acton Society Trust (1959): *Creative Leadership in a State Service*, vol. 6 of *Hospitals and the State*, London: The Acton Society Trust.
Acton Society Trust (1962). *Buying Better Health*, London: The Acton Society Trust.

Airth A. D. and Newell, D. J. (1962). *The Demand for Hospital Beds: Results of an Enquiry on Tees-side*, Newcastle-upon-Tyne: King's College.

American Hospital Association (1957). *Cost Finding for Hospitals*, Chicago: American Hospital Association.

Anderson, O. W. and Feldman, J. J. (1956). *Family Medical Costs and Voluntary Health Insurance: A Nationwide Survey*, New York: McGraw-Hill Book Company.

Anderson, O. W., Colette, P. and Feldman, J. J. (1963). *Changes in Family Medical Care Expenditures and Voluntary Health Insurance: A Five-Year Resurvey*, Cambridge: Harvard University Press.

Andrews, P. W. S. (1949). *Manufacturing Business*, London: Macmillan.

Arrow, K. J. (1963). "Uncertainty and the Welfare Economics of Medical Care", *American Economic Review*, p. 941.

Arrow, K. J. *et al.* (1961). "Capital-Labor Substitution and Economic Efficiency", *Review of Economics and Statistics*, p. 225.

Axelrod, S. J. (ed.) (1964). *The Economics of Health and Medical Care*. Ann Arbor, Michigan: Michigan University of Michigan.

Bailey, N. T. J. (1954). "Queuing for Medical Care", *Applied Statistics*, p. 137.

Bailey, N. T. J. (1956). "Statistics in Hospital Planning and Design", *Applied Statistics*, p. 146.

Bailey, N. T. J. (1957). "Operational Research in Hospital Planning and Design", *Operational Research Quarterly*, p. 149.

Bailey, N. T. J. (1960). *A Survey of the Surgical Needs of the United Oxford Hospitals*, London: The Nuffield Foundation.

Bailey, N. T. J. (1962). "Calculating the Scale of Inpatient Accommodation" in J. O. F. Davies, *et al.*, *Toward a Measure of Medical Care*, London: Oxford University Press.

Beer, S. H. (1957). *Treasury Control: The Coordination of Financial and Economic Policy in Great Britain*, Oxford: Clarendon Press.

Benjamin, B. and Perkins, T. A. (1961). "The Measurement of Bed Use and Demand" *The Hospital*, p. 31.

Blumberg, M. (1961). "DPF Concept Helps Determine Bed Needs", *Modern Hospital*, p. 75.

Borts, G. H. (1952). "Production Relations in the Railway Industry", *Econometrica*, p. 71.

Borts, G. H. (1960). "The Estimation of Rail Cost Functions", *Econometrica*, p. 108.

British Medical Association (1962). *The Hospital Gazetteer*, 1962, London: British Medical Association.

Brittain, Sir H. (1959). *The British Budgetary System*, London: George Allen and Unwin.

Brotherston, J. H. F. (1963a). "The Use of the Hospital: Review of Research in the United Kingdom", *Medical Care*, p. 142.

Brotherston, J. H. F. (1963b). "The Use of the Hospital: Review of Research in the United Kingdom", *Medical Care*, p. 225.

Buchanan, J. M. (1965). *The Inconsistencies of the National Health Service*, London: Institute of Economic Affairs.

Butler, N. R. and Bonham, D. G. (1963). *Perinatal Mortality: the First Report of the 1958 British Perinatal Mortality Survey*. Edinburgh: E. and S. Livingstone.

Cartwright, A. (1964). *Human Relations and Hospital Care*, London: Routledge and Kegan Paul.

Central Health Services Council (1952). *Report on Cooperation between Hospital, Loca Authority, and General Practitioner Services*, London: H.M.S.O.

Central Health Services Council (1954). *Report of the Committee on the Internal Administration of Hospitals*, London: H.M.S.O.

Central Office of Information (1964). *Health Services in Britain* (Reference Pamphlet 20), London: H.M.S.O.

Chisholm, M. (1959). "Economies of Scale in Road Goods Transport: Off-farm Milk Collection in England and Wales", *Oxford Economic Papers*, p. 282.

Chisholm, M. (1961). "Economies of Scale in Road Goods Transport: A Reply", *Oxford Economic Papers*, p. 119.

Clark, J. M. (1923). *Studies in the Economics of Overhead Costs*, Chicago: University of Chicago Press.

Cowan, P. (1963). "The Size of Hospitals", *Medical Care*, p. 1.

Davies, J. O. F. *et al.* (1962). *Towards a Measure of Medical Care: Operational Research in the Health Services*, London: Oxford University Press.

Dean, J. (1941). *Statistical Cost Functions of a Hosiery Mill*, Chicago: Chicago University Press.

Dean, J. (1951). *Managerial Economics*, New York: Prentice Hall.

Dean, J. and James, R. W. (1942). *The Long Run Behavior of Costs in a Chain of Shoe Stores*, Chicago: Chicago University Press.

Deeble, J. S. (1965). "An Economic Analysis of Hospital Costs", *Medical Care*, p. 138.

Dhrymes, P. (1962). "On Deriving Unbiased Estimators for the Parameters of the Cobb-Douglas Production Function", *Econometrica*, p. 287.

Dhrymes, P. J. and Kurz, M. (1964). "Technology and Scale in Electricity Generation", *Econometrica*, p. 297.

Douglas, J. W. B. *et al.* (1948). *Maternity In Great Britain*, London: Oxford University Press.

Durbin, R. L. and Antelman, G. (1964). "A Study of the Effects of Selected Variables on Hospital Utilization", *Hospital Management*, (August 1964), p. 57.

Eckstein, H. (1958). *The English Health Service*, Cambridge, Mass: Harvard University Press.

Eckstein, H. (1960). *Pressure Group Politics: The Case of the B.M.A.*, London: George Allen and Unwin.

Farndale, J. (ed.) (1964). *Trends in the National Health Service*, Oxford: Pergamon Press.

Farrell, M. J. (1957). "The Measurement of Productive Efficiency", *Journal of the Royal Statistical Society*, Series A, p. 253.

Fein, R. (1958). *The Economics of Mental Illness*, New York: Basic Books.

Feldstein, M. S. (1963a). "Economic Analysis, Operational Research, and the National Health Service", *Oxford Economic Papers*, p. 19.

Feldstein, M. S. (1963b). "Operational Research and Efficiency in the Health Service", *The Lancet*, p. 491.

Feldstein, M. S. (1963c). "Developments in Health Service Administration and Financial Control", *Medical Care*, p. 171.

Feldstein, M. S. (1963d). Review of B. A. Weisbrod, "Economics of Public Health", *Economic Journal*, p. 129.

Feldstein, M. S. (1964a). "Hospital Planning and the Demand for Care", *Bulletin of the*

307

Oxford University Institute of Economics and Statistics, p. 361.

Feldstein, M. S. (1964b). "Effects of Differences in Hospital Bed Scarcity on Type of Use", *British Medical Journal*, p. 561.

Feldstein, M. S. (1965a). "Studying Hospital Costliness", *Hospital Service Finance*, p. 3.

Feldstein, M. S. (1965b). "Improving the Use of Hospital Maternity Beds", *Operational Research Quarterly*, p. 65.

Feldstein, M. S. (1965c). "Hospital Bed Scarcity: An Analysis of the Effects of Inter-regional Differences", *Economica*, p. 393 f.

Feldstein, M. S. (1965d). "Hospital Cost Variation and Casemix Differences", *Medical Care*, p. 95 ff.

Feldstein, M. S. (1965e). "A Method of Evaluating Perinatal Mortality Risk", *British Journal of Preventive and Social Medicine*, p. 135.

Feldstein, M. S. (1966). "A Binary Variable Multiple Regression Method of Analyzing Factors Affecting Perinatal Mortality and Other Outcomes of Pregnancy", *Journal of Royal Statistical Society*, Series A, p. 61.

Feldstein, M. S. (1968). "Alternative Methods of Estimating a CES Production Function for Britain". *Economica*, (forthcoming).

Feldstein, M. S. (forthcoming). "An Aggregate Policy Model of the Health Care Sector".

Feldstein, M. S. and Butler, N. R. (1965). "Analysis of Factors Affecting Perinatal Mortality", *British Journal of Preventive and Social Medicine*, p. 128.

Feldstein, P. J. (1961). *An Empirical Investigation of the Marginal Cost of Hospital Services*, Chicago: University of Chicago Graduate Program in Hospital Adminis-tration.

Ferguson, A. E. (1950). "Empirical Determination of a Multidimensional Marginal Cost Function", *Econometrica*, p. 217.

Ferguson, T. and MacPhail, A. N. (1954). *Hospital and Community*, London: Oxford University Press.

Forsyth, G. and Logan, R. F. L. (1960). *The Demand for Medical Care: A Study of the Case-Load in the Barrow and Furness Group of Hospitals*, London: Oxford University Press.

Freeman, H. E., Levine, S. and Reeder, L. G. (1963). *Handbook of Medical Sociology*, Englewood Cliffs, New Jersey: Prentice-Hall.

Friedman, M. (1955). "Comment" on C. A. Smith, "Survey of the Empirical Evidence on Economies of Scale" in G. Stigler (ed.) *Business Concentration and Price Policy*, Princeton: Princeton University Press.

Fuchs, V. R. (1965). *Some Economic Aspects of Mortality in the United States* (preliminary draft), New York: National Bureau of Economic Research.

Gemmill, P. F. (1960). *Britain's Search for Health: The First Decade of the National Health Service*, Philadelphia: University of Pennsylvania Press.

General Register Office (1964a). *Census of England and Wales for* 1961. *Age, Marital Condition and General Tables.* London: H.M.S.O.

General Register Office (1964b). *Census of England and Wales for* 1961. *Housing Tables, Part III.* London: H.M.S.O.

Gillespie, R. P. (1954). *Partial Differentiation*, (2nd edit.), Edinburgh: Oliver and Boyd.

Goldberger, A. S. (1964). *Econometric Theory*, New York: John Wiley and Sons.

Goodman, N. R. (1963). *Alternatives to Hospital Care.* Strasbourg: Council of Europe.

Gribbin, T. K. (1963). "Production Costs in the Gas Industry", *Oxford Economic Papers*, p. 190.

Griliches, Z. (1957). "Specification Bias in Estimates of Production Functions", *Journal of Farm Economics*, p. 8.

Grundy, F. (1960). *Preventive Medicine and Public Health*, Luten: Leagrove Press.

Hadley, G. (1963). *Linear Programming*. Reading, Massachusetts: Addison-Wesley Publishing Company.

Hadley, G. (1964). *Non-Linear and Dynamic Programming*. Reading, Massachusetts: Addison-Wesley Publishing Company.

Hall, M. and Winsten, C. B. (1959). "The Ambiguous Notion of Efficiency", *Economic Journal*, p. 75.

Hall, P. (1952). *Social Services of Modern England*. London: Routledge and Kegan Paul.

Harris, S. E. (1964). *The Economics of American Medicine*, New York: Macmillan.

Hayes, J. H. (ed.) (1954). *Factors Affecting the Costs of Hospital Care*, New York: Blakiston.

Heady, J. A. and Heasman, M. A. (1959). *Social and Biological Factors in Infant Mortality*. London: H.M.S.O.

Hitch, C. J. and McKean, R. N. (1960). *The Economics of Defence in the Nuclear Age*, Cambridge: Harvard University Press.

Hoch, I. (1955). "Estimation of Production Function Parameters and Testing for Efficiency", *Econometrica*, p. 326.

Hoch, I. (1958). "Simultaneous Equation Bias in the Context of the Cobb-Douglas Production Function", *Econometrica*, p. 566.

Hoch, I. (1962). "Estimation of Production Function Parameters Combining Time-series and Cross-section Data", *Econometrica*, p. 34.

Hoch, I. (1963). "Reply to Kmenta and Joseph", *Econometrica*, p. 386.

Hoel, P. G. (1962). *Introduction to Mathematical Statistics*, (3rd edition). New York: John Wiley and Sons.

Holmes, J. M. (1964). *Obstetrics*, London: Bailliere, Tindall and Cox.

Institute of Municipal Treasurers and Accountants, and the Society of County Treasurers (1956). *Local Health Service Statistics*, 1954–55. London: Institute of Municipal Treasurers and Accountants and the Society of County Treasurers.

Institute of Municipal Treasurers and Accountants, and Society of County Treasurers (1962). *Local Health Service Statistics*, 1960–61. London: Institute of Municipal Treasurers and Accountants and the Society of County Treasurers.

Jaco, E. G. (ed.) (1958). *Patients, Physicians and Illness*, Glencoe, Illinois: The Free Press.

Jewkes, J. and Jewkes, S. (1961). *The Genesis of the British National Health Service*, Oxford: Basil Blackwell.

Jewkes, J. and Jewkes, S. (1963). *Value for Money in Medicine*, Oxford: Basil Blackwell.

Johnson, E. A. and Vivaldo, L. (1960). *A Method for the Qualitative Analysis of Hospital Performance*. Chicago: University of Chicago Graduate Program in Hospital Administration.

Johnston, J. (1952). "Statistical Cost Functions in Electricity Supply", *Oxford Economic Papers*, p. 68.

Johnston, J. (1953). "Cost-Output Variations in a Multiple Product Firm", *Manchester School*, p. 140.

Johnston, J. (1956). "Scale, Costs and Profitability in Road Passenger Transport", *Journal of Industrial Economics*, p. 207.

Johnston, J. (1958). "Statistical Cost Functions: A Reappraisal", *Review of Economics and Statistics*. p. 339.

Johnston, J. (1960). *Statistical Cost Functions.* New York: McGraw-Hill Book Company.

Johnston, J. (1963). *Econometric Methods*, New York: McGraw-Hill Book Company.

Johnstone, R. W. (1963). *A Text-Book of Midwifery*, (19th edition). London: Adam and Charles Black.

Jones, A. W. and Thomas F. K. (1938). *Report of the Hospital Survey for New York*, (vol. 3). New York: United Hospital Fund.

Kendall, M. G. (1957). *A Course in Multivariate Analysis.* London: Charles Griffin and Company.

Kendall, M. G. and Stuart, A. (1961). *The Advanced Theory of Statistics*, vol. I, (3-volume edition; 2nd edition). London: Charles Griffin and Company.

Kendall, M. G. and Stuart, A. (1961). *The Advanced Theory of Statistics*, vol. II, (3-volume edition). London: Charles Griffin and Company.

King Edward's Hospital Fund (1952). *Report on Costing Investigation for the Ministry of Health.* London: King Edward's Hospital Fund.

Klarman, H. E. (1965a). *The Economics of Health*, New York: Columbia University Press.

Klarman, H. E. (1965b). "Syphilis Control Programs" in R. Dorfman (ed.) *Measuring Benefits of Government Investments.* Washington, D.C.: The Brookings Institution.

Klein, L. R. (1953). *A Textbook of Econometrics.* Evanston: Row, Peterson, and Company.

Kmenta, J. (1964). "Some properties of alternative estimates of the Cobb-Douglas Production Function". *Econometrica*, p. 183.

Kmenta, J. and Joseph, M. E. (1963). "A Monte Carlo Study of Alternative Estimates of the Cobb-Douglas Production Function", *Econometrica*, p. 363.

Lees, D. S. (1960), "The Economics of Health Services", *Lloyds Bank Review*, (April, 1960), p. 26.

Lees, D. S. (1961). *Health through Choice*, London: Institute of Economics Affairs.

Leser, C. E. V. (1955). "Production Functions and British Coal Mining", *Econometrica*, p. 442.

Lesser, H. (ed.) (1953). *Making the Most of Present Resources*, London: Institute of Public Administration.

Lesser, H. (ed.) (1954). *Making the Most of Present Resources: Report of the Second Conference on Health Services*, London: Institute of Public Administration.

Lindsey, A. (1962). *Socialised Medicine in England and Wales: The National Health Service 1948–61.* Chapel Hill, N. Carolina: The University of North Carolina Press.

Lomax, K. S. (1951). "Cost Curves for Gas Supply", *Bullitin of the Oxford University Institute of Statistics*, p. 243.

Lomax, K. S. (1952). "Cost Curves for Electricity Generation", *Economica*, p. 193.

Long, F. (1964). "Efficient Use of Hospitals" in S. J. Axelrod (ed.) *The Economics of Health and Medical Care.* Ann Arbor, Michigan: University of Michigan.

Lytton, H. D. (1959). "Recent Productivity Trends in the Federal Government: An Exploratory Study", *Review of Economics and Statistics*, p. 341.

Lytton, H. D. (1961). "Public Sector Productivity in the Truman-Eisenhower Years", *Review of Economics and Statistics*, p. 182.

Malinvaud, E. (1964). *Méthodes statistiques de l'économétrie*, Paris: Dunod.

Malmgren, H. B. (1959). "What Conclusions are to be Drawn from Empirical Cost Data? *Journal of Industrial Economics*, p. 136.

Marschak, J. and Andrews, W. H. (1944). "Random Simultaneous Equations and the Theory of Production". *Econometrica*, p. 143.

Mason, E. S. (ed.) (1943). *Cost Behavior and Price Policy*. New York: National Bureau of Economic Research.

Maternity Services Emergency Informal Committee (1963). *Report of the Maternity Services Emergency Informal Committee*, London: The National Birthday Trust Fund.

McKean, R. N. (1958). *Efficiency in Government through Systems Analysis*, New York: John Wiley and Sons.

McKenzie, M. *et al.* (1962). *Further Studies in Hospital and Community*, London: Oxford University Press.

McLachlan, G. (ed.) (1964). *Problems and Progress in Medical Care*, London: Oxford University Press.

McNerney, W. J. *et al.* (1962). *Hospital and Medical Economics*, (2 vols.). Chicago: Hospital Research and Educational Trust.

Medical Services Review Committee (1963). *A Review of the Medical Services in Great Britain*. London: Social Assay.

Meyer, J. R., (1958). "Some Methodological Aspects of Statistical Costing as Illustrated by the Determination of Rail Passenger Costs". *American Economic Review, Papers and Proccedings*, p. 209.

Meyer, J. R. and Glauber, R. R. (1964). *Investiment Decisions, Economic Forecasting and Public Policy*. Boston: Harvard Graduate School of Business Administration.

Meyer, J. R. and Kraft, G. (1961). "The Evaluation of Statistical Costing Techniques as Applied in the Transportation Industry". *American Economic Review*, p. 313.

Ministry of Health (1950). *Development of Consultant Services*, London: H.M.S.O.

Ministry of Health (1955). *Report of the Working Party on Hospital Costing*, London: H.M.S.O.

Ministry of Health (1959). *Report of the Maternity Services Committee* (Willinck Report), London: H.M.S.O.

Ministry of Health (1963). *Hospital Costing Returns; Year Ended March 31st, 1961: Part I*. London: H.M.S.O.

Ministry of Health (1964). *List of Hospital Studies*, (H.M. (64) 13), London: H.M.S.O.

Ministry of Health (1965a). *List of Hospital Studies*, (H.M. (65) 21), London: H.M.S.O.

Ministry of Health (1965b). *On the State of the Public Health*, London. H.M.S.O.

Ministry of Health, Statistics Branch. *Digest of Health Service Statistics, Series A, No. 6*. London: Ministry of Health, 1961. (unpublished)

Ministry of Health and General Register Office (1963a). *Report on Hospital In-Patient Enquiry for the Year* 1959, (Part II, Detailed Tables and Commentary). London: H.M.S.O.

Ministry of Health and General Register Office (1963b). *Report on Hospital In-Patient Enquiry for the Year* 1960, (Part II, Detailed Tables). London: H.M.S.O.

Montacute, C. (1962). *Costing and Efficiency in Hospitals,* London: Oxford University Press.

Mood, A. M. (1950). *Introduction to the Theory of Statistics,* New York: McGraw Hill Book Company.

Morgan, J. N. *et al.* (1962). *Income and Welfare in the United States,* New York: McGraw Hill Book Company.

Morgan, J. N. and Sonquist, J. A. (1963a). "Problems in the Analysis of Survey Data, and a Proposal". *Journal of the American Statistical Association,* p. 415.

Morgan, J. N. and Sonquist, J. A. (1963b). "Some Results from a Non-Symmetrical Branching Process that Looks for Interaction Effects". Proceedings of the Social Statistics Section of the American Statistical Association, p. 40.

Mundlak, Y. (1961). "Empirical Production Functions Free of Management Bias", *Journal of Farm Economics,* p. 44.

Mundlak, Y. (1963a). "Estimation of Production and Behavioral Functions from a Combination of Cross-Section and Time-Series Data" in C. Christ. *et al., Measurement in Economics.* Standford: Stanford University Press.

Mundlak, Y. (1963b). "Specification and Estimation of Multiproduct Production Functions", *Journal of Farm Economics.*

Mundlak, Y. (1964). "Transcendental Multiproduct Production Functions", *International Economic Review,* p. 273.

Mushkin, S. J. (1962). "Health as an Investment", *Journal of Political Economy,* (October 1962, Supplement), p. 129.

Nerlove, M. (1960). "On Measurement of Relative Economic Efficiency", (abstract). *Econometrica,* p. 695.

Nerlove, M. (1963). "Returns to scale in electricity supply" in C. Christ, *et al. Measurement in Economics.* Stanford: Stanford University Press.

Nerlove, M. (1965). *Estimation and Identification of Cobb-Douglas Production Functions.* Amsterdam: North-Holland Publishing Company.

Newell, D. J. (1964a). "The Demand for Hospital Beds". *Bulletin of the International Statistical Institute,* p. 1085.

Newell, D. J. (1964b). "Problems in Estimating the Demand for Hospital Beds". *Journal of Chronic Diseases,* (1964), p. 749.

Newell, D. J. (1964c). "Statistical Aspects of the Demand for Maternity Beds", *Journal of the Royal Statistical Society,* Series A, p. 1.

Nuffield Provincial Hospitals Trust (1952). *Report of an Experiment in Hospital Costing.* London: Nuffield Provincial Hospitals Trust.

Nuffield Provincial Hospitals Trust (1955). *Studies in the Functions and Design of Hospitals.* London: Oxford University Press.

Oliver, F. R. (1962). "A Cross-section Survey of Marginal Cost", *Applied Statistics,* p. 69.

Paige, D. C. (1962). "Births and Maternity Beds in England and Wales in 1970". *National Institute Economic Review.*

Paige, D. C., and Jones, K. (1965). "Health and Welfare" in W. Beckerman and associates, *The British Economy in* 1975. Cambridge: Cambridge University Press.

Palmer, J. (1956). *Measuring Bed Needs for General Hospitals: Historical Review of Opinions with Annotated Bibliography.* Washington, D.C.: U.S. Department of Health, Education and Welfare.

Peston, M. H. (1960). "Returns to Scale", *Oxford Economic Papers*, p. 133.

Petty, W. (1691). *Verbum Sapienti*. London.

Prest, A. R. and Turvey, R. (1965). "Cost-Benefit Analysis: A Survey", *Economic Journal*, p. 683.

Querido, A. (1963). *The Efficiency of Medical Care*. Leiden: H. E. Stenfert Kroese.

Reder, M. W. (1965). "Some Problems in the Economics of Hospitals". *American Economic Review, Papers and Proceedings*, p. 472.

Revans, R. W. (1961). *The Measurements of Supervisory Attitudes*. Manchester: Manchester Statistical Society.

Revans, R. W. (1962). "Hospital Attitudes and Communications". *Sociological Review Monograph No. 5.*, p. 117.

Revans, R. W. (1964). *Standards for Morale: Cause and Effect in Hospitals*. London: Oxford University Press.

Roberts, F. (1952). *The Cost of Health*, London: Turnstile Press.

Robinson, E. A. G. (1935). *The Structure of Competitive Industry*. Cambridge: Cambridge University Press.

Robinson, G. A. (1962). *Hospital Administration*. London: Butterworth.

Roemer, M. I. and Shaïn, M. (1959). *Hospital Utilization Under Insurance*. Chicago: American Hospital Association.

Rogers, E. S. (1960). *Human Ecology and Health*. New York: Macmillan.

Rosenthal, G. D. (1962). *Hospital Utilization in the United States*. A doctoral dissertation submitted to the Department of Economics, Harvard University.

Rosenthal, G. D. (1964a). *The Demand for General Hospital Facilities*. Chicago: American Hospital Association.

Rosenthal, G. D. (1964b). "A Critical Comment: A Study of the Effects of Selected Variables on Hospital Utilization". *Hospital Management*, (October, 1964). p. 67.

Rothenberg, J. (1951). "Welfare Implications of Alternative Methods of Financing Medical Care". *American Economic Review, Papers and Proceedings*, p. 676.

Rothenberg, J. (1964). "Agenda for Research in the Economics of Health" in S. J. Axelrod (ed.), *The Economics of Health and Medical Care*. Ann Arbor, Michigan: University of Michigan.

Royal Statistical Society Working Group (1955). "Statistical Assessment of the Need for Clinical Services". *Journal of the Royal Statistical Society*, Series, A, p. 427.

Samuelson, P. A. (1947). *Foundations of Economic Analysis*. Cambridge: Harvard University Press.

Sargan, J. D. (1958). "The Estimation of Economic Relationships Using Instrumental Variables". *Econometrica*, p. 393.

Scheff, T. J. (1964). "Preferred Errors in Diagnosis". *Medical Care*, p. 166.

Select Committee on Estimates, House of Commons. *Running Costs of Hospitals; Sixth Report, Session* 1956-57. London: H.M.S.O.

Shepherd, R. (1953). *Cost and Production Functions*. Princeton: Princeton University Press.

Skinner, C. G. (1962). "Hospitals and Allied Institutions: Facilities, Programs and Costs", in W. J. McNerney *et al.*, *Hospital and Medical Economics*, vol. 2; Chicago: Hospital Research and Educational Trust.

Smith, C. A. (1955), "Survey of the Empirical Evidence on Economies of Scale" in G.

Stigler, (ed.) *Business Concentration and Price Policy*: Princeton: Princeton University Press.

Somers, H. M. and Somers, A. R. (1961). *Doctors, Patients and Health Insurance*. Washington, D. C.: The Brookings Institution.

Société pour l'Avancement et l'Utilisation de la Recherche Opérationnelle Civile (1965). "Résultats d'une étude sur les facteurs de dimensionnement des hôpitaux". *La Revue Hospitalière de France*, p. 720.

Stageman, A. and Barrey, A. M. (1962). *Hospital Utilization Studies: Selected References Annotated*. Washington, D. C.: U.S. G.P.O.

Stone, J. E. (1954). *Hospital Accounts and Financial Administration*, (3rd and Revised Edition). London: Faber and Faber.

Suits, D. B. (1957). "Use of Dummy Variables in Regression Equations". *Journal of the American Statistical Association*, p. 548.

Susser, M. W. and Watson, W. (1962). *Sociology in Medicine*. Oxford: Oxford University Press.

Theil, H. (1961). *Economic Forecasts and Policy*, (2nd revised edition). Amsterdam: North Holland Publishing Company.

Theil, H. (1963). "On the Use of Incomplete Prior Information in Regression Analysis", *Journal of the American Statistical Association*, p. 403.

Theil, H. (1964). *Optimal Decision Rules for Government and Industry:* Amsterdam: North-Holland Publishing Company.

Theil, H. and Goldberger, A. S. (1960). "On Pure and Mixed Estimation in Economics", *International Economic Review*, p. 65.

Tinbergen, J. (1954). *Centralisation and Decentralisation in Economic Policy*. Amsterdam: North-Holland Publishing Company.

Tobin, J. (1958). "Estimation of relationships for limited dependent variables". *Econometrica*, p. 24.

United States Department of Health, Education, and Welfare (1963). *Conference on Research in Hospital Use*. Washington, D.C.: U.S. G.P.O.

United States Department of Health, Education, and Welfare (1962). *Research in Hospital Use: Progress and Problems*. Washington, D.C.: U.S. G.P.O.

United States Bureau of the Budget (1964). *Measuring Productivity of Federal Government Organizations*. Washington, D.C.: U.S. G.P.O.

United States National Center for Health Statistics (1965a). *Persons Hospitalized by Number of Hospital Episodes and Days in a Year*. Washington, D.C.: U.S. Gov. P.O.

United States National Center for Health Statistics (1965b). *Weight at Birth and Cause of Death in the Neonatal Period*. Washington, D.C.: U.S. G.P.O.

United States National Committee on Vital and Health Statistics (1964). *United States Statistics on Medical Economics: Present Status and Recommendations for Additional Data*. Washington, D.C.: U.S. G.P.O.

Verhulst, M. J. (1948). "Pure Theory of Production Applied to the French Gas Industry". *Econometrica*, p. 295.

Walters, A. A. (1961a). "Some Notes on the Cobb-Douglas Production Function". *Metroeconomica*, p. 121.

Walters, A. A. (1961b). "Economies of Scale in Road Haulage: A Comment". *Oxford Economic Papers*, p. 116.

Walters, A. A. (1963). "Production and Cost Functions: An Econometric Survey", *Econometrica*, p. 1.

Weeks, H. A. (1961). *Family Spending Patterns and Health Care*, Cambridge: Harvard University Press.

Weisbrod, B. A. (1961). *Economics of Public Health: Measuring the Economic Impact of Diseases*. Philadelphia: University of Pennsylvania Press.

Weisbrod, B. A. and Fiesler, R. J. (1961). "Hospitalization Insurance and Hospital Utilization". *American Economic Review*, p. 126.

Wiles, P. J. D. (1956). *Price, Cost and Output*. Oxford: Basil Blackwell.

Wiles, P. J. D. (1961). *Price, Cost and Output*, (2nd edition). Oxford: Basil Blackwell.

Wilks, S. S. (1962). *Mathematical Statistics*. New York: John Wiley and Sons.

Winsten, C. and Hall, M. (1961). "The Measurement of Economies of Scale". *Journal of Industrial Economics*, p. 255.

Wirick, G. and Barlow, R. (1964). "The Economic and Social Determinants of the Demand for Health Services" in S. J. Axelrod (ed.), *The Economics of Health and Medical Care*. Ann. Arbor, Michigan: University of Michigan.

Wiseman, J. (1963). "Cost-Benefit Analysis and Health Service Policy" in A. T. Peacock and D. J. Robertson (eds.), *Public Expenditure: Appraisal and Control*. Edinburgh: Oliver and Boyd.

Wold, H. (1964). *Econometric Model Building*. Amsterdam: North-Holland Publishing Company.

World Health Organization (1957). *Measurement of Health Levels*, Geneva: World Health Organization.

World Health Organization, Regional Office for Europe (1965). *European Symposium on the Estimation of Hospital Bed Requirements*. Copenhagen: World Health Organization.

Zellner, A. and Lee, T. H. (1965). "Joint Estimation of Relationships Involving Discrete Random Variables". *Econometrica*, p. 382.

Cmd. 6502

    A National Health Service.

    London: H.M.S.O., 1944.

Cmd. 9663

    Report of the Committee of Inquiry into the Cost of the National Health Service (The Guillebaud Report).

    London: H.M.S.O., 1956.

Cmnd. 939

    Royal Commission on Doctors' and Dentists' Remuneration, 1957–1960.

    London H.M.S.O., 1960.

Cmnd. 1418

    Annual Report of Ministry of Health for the Year 1960.

    London: H.M.S.O., 1961.

Cmnd. 1432

    Control of Public Expenditure.

    London: H.M.S.O., 1961.

Cmnd. 1598
  Report of the Commissioners of H.M. Inland Revenue, 1960–61.
  London: H.M.S.O., 1962.
Cmnd. 1604
  A Hospital Plan for England and Wales.
  London: H.M.S.O., 1962.
Cmnd. 1973
  Health and Welfare: The Development of Community Care.
  London: H.M.S.O., 1963.
Cmnd. 2688
  Annual Report of the Ministry of Health for the Year 1964.
  London: H.M.S.O., 1965.

AUTHOR INDEX

SUBJECT INDEX